D1616017

Microstructure and Thermal Analysis of Solid Surfaces

Raouf Sh. Mikhail

*Department of Chemistry
Ain-Shams University
Abbassia, Cairo, Egypt
and
The Institute of Paper Chemistry
Appleton, Wisconsin, USA*

and

Erich Robens

*Battelle-Institut e.V.
Frankfurt am Main
West Germany*

A Wiley Heyden Publication

JOHN WILEY & SONS

Chichester · New York · Brisbane · Toronto · Singapore

6871-4890

CHEMISTRY

Library of Congress Cataloging in Publication Data:

Mikhail, Raouf Shaker.
  Microstructure and thermal analysis of solid surfaces.
  A Wiley Heyden publication.
  Bibliography: p.
  Includes index.
  1. Surface chemistry. 2. Thermal analysis.
I. Robens, Erich. II. Title.
QD506.M54 1983   541.3′453   82-17507
  ISBN 0 471 26230 (U.S.)

British Library Cataloguing in Publication Data:

Mikhail, Raouf Sh.
Microstructure and thermal analysis of solid
surfaces.
1. Solids   2. Surfaces (Technology)
I. Title   II. Robens, Erich
530.4′1   QC176.8.S8

ISBN 0 471 26230 7

Typeset by Preface Ltd, Salisbury, Wilts.
Printed by Page Bros. (Norwich) Ltd.

Contents

viii

Preface

Until some years ago it was assumed that the investigation of the fine structure of surfaces is only necessary in particular fields of technological research and production control, e.g. in the manufacture of adsorbents and catalysts. Today it is realized that characterization of the surface and pore structure is advantageous whenever quantitative data are required for reactions at the surface of a solid. This applies to physical reactions, such as adsorption or absorption, dissolution, and crystallization; to electrochemical reactions at electrodes; and to chemical reactions in which the solid is converted, e.g. corrosion. The experimental methods described in this book are furthermore of importance in the increasing application of fine porous materials in technical processes as carriers for catalysts, adsorbents and matrix material for the storage of substances.

The surface of a solid differs from the bulk basically by two features:

— the surface has an open geometric structure, and the arrangement of the atoms differs from that in the bulk
— the surface atoms are bound only unilaterally, and they have free valences ready to bind foreign atoms of the adjoining phase.

These facts have to be regarded in all processes where solid phase boundaries are present because the course and kinetics of reactions can be strongly influenced by the surface properties. With regard to the miniaturization of all devices in mechanics, electronics, optics, etc., the surface in comparison to the bulk is increased and thus surface effects like corrosion, adhesion, and surface charge gain increased importance.

The book covers the basic methods of investigating the surface with respect to its geometry, its chemistry, and its treatment by heat. Research on surface reactions and processes occurring or starting at the surface of a solid, like sorption, heterogeneous catalysis, friction, lubrication and glueing, degassing, drying, corrosion, and surface treatment, requires knowledge of some of the following parameters: surface geometry, pore structure, particle size distribution; specific surface area; chemical composition of the surface; valency spectrum; composition of adsorbed layers; and electronic work function.

The book also presents methods of surface analysis, especially based on experiments with gases and liquids in contact with the surface investigated; it touches upon microscopy and scattering experiments with light, electrons, and ions. Measurement of electric properties and valences, however, was not considered to be appropriate.

Part 1 deals with the investigation of the geometric properties of the surface, Part 2 with that of the chemical surface properties, and Part 3 describes in some detail the gravimetric techniques widely used by the authors, and some useful appendixes complete the work.

The treatise is based on many years' experience gained in experimental work at the Laboratory of Surface Chemistry, Ain-Shams University, Abbassia-Cairo, and the Interfaces Research Section, Battelle-Institut e.V., Frankfurt am Main.

RAOUF SH. MIKHAIL
ERICH ROBENS

Part 1

Geometry of Solid Surfaces

Introduction to Part 1

When examining a surface visually, even by means of the light microscope, only structures above 0.1 μm can be observed. Thus an optically smooth surface can reveal a highly rugged structure. Inspecting a well-machined piece of material we have to take into account:

— deviations from the ideal shape
— surface roughness
— internal pore structure, where we have to distinguish between open pores accessible for molecules of the surrounding atmosphere and closed pores accessible only by bulk diffusion.

A diagram of a well-machined metal surface is shown in Fig. 1 depicting:

(a) the shape deviation as seen with the aid of an optical instrument
(b) the surface roughness which can be detected by e.g. tactile response to a diamond pin; and
(c) the surface pore structure revealed by an electron microscope.

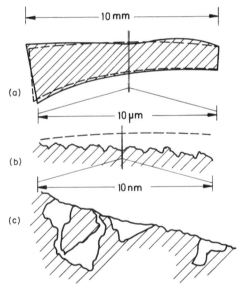

Fig. 1 Diagram of a section through a metal piece normal to the well-machined surface under increasing magnifications: (a) deviation from desired shape; (b) surface roughness; (c) micro- and mesopore structure

Many catalysts, adsorbents, and many powders dispose on surface areas of some hundred square metres per cubic centimetre, or 10^8 m²/m³. This surface area is situated mostly inside the grains, pellets, etc. Thus the visual boundary layer hides an internal surface area which is at least 1.05 up to 10^6 times larger than the geometric projection area.

The first part of this book covers the investigation of the geometry mainly in the sub-micron and nanometer range. Shape deviations, roughness and grain size determination will be dealt with briefly because these parameters can be measured just as well with methods for the analysis of the sub-micro-geometric range.

The complexity involved in the analysis of solid surfaces, especially amorphous solids, lies in the difficulty of obtaining reproducible properties of various samples of the same material. This complexity is due to several facts. Firstly, high surface area solids are formed, in the majority of instances, by polymerization processes; heterogeniety is created due to irregular packing of macromolecules as well as to incompleteness of the condensation reaction between these macromolecules. Therefore, the geometry and chemical composition of the surface depends to a large extent on the method used in obtaining these inorganic or organic polymers in a certain medium, which affects their structure. Secondly, removal of the liquid phase subsequent to preparation, and for oxides, dehydration and dehydroxylation of the bulk and the surface of the solid, are complex and irreversible processes, but the extent to which these processes take place is the factor which determines the property of solids in specific molecular interaction. Thirdly, the solids, during their synthesis and subsequent treatment, capture all the possible accompanying elements and impurities; these impurities drastically affect the chemical characteristics of the resulting solid surface.

Consequently, analysis of solid surfaces should involve analysis of both the physical characteristics (geometry) of the surface, namely the specific surface area and the pore structure, as well as the chemical composition of the surface. The last decade has witnessed the transition from surface chemistry as a branch of physical chemistry dealing mainly with capillary phenomena, to the chemistry and physics of the solid surface itself, i.e., to the study of the dependence of the properties on the extent, location, and chemical composition of solid surfaces, by use of modern methods: structural, chemical, spectral, mass-spectral, isotopic exchange, catalytic, calorimetric, etc. Various *modus operandi* must be applied to the same sample under comparable conditions[1,2].

The vast majority of practical solids are porous. Indeed, production in the laboratory of solids that are sufficiently nonporous that their internal surface and void structure can be ignored is somewhat problematical. When a solid is prepared from a parent material, e.g. by thermal treatment, the final solid is very often porous even if the parent material was nonporous. Moreover, in most cases, the pore structure either suffers from a tendency toward spontaneous irreversible changes, or is susceptible to changes caused by external variables. For the minority of solids which are nonporous, it is the chemical composition of their surfaces, beside their surface extent, which determine their surface character. For the majority of solids which are porous, the size, shape, and distribution of pores play an extremely important role, which adds a third important factor, beside the chemical composition and the extent of the surface in determining their surface character. Obviously, the first step in physical analysis of solid surfaces should involve the detection of porosity before proceeding to the actual characterization of the surface in terms of surface area determination and pore structure analysis by different methods.

Four chapters are included in this part of the book; these are:

Chapter 1: The origin of pores, and the classification of porous solids
Chapter 2: Detection of porosity in solids
Chapter 3: Methods of surface area determination
Chapter 4: Methods of pore structure analysis.

Chapter 1 will serve mainly as an introduction which will be helpful for an investigator in making a choice among alternatives for the interpretation of data. Chapter 2 is demanding, because all fundamental concepts, definitions, and methods of analysis of surface area and pore structure (Chapters 3 and 4) will mostly depend on a precharacterization of the solid, and orienting its surface character in between two extreme cases, namely nonporous or totally microporous. It is not an understatement to say that the methods to be discussed in Chapters 3 and 4 should clarify the discussion of the two extreme cases, and that for an actual solid of intermediate character, the investigator should apply the method which gives a minimum margin of error, based on the actual pore structure of the solid.

References

1. Discussions of the Faraday Society No. 52, Surface chemistry of oxides, 1971.
2. Faraday Discussions of the Chemical Society No. 60, Electron spectroscopy of solids and surfaces, 1975.

Chapter 1

The Origin of Pores, and the Classification of Porous Solids*

The analysis and classification of pore sizes, and size distributions, irrespective of their origin, has been a subject of great interest to many authors[1]. We feel, however, that it is of value to include considerations of origin in the classification scheme. This is because the methods by which pore distribution is determined are strongly dependent on certain geometric features of the pores themselves, and knowledge of the origin of pores allows an investigator to make a choice among alternatives for the interpretation of his data.

We will adopt the terminology suggested by IUPAC in 1971[2]. The narrowest pores, of width not exceeding about 2 nm, are called micropores; the widest pores, of width exceeding about 50 nm, are called macropores; and the pores of intermediate width are termed mesopores.

The origin and the stability of the pore structure of solids are extremely important, especially with regard to:

(a) the control of pore structure, e.g. the need for tailoring the pore structure to suit particular applications;
(b) the control of the conditions which cause metamorphic changes that modify the structure during preparation or afterwards, e.g. in storage and in practical use; and
(c) to serve as a guide in considering a particular pore model needed for pore structure analysis in the absence of direct observation of pore shape.

Several authors[3-6] have tried to develop a classification system for pores based in a major way upon their origin, and as a preliminary it should be noted that in essentially every practical porous system, the structure might exhibit more than one of the features that are described separately below. We will return to this question of complexity later on.

1.1 Pores in compacted powders

The simplest case to deal with is a system composed of spherical, nonporous particles, which, on compaction, generates a well developed, more or less uniform pore structure in which the pore space is made up of the interstitial voids between the particles. The pore volume will depend on the particle size and the average coordination number.

*Based largely on Ref. (6)

We will not go into detail here regarding the ideal packing of *uniform* spheres, for two reasons. First, a great many textbooks and treatises on physical metallurgy, X-ray crystallography, and crystal chemistry discuss this subject at considerable length. Second, the ideal packing is very seldom realized in practical bodies formed from powders or grains. There are three reasons for this non-ideality: (1) The grains are seldom of uniform size or shape, let alone spheres. (2) The average coordination number is rarely that of a close-packed solid, i.e. 12 for hexagonal close packed (HCP) and face centered cubic (FCC) lattices except for very local regions of the aggregate; local regions of coordination number 8 (corresponding to a body centered cubic (BCC) lattice) or lower are, in general, randomly intermixed. (3) The structures of such a system are commonly very seriously modified by the temperature and applied pressure to which the material is subjected.

The first two reasons for nonideality require little comment at this point; but the third has some manifestations that were not completely predictable before experimental studies were made. We will discuss the effects of temperature first.

With an increase in temperature, sintering commences. According to the classical work on metal powders, three stages of sintering can be distinguished.

1. Elimination of internal porosity of the discrete particles. This has been referred to as 'smoothing'[1]; this stage does not, however, include changes in the external topography of the particles. It probably occurs largely by a surface diffusion mechanism, particularly with regard to the elimination of internal micropores in primary particles.

2. Adhesion. Discrete particles, which at low temperature constitute a loose powder, develop points of contact that have sufficient mechanical strength that the powder is converted into an aggregate that has a little mechanical strength. This stage occurs near the Tammann temperature, which is approximately half the absolute melting point. There is some surface transport in this stage (though little loss of surface area) and bridging between particles, by curved-neck connections, commences. The solid mass contains macro- and mesopores, at this stage. If surface transport is extensive, closed-off pores may develop, which are not connected to the exterior surface.

3. Shrinkage. Further heating causes onset of the third stage, during which pore shrinkage occurs, with fastening of the bridges between particles; and crystal grain growth takes place. More pores lose their connection to the exterior. The entire porous body shrinks. In the final stage of this process, the isolated voids are eliminated by diffusion of vacancies, which readily occurs at grain boundaries.

The classical mechanism of sintering, outlined above, does not seem to hold for certain very fine particles. It has been demonstrated by Teichner and co-workers[7] that, in the case of TiO_2 particles of diameter 100 nm or less, the contact between two adjacent particles does not form a curved neck. The initial step is for spheroidal particles to become polyhedral. Adhesion then occurs between the flat surfaces of the neighbouring particles. It is to be expected that this behaviour will be present with solids for which the surface energy of faces other than one or two low-index planes is much higher than that of the low-index planes.

Compaction pressure, which is the second external variable for this group of solids, leads to a decrease in the pore volume and, in most (but not all) cases, a diminution in surface area as well. Mica constitutes a clear example of a decrease in surface area under compaction. This decrease is attributed to the fact that the particles are flaky, with an extensive area of very flat surface, which is eliminated when particles adhere to each other.

The effect of pressure has been found to depend strongly on the mechanical properties of the solid. For example, plastic deformation governs the response of sodium chloride, whereas particle fracture governs the compaction of both sucrose and coal[8]. With sucrose, the fragments move to occupy the available space, while with coal, there is tendency for fragments to remain wedged, in the form of bridges, which help to preserve an open structure. There is, as might be expected, only a modest change (decrease) in surface area when hydrostatic pressure causes particle fracture as well as compaction. It is sometimes found that when pressure has caused fracture, higher temperatures are required to produce significant sintering than when pressure has not been applied.

As already noted, the particles from which a porous solid are formed are rarely spheres; and they are seldom of equal size, whatever their shape. Even when they are relatively uniform and nearly spherical, they are seldom in close-packed arrays. The mean coordination number for random particle-packing is, in general, less than the closest-packed value, 12; and it may be lower than the BCC value, 8. If the particles are all of equal size, the more irregular the particles, the lower the mean coordination number will be, and the larger and more irregular the voids. Initial nonuniformity of voids will (to a considerable extent) persist in sintered or otherwise consolidated bodies.

In the far more common case of unequal particle size, the void volume is frequently (but not always) reduced below the volume fraction of voids in beds of uniform particles. The pore structure becomes correspondingly more complex in such systems.

1.2 Pores in gels

1.2.1 Precipitated gels

Metal hydroxide or hydrous oxide gels and precipitates, formed from solution, can be obtained in a wide range of pore structures. Once the gel is formed from solution, it starts ageing, i.e. it undergoes irreversible structural and textural changes, which continue during and after the removal of the liquid phase. Three distinct stages have been described[9] for the ageing of flocculated, hydrous gels. There are no sharp demarcations separating them; and any two consecutive steps can overlap with each other.

The three ageing stages are: (a) condensation polymerization, (b) aggregation-cementation, and (c) crystal growth and recrystalization. Stage (a) is often accompanied by the development of a large surface area and the creation of uniform microporosity. Stage (b) involves the loss of area, often with concomitant loss of micropores and development of mesopores. Stage (c), which is a slow process unless accelerated by heat, can lead to the elimination of pores and the ultimate production of stable, crystalline solids of low or negligible porosity.

Elimination of the liquid phase generally leads to a slowing down in the rate by which the three processes can take place. In certain cases, elimination of the liquid phase can by itself lead to unusual but characteristic pore structures. A well-known example is the aerogel structure, which is an open gel system with a large pore volume. The particles that make up the solid phase have a small average coordination number, typically between 2 and 2.5. Such a system collapses upon heating, with a tremendous reduction in pore volume but only a small change in specific surface area. This occurs to a lesser extent in the conversion of a hydrogel to a xerogel, which involves only a partial collapse of the structure and an increase in average coordination number to something in the range of 6.

Precipitation of insoluble compounds other than hydroxides can lead to gels; but the steps following primary precipitation are commonly much simpler than those with metal hydroxides. Usually, such steps consist principally of crystal growth, with disappearance of the smaller and more imperfect crystals. Porous solids prepared from such precipitates commonly have pore morphologies resembling those obtained with a compacted powder (see section 1.1), unlike the gels obtained from metal hydroxides.

1.2.2 Topochemical and through-solution gels

In some cases, a primary solid is capable of further chemical interaction with water, leading to the formation of a gel, either by a topochemical or through-solution mechanism. The gel is precipitated in the water-filled spaces of the primary structure; and it can undergo a subsequent change of composition, and shrinkage, leading to a characteristic micropore structure. Typical examples are Portland cement and other types of cements, as well as gypsum. The following discussion is based on the theory of cement hydration and aging proposed by Powers[10].

When dry cement is mixed with a limited volume of water, it forms a cement paste. Extensive studies of cement paste have led to the conclusion that it exists, initially, as a conglomerate of relatively discrete particles of the unhydrated cement grains and calcium sulphate. In the presence of water, this develops into a conglomerate of (1) 'cement gel'; (2) calcium hydroxide and small amounts of other coarsely crystalline hydration products; (3) residual unhydrated cement grains and portions of grains; and (4) 'capillary pores', which are in the macropore and mesopore ranges. These are the remnants of water-filled void space that had existed between the cement grains at the time of the start of setting.

The most important of these constituents is thought to be the cement gel, which has an unusual structure. It is viewed as consisting of a solid part, the finely divided or colloidal hydration products, which are mostly calcium silicate hydrate; and a non-solid part, the 'gel pores'. The pores are treated as an intrinsic part of the gel. The gel pores are initially filled with water, but the water can be removed by evaporation, as can the water in the capillary pores. The average size of the gel pores may be interpreted in terms of the hydraulic radius, and estimates of hydraulic radii of the order of 0.75 nm have been cited[10]. This value implies an average distance from surface to surface of 1.5 to 3 nm, depending on the pore shape.

In contrast to the characteristic volume and size of the gel pores, the capillary pore constituent of the paste is thought to vary in volume (and perhaps in void size), depending mainly on the water/cement ratio and the degree of hydration of the particular paste. An interesting conclusion has also been reached[10] that in pastes of water/cement ratio less than about 0.38 that have been allowed to hydrate continuously, all the capillary voids eventually become filled with gel. Quantitative evaluation of the size ranges to be ascribed to capillary pores are virtually nonexistent. Nevertheless, it is maintained that those are generally order of magnitude larger than gel pores.

Finally, it is believed that the capillary pores constitute an interconnected, continuous network in fresh cement paste; but for pastes of normal water/cement ratio ('normal' meaning ratios between 0.4 and 0.7) it is considered that the capillary pores become discontinuous as hydration proceeds. When this occurs, transmission of fluid between capillary pores must involve passing through gel pores, whose size is very much smaller. Thus, in this kind of material, additional hydration offsets ageing effects.

The pore structure of this group of solids is particularly important because of its direct effect on the mechanical and other engineering properties of the pastes.

1.3 Pores in stable crystals

The well-known zeolites and 'molecular sieves' are examples of this group of solids, in which an intracrystalline micropore structure is distributed as channels, slits, or cavities within the lattice. The dimensions and patterns of these micropores are regular. In zeolites, the cavities are interconnected by 'windows' of diameter 0.4 or 1 nm. Zeolites and molecular sieves can be used, by virtue of their stability towards heat treatment, for trapping otherwise inert gas molecules. At high temperatures and pressures, small molecules can pene-

10

trate into such crystals; but when the temperature or pressure is reduced, the gas molecules are trapped, until the crystals are again heated[11,12].

The behaviour of zeolites towards guest molecules differs greatly from that of clathrates. Clathrate lattices contain isolated cavities, and the lattice is not stable in the absence of guest molecules; once the lattice has formed, the molecules are trapped until the whole structure decomposes.

Chrysotile asbestos, an interesting porous mineral[13] with regard both to its range of possible applications in technology and its health hazards: probably because of their geometric shape (length and diameter), fibrils, when breathed in from the air, can cause not only asbestosis, but can also generate mesothelioma. Chemically it is a pure magnesium silicate (Fig. 1.1) the molecules forming spiral layers wound up to small fibrils of about 20 nm in diameters (Fig. 1.2). The fibrils are densely packed to fibres of diameters in the mircometer range which in their technical application as filters or gaskets are worked up to felt. The voids in the felt are of macropore dimensions, the interstices between the fibrils and the holes in the axis of the fibrils are meso- and

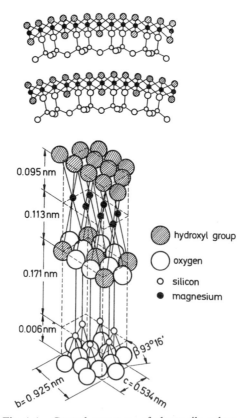

Fig. 1.1   Crystal structure of chrysotile asbestos consisting of parallel connected fibrils

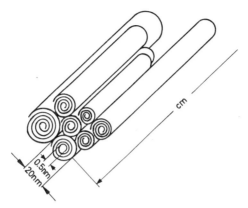

Fig. 1.2   Schematic drawing of a Chrysotile
Asbestos Fibre

microporous. The gaps between the spiral layers in general are not accessible for gases and, hence are ultramicropores.

1.4 Pores produced by thermal and chemical processes

1.4.1 Calcination

When a solid parent material (A) calcines to yield a solid product (B) and a gas (C) it is generally observed that the product is formed with well-developed porosity, and tremendous increase in surface area, even when the parent solid (A) is nonporous. Examples are the calcination of hydroxides, carbonates, and oxalates. It is believed that upon decomposition, each crystallite of the parent material (A) gives rise to a number of B crystallites, the number depending on the number of decomposition nuclei in the parent crystal. The crystallites of B are formed in a metastable condition or as a pseudo-lattice of A; and they tend to recrystallize and sinter if heated at a higher temperature than the decomposition temperature, or if heated for a longer period at the same temperature. The overlap of the two processes, activation (decomposition) and sintering (recrystallization), leads to a maximum in the curve of surface area *vs.* calcination temperature. The presence of water is often found to accelerate the second stage of sintering. Although this is the most common mechanism prevailing during calcination, other mechanisms can also operate, as explained by Gregg[14].

Control of the pore structure in this group of solids is not an easy task. The external variables are temperature, time of heating, and the ambient atmosphere. An essential, internal variable, which is not easily controllable, is the number of nucleation sites for decomposition in the parent material.

1.4.2 Chemically induced porosity

Another way to produce porosity in the non-porous or inactive solid is by treating it with a reagent that dissolves out some constituents, leaving others in the form of a porous framework. Among the more familiar examples is the preparation of porous Vycor glass by acid treatment, and the production of activated fullers' earth, also by mineral acid treatment. The pore structure of the leached or chemically treated material depends on at least two variables: (a) time and the rate constants of the reaction, together with kinetic factors such as concentration and temperature; and (b) the physical structure of the parent solid. The pore structure that is to be expected in systems of chemically induced porosity depends in a major way upon the structure of the parent material. In the case of porous Vycor, the material that gets leached out is present as a discrete phase that had been precipitated during an earlier stage in the thermal treatment of the glass. The pores that are produced by leaching follow the structure of the precipitated phase, which is a structure resembling a three-dimensional network, so the pore structure that is produced by leaching resembles interconnected wormholes.

There are cases in which a liquid converts a solid into another solid by the removal of a constituent of the primary solid, with collapse of the primary lattice. The production of Raney nickel[15] no doubt occurs in this fashion (see Section 7.2.4. The pore structure of the product must be quite different from that in the two cases just mentioned, in which the primary structure is skeletonized on one scale of dimensions or another. The structure is likely to be quite different from that of an inorganic gel prepared by precipitation from solution. Indeed, we can say rather little in the way of *a priori* argument about the pore structures of such solids. If, as with Raney nickel, the product has (in its pure state) a high melting point and very low solubility in water, the mechanisms of crystallite growth by solid state diffusion and by through-solution transport are unlikely to lead to such activity in restructuring the solid under the usual conditions of preparation. There remains the reaction of local electrochemical cells, anodic oxidation and cathodic reduction, as a transport mechanism. In the presence of hydroxyl ions and aluminium ions (aluminate, certainly), the electrochemistry of metallic nickel is very complex, and it may be appreciably different from the behaviour of nickel in more familiar chemical conditions.

1.4.3 Joint thermal and chemical processes

Pyrolysis is a common process, used for the production of active carbon by the carbonization and activation of organic materials. The carbon produced in the absence of air possesses a low surface area. It can be activated by steam or carbon dioxide. The development of the porosity, in this latter stage, is induced by joint chemical and thermal actions, which take place by oxidation and preferential burn-out of some components, with both a great increase in area and the production of active adsorption sites. Chemical additives or agents which catalyse these processes have been suggested for carbonizing material of vegetable origin. By careful adjustment of the reaction conditions and temperature, pore sizes covering the three regions, namely micro-, meso-, and macropores, can be obtained. The ultimate pore structure will depend on the nature of the solid in its state before activation.

The solid that is being pyrolysed may, initially, be a cross-linked polymer. If so, it may retain much of its original configuration during heating, even while gaseous products are being evolved. The surface tension of the developing solid may not play an important role in determining the pore configuration. But many materials that are pyrolysed are, initially, linear polymers, or relatively low-molecular substances (as in the case of coal) that polymerize when heated, before they evaporate, and that form soft solids or very viscous liquids before decomposition is complete. Gas that is evolved is held as bubbles; and surface tension will cause the pores that are produced to be roughly spherical in shape. As a final step, cross-linking occurs and reaches a degree of completion that fixes the over-all pore structure. Porous solids of this type are of little interest for applications such as catalysis, adsorption, etc., because the pores tend to be of very large size and of low area, as well as being often closed or not connected to the surface of the solid.

Thus, the production of interesting and useful porous solids by pyrolysis occurs only if there is the right balance among the chemical reactions of polymerizing or chain extension, cross-linking, and decomposition, and if an activation process can be employed that increases final surface area.

1.5 Composite pore structures

As already mentioned, pore structures in most practical systems are complex; they may be composites of the various types already discussed. For example, the micropores in the 'gel pores' of cement paste have already been described; they develop in a secondary reaction, after the formation of the primary pore structure. Another kind of secondary pore structure consists of the regions in which the surfaces of primary particles approach each other, and come in contact. These have already been alluded to.

Another example of a complex pore system is paper, where the felted cellulose fibres form a macropore system (type A solid) whereas the pores of the cell wall (type B) are of meso- and micro- size[16,17]. With regard to the gel nature of this material, it is subject to swelling processes in water, but the swelling can be reduced, for example by cross-linking acetal cross-links in the cellulose fibre as a result of treatment with formaldehyde (Fig. 1.3). The pore structure can be frozen by forming an aerogel by means of critical-point drying. This method is used widely to prepare porous samples for electron microscopy.

A further kind of secondary porosity consists of what might be termed 'internal fuzz'. The internal surfaces of pores will rarely be smooth on a

14

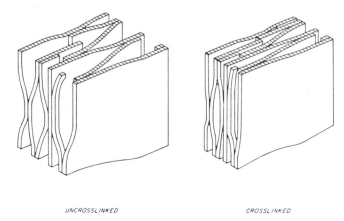

Fig. 1.3 A segment of water-swollen cellulose cell-wall, un-cross-linked or cross-linked with formaldehyde[16] (Courtesy R. C. Weatherwax)

molecular scale. Electron micrographs such as Figs 1.4 and 1.5 indicate that crystalline material is often present, which is of an order of magnitude smaller than the effective pore diameter. This material may have the same chemical composition as the principal solid material of the pores, or the composition may be different. Examples in which the substructure composition is different from the main material are clay in sandstone or porous limestone which may

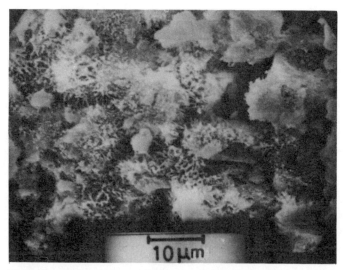

Fig. 1.4 SEM micrographs for autoclaved slag-quartz-lime specimen after 2 hours autoclaving at 10 bar of saturated steam[6]

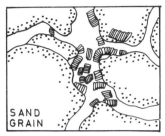

Fig. 1.5a "Discrete particle" kaolinite

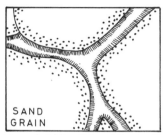

Fig. 1.5b "Pore-Linning" chlorite

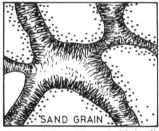

Fig. 1.5c "Pore-bridging" illite

Fig. 1.5 Three general types of pore morphology of clay in sandstone, based on electron micrographs of J. W. Neasham[18]

constitute a fuzz in the pores. Figures 1.6 and 1.7 show some models for the structure and substructure, of different degrees of complexity[6].

Neasham[18] has recently published scanning electron microscope (SEM) photographs of sandstone oil-reservoir rocks containing dispersed clay (see Fig. 1.5). The line drawings in this figure show Neasham's interpretation of the structures, for three different kinds of clays. Figure 1.5(b) is particularly notable, because the chlorite clay is present as flakes, needles, or fibres, forming something resembling a velvet lining of the main pores. Neasham pointed out that the clay undoubtedly was formed hydrothermally in the sandstone, in processes that occurred long after the primary rock formation.

16

1.6 Classification of pore systems

A catalogue of pore structures starting with a few elementary types and building up combinations of types can now be constructed. We will do this in a fashion that is appropriate for modelling processes, e.g. fluid flow, liquid penetration, and gas adsorption in monolayer and multilayer regimes.

In Fig. 1.6, models are shown based on the proper 'pore or sponge concept': the existence of voids in solids. Figure 1.6(a) is the classical cylindrical

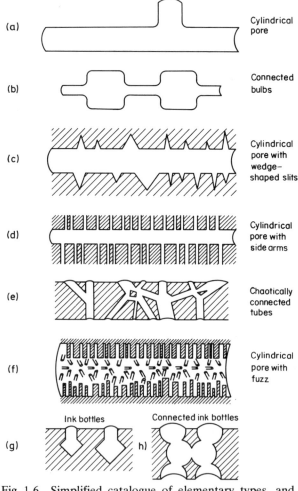

Fig. 1.6 Simplified catalogue of elementary types, and build-up of combinations of types of pores (sponge concept): (a) cylindrical pore; (b) connected bulbs; (c) cylindrical pore with wedge-shaped slits; (d) cylindrical pore with side arms; (e) chaotically, connected tubes; (f) cylindrical pore with fuzz; (g) ink bottles; (h) connected ink bottles

pore. A branch has been added, which is of the same size as the main pore; and the radius of curvature of the wall at the branching point is comparable to the radius of the pore itself. This kind of pore model is useful for certain elementary calculations. Figure 1.6(b) is a series of connected bulbs. This is a useful model for calculations involving liquid flow. A model of this type has previously been suggested by Dullien[19]. The resistance to flow would be that of the necks, and the capacity would be that of the bulbs. The connected bulb may, of course, be combined with models in which branches are present (Figs 1.6(d)–(f). When this is done, the result is a model which is relatively close to that of certain real structures that occur in sintered, powdered solids.

Figure 1.6(c) is a model in which side pores in the form of wedge-shaped slits, or conical or pyramidal void spaces, exist as dead-end side-pores of a central pore. This model may be considered as representing certain features of a solid that consists of spheroidal or polyhedral particles in contact, consolidated but without the degree of sintering that converts points or areas of tangent contact of particles to rounded bridges between the particles. The central cylinder in the drawing represents the largest-diameter through-pore in the local region of the solid. The model (and the models indicated in (d) to (f) are useful for the treatment of Washburn pore penetration by a fluid that forms a nonzero contact angle on the solid. Figure 1.6(d) is clearly related to 1.6(c) with the wedge-shaped or conical slits being replaced by through-pores which connect to other pores. In 1.6(c) this model has been made more typical using randomly connected tubes of various diameters. This model may be used for the statistical calculation of penetration or flow through a porous system as done by Pismen[20] Nicholson and Petropoulos[21]. Figure 1.6(f) is based on the existence of a fuzz of particles (rods or sheets) extending inward from the pore walls (compare the electron micrographs, Fig. 1.4).

Another approach to a description of a porous material, the corpuscular concept, starts from interspaces between particles more or less in contact and more or less packed. An example of such a model is the well-known slit pore model as depicted in Fig. 1.7(a). The model gives a basis for the discussion of swelling phenomena and for the calculation of condensation phenomena for which it is in contrast to the cylinder pore model.

Figure 1.7(b) is an array of cylinders in contact. A corresponding drawing could be made for lath-shaped crystallites in contact. In Fig. 1.7(b) the average coordination number is lower than that for closest packing; while Fig. 1.7(c) illustrates a random array of cylinders *not* in contact. These cylinders correspond to fibres anchored in the wall of a pore; Neasham's chlorite pore-lining clay. Figure 1.7(d) shows a system of crossed rods as suggested by Karnaukhov[22]. Obviously the interspaces exhibit rather complicated geometric bodies. Figure 1.7(e) is a structure of uniform spheres in contact, in a similar arrangement as Fig. 1.7(b).

Karnaukhov[22] stresses the idea that each solid/pore system can be converted mathematically into a reciprocal pore/solid system with respective coordination numbers. This is important in so far as the geometry of the pores

18

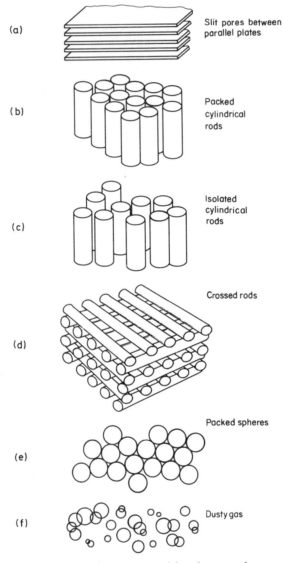

(a)   Slit pores between parallel plates

(b)   Packed cylindrical rods

(c)   Isolated cylindrical rods

(d)   Crossed rods

(e)   Packed spheres

(f)   Dusty gas

Fig. 1.7 Pores between particles (corpuscular concept): (a) slit pores between parallel plates; (b) packed cylindrical rods; (c) isolated cylindrical rods; (d) crossed rods; (e) packed spheres; (f) dusty gas

between particles is much more complicated than that of the particles themselves. According to the rule of inversion, description of one fragment of the system provides complete information about the other. In this way Karnaukhov calculated surface area, porosity, and some filling curves for some simple geometrics of particles of uniform size (e.g. Figs. 1.6(h), 1.7(d)). For more complicated systems the use of a computer is necessary.

A very general approach using the corpuscular concept is given by the 'dusty gas' model[23]. It starts from isolated solid particles scattering the incoming gas molecules. The first calculation of a highly diluted suspension of spheres in a gas was made by Derjaguin[24] in 1946. Later on, Prager, Strieder and Weissberg[25-27], and Evans, Mason and Watson[28-30], hit on the same idea. They extended the model to more concentrated suspensions, e.g. true pore systems. However, mathematical difficulties led Weissberg[25] to a model in which the positions of the sphere centres are assumed to be statistically independent. Even at moderate void fractions, the model leads to considerable overlap of the spheres, as is exemplified by Weissberg's estimate that the void fraction U is

$$U = e^{-V}$$

where V is the volume fraction of all spheres making up the porous material. With $U = 0.5$, V is calculated at 0.69, about 40 per cent too large because, physically, U cannot exceed $1 - V$. The distribution function of the sphere radii is adjusted in such a way that the experimentally determined surface area equals the total surface area of all spheres, multiplied by the void fraction. Thus, the model will not be very useful for porous systems of moderate or low porosity and, furthermore, the particle radius is essentially an adjustable parameter.

Van Eekelen[31] has shown that in Weissberg's model, very different sphere radius distributions can lead to very similar pore radius distributions. He stresses the fact that it is impossible to deduce particle size distributions from pore radius distributions when assuming Weissberg's model.

The final conclusion is that a satisfactory statistical description of a porous composite, even of isometric crystals or spheres, is still lacking.

We may summarize the classification from the point of view of void morphology, in the most simplified form, as follows:

(a) Voids in particles-in-contact aggregates. Their shapes depend on the solid morphology (spherical particles versus platelets) and on the coordination number. Spherical particles can lead in most cases to quasi-cylindrical pores, and depending on the mode of stacking, to isolated cavities, or to voids like worm-holes. Platelets lead in most cases to slit-shaped voids.

(b) Voids like wormholes, mostly in solids of section 1.4, which topologically can be considered as straight cylinders with interconnections but closed at one end.

(c) Voids of above types, with fuzz mostly in solids of section 1.2.2. With some approximation, the fuzz acts as 'neck' to the wider voids, and in this sense it is an ink-bottle void.

(d) Voids of the zeolitic type (solids of section 1.3). These are stable voids controlled by the 'neck' and can be considered as intermediate between cylindrical and ink-bottle voids.

(e) Voids in a thermoplastic-thermoset solid, which are mostly spherical bulbs.

(f) Composite void structures.

The above presentation shows that the four common void morphologies are the spherical, cylindrical, slit-shaped, and ink-bottle, and a fifth that is less common, namely of an intermediate morphology between the cylindrical and the ink-bottle.

The discussion presented so far indicates that the origin of a solid is an essential parameter in developing the pore and void morphology. Beside pore structure analysis, the specific area of the solid represents a main parameter involved in describing the morphology of a solid.

An interesting conclusion is developed in this discussion, that even when the primary particles are nonporous, an aggregate or an agglomerate of particles is expected to develop a porous body, unless the particle size and shape allow a certain minimum coordination number between the particles to keep the nonporous character of the individual particles predominating. The vast majority of solids are therefore porous, and the next chapter will deal with the detection of solid porosity and the existence of various types of pores in solids.

References

1. See, e.g. D. Dollimore and G. R. Heal, *Surface Technology*, **6**, 231, (1978), and references cited there
2. IUPAC Manual of Symbols and Terminology. Appendix 2, Part I, *Coll., Surface Chem. Pure Appl. Chem.*, **31**, 578 (1972)
3. K. S. W. Sing, in Pore structure and properties of materials, *Proceedings of the International Symposium*, Prague, Sept., 18–21, 1973, Final Report-Part I. Academia, Prague, P.B-5
4. J. C. P. Broeckhoff and B. G. Linsen in: B. G. Linsen (ed.), *Physical and Chemical Aspects of Adsorbents and Catalysts*, Academic Press, London and New York, 1970, p. 5
5. A. P. Karnaukhov, in Pore Structure and properties of materials, *Proceedings of the International Symposium* RILEM/IUPAC, Prague, Sept., 18–21, 1973, Preliminary Report, Part I, Academia, Prague
6. R. Sh. Mikhail, S. A. Abo-El-Enein and R. J. Good. (To be published.)
7. F. Vergnon, M. Astler and S. J. Teichner, *Materials Science Research*, **6**, (301), 1972, Plenum, New York
8. J. S. Hardmann and B. A. Lilley, *Proc. Roy. Soc., London A.*, **333**, 183 (1973)
9. G. C. Bye and K. S. W. Sing, in: A. L. Smith (ed.), *Particle Growth in Suspensions*, Academic Press, London, 1973, p. 29
10. T. C. Powers, in Chemistry of cement, *Proceedings of the 4th International Conference on the Chemistry of Cement*, Washington, D.C., 1960, p. 577
11. R. M. Barrer and D. E. W. Vaughan, *Trans. Faraday Soc.*, **67**, 2129 (1971)
12. R. M. Barrer and D. E. W. Vaughan, *J. Phys. Chem. Solids*, **32**, 731 (1971)
13. E. Robens, H. Heide and G. Walter, *GIT—Glas Inst. Techn.* (1983).
14. S. J. Gregg, *J. Chem. Soc.*, 3940, (1953)
15. H. Binder, A. Köhling, K. Metzelthin, G. Sandstede and M.-L. Schrecker, *Chemie-Ing.-Techn.* **40**, 586 (1968)

16. R. C. Weatherwax and D. F. Caulfield, *J. Colloid Interface Sci., 67*, 498 (1978)
17. R. C. Weatherwax and D. F. Caulfield, *J. Colloid Interface Sci., 67*, 506 (1978)
18. J. W. Neasham, Paper presented at the 52nd Annual Fall Technical Conference of the Society of Petroleum Engineers of AIME, held in Denver, Colorado, October 9–12, 1977
19. F. A. L. Dullien and V. K. Batra, *Ind. Eng. Chem., 62*, 25 (1970)
20. L. M. Pismen, *Chem. Engineering Sci., 29*, 1227 (1974)
21. D. Nicholson and J. H. Petropoulos, in: S. J. Gregg, K. S. W. Sing, and H. F. Stoeckli (eds.), *Characterisation of Porous Solids*, Soc. Chemical Ind., London, 1979, p. 211
22. A. P. Karnaukhov, in: S. J. Gregg, K. S. W. Sing, H. F. Stoeckli (eds.), *Characterisation of Porous Solids*, Soc. Chemical Ind., London 1979, p. 301.
23. G. Walter and E. Robens, in: E. Drauglis, R. I. Jaffee (eds.), *The Physical Basis for Heterogeneous Catalysis*, Plenum Publishing, New York, 1975, p. 367
24. B. Derjaguin, *Comp. Rend. Acad. Sci. USSR, 53*, 623 (1946)
25. H. L. Weissberg, *J. Appl. Phys., 34*, 2636 (1963)
26. W. C. Strieder and S. Prager, *Physics of Fluids, 11*, 2544 (1968)
27. W. Strieder, *J. Chem. Phys., 54*, 4050 (1971)
28. R. B. Evans III, G. M. Watson and E. A. Mason, *J. Chem. Phys., 35*, 2076 (1961)
29. R. B. Evans III, G. M. Watson and E. A. Mason, *J. Chem. Phys., 36*, 1894 (1962)
30. E. A. Mason, R. B. Evans III and G. M. Watson, *J. Chem. Phys., 38*, 1808 (1963)
31. H. A. M. Van Erkelen, *J. Catalysis, 29*, 75 (1973)

Chapter 2

Detection of Porosity in Solids

Many of the useful properties of solids arise from reactions between the solid surfaces and various gases, the reaction being limited to the interfacial regions. Hence, adsorbents comprise the group of solids of major theoretical and practical importance. Irrespective of their chemical nature, adsorbents are usually classified as nonporous or porous. The nonporous adsorbents include those in which the radii of curvature of their surfaces are very large and basically tend to infinity. In actual fact, however, in most cases study is made of nonporous adsorbents with a specific surface area of the order of tens of square metres per gram, which are already highly dispersed solids. A typical example is graphitized carbon black with spherical particles having radii of about 15 nm and a specific surface area close to $100 \ m^2/g$.

Adsorbent pores are voids or cavities in solids which usually communicate with each other. As already pointed out in Chapter 1, their shapes and sizes differ widely and depend on the nature of the adsorbent and the method by which it is obtained. The linear sizes of pores of any cross-sectional shape are characterized by the ratio of the area of the normal cross-section of the pore to its perimeter (Eqn. (2.4)). This ratio has the dimension of length and is termed the hydraulic radius. For cylindrical pores, the hydraulic radius is equal to half the pore radius, and for slit-shaped pores between parallel plates, the hydraulic radius is equal to half the distance between the plates. The conversion of the hydraulic radius and of the relation volume to surface to the radius of some pore models is compiled in Fig. 2.1.

From the point of view of pore sizes, which essentially determine the mechanism of adsorption and capillary phenomena occurring in them, it is expedient to divide adsorbents into three basic varieties: macroporous, mesoporous, and microporous. Adsorbents of mixed structural types may contain two or all three pore varieties. This brings paper, fabrics, and cloth (wool, cotton, nylon, etc.), building stone, coke, and wood mainly into the group of macroporous materials, and synthetic or natural adsorbents and catalysts mainly into the other two groups, being either mesoporous or microporous, or a mixture of both. This does not mean that the first group does not contain micropores and/or mesopores, or that the second group is devoid of macropores but, rather, that the characteristic properties of these materials are mainly determined by macropores in the first case and by mesopores or micropores in the second. Because with both the adsorbents and catalysts the chemical processes take place at their surface, the surface area which is available for these processes is of major importance. This surface area is determined by the surface area in micro- and in mesopores. Macropores, nevertheless, play an important role in the operational use of these substances, since the kinetics of the whole process depends as well on the rate of diffusion in these pores.

2.1 Definitions and survey of measuring methods

The properties of porous materials differ widely from those of the compact bulk: the apparent density is lower, in the case of open pores, a flow of liquids or gases through the material is possible, heat flow is reduced, foreign molecules can be stored in the voids, the internal surface of open pores is much larger than the outer geometric projection surface and is available for catalytic and other chemical or physical surface reactions.

All these properties and effects can be used for the detection of porosity which is characterized in geometric terms mainly by the specific surface area, the porosity, the pore size distribution and the characteristic pore shape. The *specific surface areas* customary (and generally in this book) is related to unit mass,

$$S = S_s m_s^{-1} \tag{2.1}$$

where S_s and m_s denotes the sample surface and mass respectively. It may be more useful to relate the specific surface area to the total volume V_s of the sample resulting in a value Σ which has the dimension [length^{-1}]:

$$\Sigma = S_s V_s^{-1} = S_s (V_{m,s} + V_{p,s})^{-1} \tag{2.2}$$

where $V_{m,s}$ is the volume of the matrix material and $V_{p,s}$ the volume of the pores in the sample. The two quantities can be converted into each other by means of the apparent density of the sample, ρ_a:

$$\Sigma = S \rho_a \tag{2.3}$$

It may be mentioned here that the volume-related specific surface area has the reciprocal dimension of the *hydraulic radius* which, however, has quite another physical meaning. It is usually defined as the ratio of the cross-sectional area S_c of a cylindrical tube to its perimeter d_c:

$$r_h = S_c d_c^{-1} \tag{2.4}$$

or as in Eqn. (4.23) as the ratio of pore volume to its surface area,

$$r_h = V_p S_p^{-1} \tag{2.5}$$

Both definitions result in identical values for cylindrical or slit-shaped pores but not for some other geometries (compare Fig. 2.1).

24

Pore model	$r_h = \dfrac{S_c}{d_c}$	$\dfrac{V}{A}$
Cylindrical tube	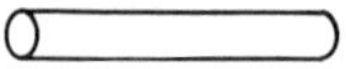 $\dfrac{r}{2}$	$\dfrac{r}{2}$
Hollow sphere	 $\dfrac{r}{2}$	$\dfrac{r}{3}$
Hollow cube	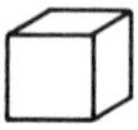 $\dfrac{r}{2}$	$\dfrac{r}{3}$
Slit	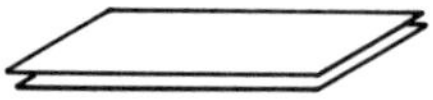 $\dfrac{r}{4}$	$\dfrac{r}{4}$

Fig. 2.1 Relation between the hydraulic radius (ratio of cross-sectional area to perimeter of a cylindrical tube) and of the ratio volume/radius and the radius or half the distance r of various pore types

The *specific pore volume* V_p is related to unit mass

$$V_p = V_{p,s} m_s^{-1} = \rho_a^{-1} = \rho_s^{-1} \tag{2.6}$$

and the porosity Π to unit volume

$$\Pi = V_{p,s} V_s^{-1} = V_{p,s}(V_{p,s} + V_{m,s})^{-1}$$
$$= V_p(V_p + V_m)^{-1} = V_p(V_p + \rho_m^{-1})^{-1} \tag{2.7}$$

where ρ_m denotes the density of the matrix material, and ρ_a the apparent density: mass related to the geometric volume.

Extending the IUPAC classification, pores can be classified by their characteristic pore width $2r$ into:

macropores $\qquad\qquad 2r \geqslant 50$ nm
mesopores $\qquad 50$ nm $\geqslant 2r \geqslant 2$ nm
micropores $\qquad 2$ nm $\geqslant 2r$
ultramicropores $\leqslant$ molecular diameter of adsorptives (about 0.6 nm)

Macropores determine widely the apparent material density and are responsible for the transport of gases and liquids in the system. Mesopores contribute significantly to the specific surface area and thus play an important role in chemical surface reactions. Micropores contribute to the accessible surface. Because transport in micropores is difficult, they contribute less to surface reactions. Micro- and ultramicropores are responsible for the mechanical properties of a solid.

Futhermore, a distinction has to be made between closed and open pores, the sum of which constitutes the total pore volume. A variety of materials containing closed pores is manufactured because of their low (apparent) density and heat conductivity. The pore width in general corresponds to that of macropores. Closed pores sometimes are generated during corrosion processes; these pores may be in the range of meso- and micropores. Closed pores do not contribute to the specific surface area, but to the apparent density, thus disturbing some gravimetric measurements and calculations, e.g. that according to Eqn. (2.3).

Materials containing open pores, which are accessible from the surface, may be used as adsorbents, desiccants, catalysts or carrier materials for catalysts, as storage matrices for greases, drugs, etc. In this book, unless stated otherwise, pores are to be understood as open pores.

Delle[1,2] gives a survey of methods applicable to the measurement of total and open porosity, respectively (see Tables 2.1 and 2.2). Performing both measurements, the portions of closed and open pores of a material can thus be determined.

All methods for the determination of porosity discussed in the following sections differ not only in the measuring range but also in applicability and results. In many cases it is advisable to use two or more methods for the characterisation of a material.

— Density measurements by buoyancy in a gas or in liquids and comparison of the results with the theoretical density of the nonporous material can be used to determine the total porosity and, after wetting of the accessible pores, to determine the porosity due to closed pores. Irregularities like lattice defects of the bulk may be sources of error. The method is described in section 2.2.
— Touch methods and light microscopy provide information on the outer surface structure with a resolution down to the micrometer range. These methods are described in sections 3.12 and 3.9, respectively.
— Electron microscopy permits measurements down to the nanometer range but is restricted to the outer surface or to sections (see section 3.9).
— Quantitative image analysis can be used in some cases to investigate the macropore system using the gray value contrasts between bulk material and pores. Pore models of the resulting cross-sectional pore areas can be used to derive pore volumes and specific surface areas. Application of quantitative image analysis to transmission electron micrographs extends the investigations to meso- and microporosity.
— X-ray small-angle scattering (see section 3.10) gives the total pore volume in the mesopore range.

Table 2.1   Methods for the determination of total porosity (after Ref. 3)

Procedure	Range of pore sizes	Assumptions	Advantages	Disadvantages
Calculation of apparent density	Total		Easy calculation from commonly known property	
Small angle X-ray scattering	$1\ \mathrm{nm} \leqslant d \leqslant 100\ \mathrm{nm}$		Short time method	Complicated valuation programme
Small angle neutron scattering	$1\ \mathrm{nm} \leqslant d \leqslant 100\ \mathrm{nm}$		Short time method	Much experimental effort, limited to nuclear centres
Quantitative image analysis	$d > 20\ \mathrm{nm}$	Spherical pores	Large pores can be measured, optical checking is possible, also microporosity can be measured by analysing TEM photograph	Limitation to large pores, significant errors in coarse grain materials, area information, for spatial informations large mathematical effort
Image analysis system	$d > 20\ \mathrm{nm}$		Size measurements on pores of irregular shapes, application on ceramographic sect., fig., microphot., view graphs	Subjective measurement, area information

Table 2.2 Methods for the determination of open porosity (after Ref. 3)

Procedure	Range of pore sizes	Assumptions	Advantages	Disadvantages
Xylene and water impregnation	$d > 100$ nm		Simple method, short time	No pore size distribution, specimens with small diameter
Liquid metal impregnation			True pore network	No measurable pore size distribution, carbon burn-off
Air/He penetration	Some nm depending upon gas applied		Very short time method ~1 min good reproducibility, no influence on sample	No pore size distribution
N_2 adsorption	$d < 50$ nm		Correlation with BET surface	Complicated evaluation programme
Mercury impregnation	~4 nm $< d \approx 4$ μm	Cylindrical pores	Much in use, comparable data, extended range of pore sizes	Danger of breaking pore walls, large pores are filled at atmosph. pressure

			Total porosity	Saccate porosity	Open porosity	Permeable poros.	Micropore volume	Specific surface	Mean pore size	Pore size distn.	Pore shape
DIRECT	STEREOLOGY	Phase integration; areal analysis	×								
		Lineal analysis; point-counting	×								
		Intercept analysis						×	×	×	×
		Serial sectioning								×	×
INDIRECT	FLUID DISPLACEMENT	Buoyancy	×		×						
		Pycnometry	×		×						
		Gas volumetry			×						
	FLUID FLOW	Transient gas flow		×	×						
		Steady gas or liquid flow				×		×	(a)		
	INTERFACIAL CURVATURE	Suction & pressure porosimetry						(b)		×	
		Capillary condensation			×			(b)		×	
		Freezing-point depression						(b)		×	
	ADSORPTION	Adsorption of gases & vapours					×	×	(c)		
		Adsorption from solution						×	(c)		
		Molecular sieve effects					(d)				
		Heat of wetting						×			
	OTHER	Electrical conductance				×					(e)
		Radiation attenuation	×								
		Radiation scattering						×	×		
		Wetting kinetics			×				×		

(a) Size of equal cylindrical pores of same total volume, giving same permeability.
(b) Calculated by integration
(c) Calculated from surface-to-volume ratio, if porosity is also known.
(d) Can give size-distribution of micropores.
(e) By Astbury's method, based on wetting kinetics.

Fig. 2.2 Methods for the determination of pore properties according to Haynes[4]

— Flow methods (section 3.7) can be used to measure the porosity, the flow resistance, and the specific surface area of through pores and of compacted powders.
— Impregnation of the pore system (after evacuation) with a suitable liquid (xylene, water) and measurement of the mass increase results in the open pore volume, using the density of the liquid. The variation in buoyancy has to be taken into account.
— Measurement of the displacement of a non-adsorbing gas (helium) and comparison of the results with the displacement of a similar nonporous sample or of the sample impregnated with substance like wax gives the open porosity.
— With intrusion of liquids (mercury, water) or displacement of liquids (water) by gases (air) the pore radius distribution in the macropore range and to some extent in the mesopore range can be determined. These methods are discussed in Chapter 4.

— Adsorption and condensation methods give the specific surface area, the pore radius distribution in the meso- and micropore range and to some extent deliver results for a discussion of pore shape. These methods are discussed in detail in the following, and in Part 3.
— In addition to these physical methods, chemical and spectroscopic methods may be applied for porosity measurements, as discussed in Part 2.

In Fig. 2.2 Haynes[4] gives a survey of many methods in use (compare as well Appendix A). A survey of the range of the most common methods is shown in Fig. 2.3.

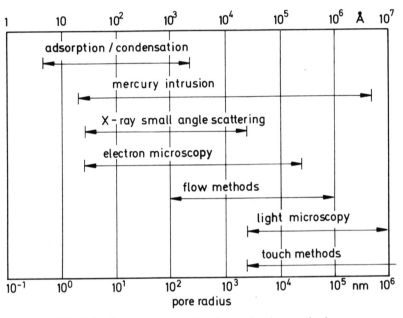

Fig. 2.3   Survey on pore size determination methods

2.2 Density measurements

If the density of the matrix material is known, the porosity Π can be determined by measuring the apparent density ρ_a of the porous material[5] according to

$$\Pi = 1 - \rho_a/\rho_m \qquad (2.8)$$

where ρ_m denotes the theoretical density of the nonporous matrix material. According to the definition of density,

$$\rho = mV^{-1} \qquad (2.9)$$

the parameters can be measured in the usual way by mass and volume determination. In the case of large and compact materials the total volume of a porous body may sometimes be found from measurement of the external dimensions.

In the case of irregular shaped bodies or powders the displacement of a non-wetting liquid can be measured. If necessary, the solid may be rendered non-wettable by a surface treatment. A certain error resulting in a too high apparent density arises because the hydrostatic pressure can force some liquid into the pores. This effect can be avoided by covering the surface with an impermeable coating of known or negligible density, or impregnation of the sample, thus filling up the pore entrances with low density material.

Another method is to saturate a compact sample with a wetting liquid after evaporation of the pore system in vacuum[5]. Then the wet sample is weighed in air (m_g) and under the liquid (m_l) of density ρ_e. The total volume V_t results as

$$V_t = (m_g - m_l)\rho_l^{-1} \tag{2.10}$$

The weak point of this method is the measurement of the wet sample in air which is subject to an error of about 0.02%.

By the same method we obtain the density of the matrix material using the equation

$$\rho_m = \frac{1}{1 - m_l/m_m} \tag{2.11}$$

with m_m mass of the dry matrix. In both cases the influence of closed pores is negligible.

The volume of the matrix furthermore can be found by the measurement with a pycnometer after having saturated the pores under vacuum with the wetting liquid used in the pycnometer. In the case of micro- and mesoporous material this takes a considerable time. Difficulties arise if the material changes the dimensions of the pore system during drying. In special cases, e.g. hollow glass beds, the apparent density, and with nonporous particles, the true density can be determined, by immersing the material into a liquid with a density slightly lower than the particle density. The material floats to a certain level corresponding to its hydrostatic pressure (Andreasen method). In the case of crystalline material the matrix density can be determined by means of X-ray diffraction.

Alternatively, the volume of the matrix can be measured by gas volumetry. After placing the sample in a gas-filled vessel this is connected to an evacuated second vessel, both of known volume. After temperature equalization the volume can be calculated using Boyle's law. Some error arises from unexpected adsorption (see section 2.3). To minimize this effect, helium is customarily used because of its negligible adsorption.

The void volume can be determined by filling the pores completely with adsorbate, when approaching the saturation pressure. Using the density of the liquid the total pore volume can be estimated (Gurvitsch rule).

2.3 The measurement of the adsorption isotherm

Detection of porosity in solids, especially with regard to micro- and meso-porosity, is based largely on comparison of adsorption isotherms measured on both a nonporous (reference) sample and the sample under test; comparison can either be direct or indirect (*vide infra*). The two commonly utilized methods of measurement of adsorption isotherms are the volumetric procedure and the gravimetric technique, although other methods may be used, such as chromatography or certain dynamic systems. Joy[6] has reviewed all existing techniques. The decision of which method to use is usually influenced by the nature of the gas or vapour used and the time which is needed to reach equilibrium at different pressures. Many details of gravimetric methods will be described later in this book, and we will deal in this part mainly with the volumetric techniques.

A volumetric unit measures the volumes of gases adsorbed using the gas laws. Gases which approximate to the ideal gas laws in their behaviour are expected, therefore, to yield more reliable results, and one finds that the gases used extensively are nitrogen[7-10], nitrous oxide[11], argon[12] and krypton[13].

The volumetric unit is most commonly used with nitrogen as the adsorbate at a temperature of 77 K. A detailed description of a conventional apparatus used for this purpose has been given, for example by Lippens and Hermans[14], but the conventional BET apparatus has various disadvantages:

(a) the difficulty of removing the heat of adsorption as a result of the rather large amount of substance used;
(b) the difficulty of detecting equilibrium as a result of the rather large dead volume present;
(c) the volumes adsorbed are added cumulatively;
(d) the difficulty in detecting and preventing any leakage during the measurement;
(e) the difficulty in interrupting the measurement.

These difficulties were remedied by the development of a micro-BET apparatus[14,15], a diagram of which is shown in Fig. 2.4. The principal parts of this apparatus are as follows:

1. Gas burette (A), filled with mercury, of capacity 100 ml, graduated in 0.1 ml.
2. Adsorption vessel (C) closed off from the system by means of a filter plate (b) to prevent contamination of the apparatus by solid matter.
3. Mercury pump (B) for the transport of gas from burette (A) to adsorption vessel (C).
4. A capillary differential manometer (E).
5. Vacuum and pressure chamber (H) to equalize the pressure in the left part of the manometer (E) and that in the adsorption vessel (C).
6. Manometer (G) indicating the pressure in the left part of manometer (E).

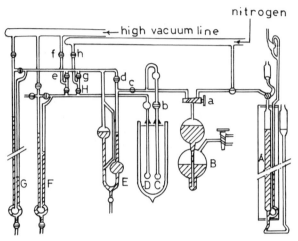

Fig. 2.4 Apparatus for the measurement of nitrogen adsorption isotherms[15]. (Courtesy Lippens, Linsen, and de Boer)

7. Manometer (F) connected to vessel (D), which is immersed in liquid nitrogen and contains some pure condensed nitrogen. This manometer acts as a liquid nitrogen thermometer.

Under all circumstances, the adsorbent must be degassed prior to undertaking the measurements, and here knowledge of the prehistory of the sample determine the set of conditions to be used during degassing, and whether pumping should be carried out at room temperature or at elevated temperatures. In most cases a high vacuum of 10^{-3} Pa is sufficient. That the apparatus is gas-tight is much more important than the final vacuum reached. A liquid nitrogen filled cold trap should be inserted in the main pumping line to prevent back diffusion of mercury or oil from the pump to the sample. Outgassing should be continued until the normal final vacuum of the apparatus is approximated. To ensure that no further gas is evolved from the sample the pumping line including the cold trap is shut off, and the pressure should remain at that pressure for some minutes. In general a degassing temperature of 400 K is sufficient. For sensitive materials and for materials that degas slowly (e.g. microporous), the most suitable degassing conditions must be selected.

Details for the calibration of the apparatus have been given[4,5]. For the calibration of the dead volume (C), the stopcocks c,d,e, and f are opened for degassing till the pressure falls below 10^{-3} Pa, then the stopcocks are closed. Liquid nitrogen is then placed around (C), and by means of the mercury pump (B), a certain amount of nitrogen is transferred from the gas burette (A) to the measuring system (C). If the pressure in (C) increases, the mercury level in both arms of (E) is balanced by increasing the pressure in the left-hand limb of (E) by opening stopcocks (g) and (h). If the pressure indicated by (G) is equal to p_G (mm Hg) and the difference between the mercury levels of (E) is p_E (mm Hg), the pressure in (C) is:

$$p = p_G - p_E \tag{2.12}$$

The dead volume V_d is defined as the volume of nitrogen (in ml at STP) giving a pressure in (C) of 1000 mm Hg under the prevailing experimental conditions. If the volume of gas (ml at STP) introduced from (A) into (C) is equal to V,

$$V = 0.001 \, p \, (V_d - Kp_E) \tag{2.13}$$

in which K is a constant given by the diameter of the capillary of (E). The quantities V_a and K can be determined by varying V as a function of p_E. When measuring the adsorption isotherm, V_d must be diminished by an amount of gas at 1000 mm Hg under the measuring conditions, namely the amount of gas that has been replaced by the volume of the sample to be measured. This amount V_s is given by:

$$V_s = \frac{1000}{760} \times \frac{273}{78} \times V_{sp} \times G \times 1.04 = 4.78 \times V_{sp} \times G \tag{2.14}$$

in which V_{sp} is the specific volume of the substance, G (the weight in grams, and 1.04 is the correction for the ideal gas law.

The adsorption isotherm is measured in the same manner as the dead volume. If the total volume of the gas in (C) is equal to V, the volume V_a adsorbed by 1 g of the solid to be investigated is given by

$$V_a = \frac{1}{G}\left[V - \frac{p_G - p_E}{1000} \times (V_d - V_s - Kp_E)\right] \tag{2.15}$$

The readings should always maintain equilibrium, and the maximum equilibrium pressure obtainable measured in (C) is taken as the saturation pressure.

It has been reported that the presence of mercury vapour can materially affect the nitrogen adsorption isotherm of certain solids[16]. The use of a pressure transducer with a fixed doser system was suggested by Dollimore et al.[17] to overcome this difficulty. A diagram of this unit is shown in Fig. 2.5. A thermostatically controlled volume doser (A) is calibrated by both mercury and gaseous expansion experiments. A pressure transducer (B), thermostatically controlled, is incorporated into the constant volume, and it measures the pressure of the adsorbate. A Toepler pump (C) may be used to obtain relative pressures approaching unity. The adsorption sample bulb (D) has a capacity of approximately 3 ml.

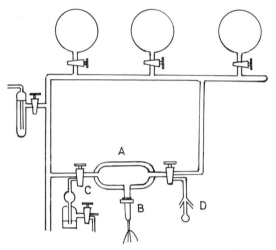

Fig. 2.5 The basic features of the fixed doser volumetric unit incorporating a transducer for pressure measurements[69]. (Courtesy Dollimore, Spooner, and Turner)

In the United Kingdom a volumetric BET apparatus has been standardized[18]. Details of the design are shown in Figs 2.6 to 2.8. The vacuum manifold consists of a rotary vane pump followed by a mercury or oil diffusion pump with cold trap. A McLeod gauge is added for the vacuum measurement and leak detection. The mercury manometer which is an integral part of the gas burette is accurate to within 0.1 mm Hg (~10 Pa). Because this instrument is used especially for surface area determination (see Chapter 3), the volume of the gas burette is chosen so that it can deliver the appropriate volume of gas expected to be adsorbed at a relative pressure of 0.5 in a limited number of increments. A sample size with a surface area between 20 and 200 m² is recommended. Designs of sample bulbs of 5 and 10 cm³ are shown in Fig. 2.7. The narrow tube connecting the bottom of the bulb shown in Fig. 2.7(b) should impede the scattering of powder during degassing.

Measurements with krypton have been reported, for example, by Haul[19], Litvan[20] and Jaycock[21]; units are described by Dollimore *et al.*[22] and by Sing and Swallow[13]. The low vapour pressure of krypton (231 Pa at 77 K) means that the dead space error is minimized[23]. With gravimetric units krypton isotherms are usually measured at 90 K[19]; there the buoyancy error is negligible. The use of krypton labelled with [85]Kr has been reported[24]; a formerly commercial unit is described by Houtman and Medema[25,26] (Fig. 3.29). The adsorbed mass in this apparatus was determined by means of a Geiger–Müller counter.

With xenon, surface area measurements have been performed by Kini *et al.* at 195 K[27], by Watanabe and Yamashina[28] and by Chènebault and Schürenkämper at 77 K[29] using a mixture of natural and [133]Xe. Benzene and water isotherms are usually used[30] for the characterization of activated carbon.

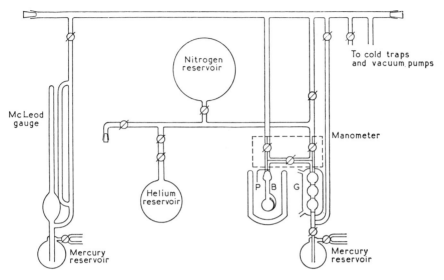

McLeod
gauge

Nitrogen
reservoir

To cold traps
and vacuum pumps

Manometer

Helium
reservoir

P B G

Mercury
reservoir

Mercury
reservoir

B Sample bulb
G Gas burette
P Wire level probe

Fig. 2.6　Volumetric BET apparatus according to the British Standard 4359

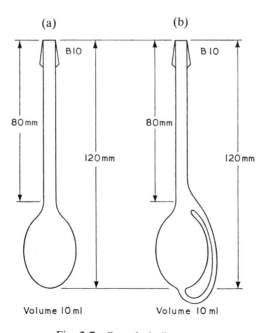

(a)　　　　　　(b)

B10　　　　　　B10

80mm　　　　　80mm

120mm　　　　　120mm

Volume 10 ml　　Volume 10 ml

Fig. 2.7　Sample bulbs

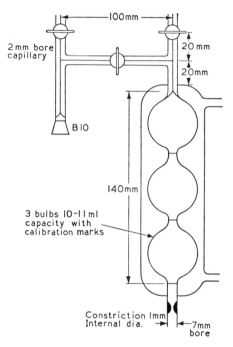

Fig. 2.8 Gas burette

Nineteen commercialized instruments which are mostly out of production today are described in Ref. (31); the most interesting designs are reported briefly as follows. An automated form of the conventional apparatus 'Adsorptomat' for nitrogen (and other gases) adsorption has been designed by Ballou and Doolen[32] to provide automatic injection (or withdrawal) of small standard volume increments (or decrements) of gas while giving a continuous record of the gas pressure above the adsorbent. The pressure is measured by means of a differential pressure gauge so arranged as to maintain constant volume of the adsorption system. A particular advantage of the apparatus is that one can without difficulty obtain fifty points on each branch of the isotherm. The isotherm, therefore, can be plotted in considerable detail. In Schlosser's Betograph[33], argon is allowed to enter the adsorbent very slowly and the pressure is recorded continuously. As the passage of gas is very slow, it is assumed that the system is always in a state of adsorption equilibrium. This assumption is not necessarily justified, particularly in the range of pressures where capillary condensation takes place, and it is doubtful, therefore, whether this technique can be used for the determination of pore size distribution.

The Areatron of Hansen and Littman[34] was designed for a single-point argon adsorption measurement at 77 K. The injection of gas is throttled by a capillary. The time to obtain the preset equilibrium pressure is used as a measure for the adsorbed amount.

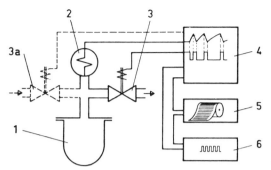

Fig. 2.9 Sorboprint after Kraus; 1 measuring chamber, 2 pressure transducer, 3, 3a solenoid valves, 4 amplifier and governor, 5 impulse counter, 6 impulse generator

The Sorboprint (Fig. 2.9) according to Kraus[35,36], designed for degassing determination, was able to measure adsorption in the range of 1 to 3000 Pa. It consisted of a calibrated sample vessel, a Pirani actuated pressure control and two solenoid valves, one connected to a gas reservoir, the other one to a rotary vane vacuum pump. As a measure for the gas quantity injected or sucked off, the number of times of actuation of the solenoid valve to attain a preset pressure was noted.

Also out of production are most of the widely used carrier gas instruments, where the adsorptive nitrogen was mixed with the non-adsorbable helium (Fig. 2.10). The advantage of these instruments (Sor-BET, Sorptometer[37], Isorpta Analyser, Surfalyser) was that a vacuum was avoided, the degassing being carried out at elevated temperatures in a helium gas stream. This, however, is a doubtful measure in the case of a sample containing small pores. The adsorption of nitrogen at 77 K from the mixture was measured either by gas chromatographic methods (change of heat conduction of the mixture) or by the pressure decrease. As a supplement to a gas chromatograph, the equipment is rather inexpensive[38-40].

In 1981, only four manufacturers were producing volumetric nitrogen sorption measuring instruments, one gravimetric and one-carrier gas apparatus. In addition, some manufacturers of vacuum balances and thermogravimetric instruments offer ancillary equipment for sorption experiments. These are mentioned in Part 3. Manufacturers addresses are listed in Appendix D.

Quantachrome produces two compact instruments after Lowell[41] working on the carrier gas method with a helium/nitrogen mixture at 77 K. With the 'Quantasorb' the measurement of a complete isotherm is possible; with the 'Monosorb' only one point in the BET region is measured. Mixtures of helium and nitrogen with various partial pressures are passed through a small U-shaped cell containing the sample, the gas flow being controlled by a flowmeter. Adsorption and desorption occur when the sample is immersed into and then withdrawn from the liquid nitrogen bath. Changes in the ratio of

38

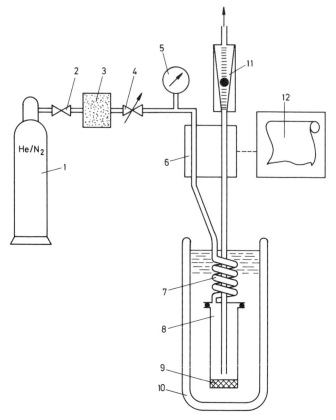

Fig. 2.10 Carrier gas apparatus for sorption measurements; 1 cylinder with carrier gas/sorptive mixture, 2 reducing valve, 3 gas scrubber, 4 control valve, 5 pressure gauge, 6 heat conductivity cell, 7 gas cooler, 8 sample container, 9 sample, 10 Dewar vessel with liquid nitrogen, 11 flow meter, 12 recorder

helium to nitrogen in the flowing stream due to adsorption or desorption are sensed by a thermal conductivity detector. The signals delivered are approximately Gaussian in shape. The instantaneous signal height is proportional to the sorption rate, and the total integrated area under the curve is proportional to the quantity of gas adsorbed. In Fig. 2.11 a typical signal is shown. The signal has to be calibrated. A separate apparatus is used for prior degassing of the sample in a helium stream. The degassing is controlled by a thermal conductivity detector.

Figure 2.12 is a diagrammatic sketch of the particularly simple 'Areameter' of Haul and Dümbgen[42,43] produced by Ströhlein. The influence of volume (dead space) error is minimized by pressure difference measurements. The sample in one bulb is first degassed at elevated temperature under flowing nitrogen in a separate apparatus. A second identical bulb is filled with glass

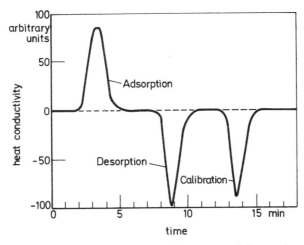

Fig. 2.11 Response on a gas chromatographic sorption measurement

spheres of the same volume. Then both volumes are filled with nitrogen at ambient temperature up to a pressure fixed by a pressure relief valve. The both vessels are cooled with liquid nitrogen. The pressure difference gives one value of the isotherm in the BET range.

Two types of sorption measuring apparatus are produced by Carlo Erba, both working on a static-volumetric principle, where adsorbate volumes are

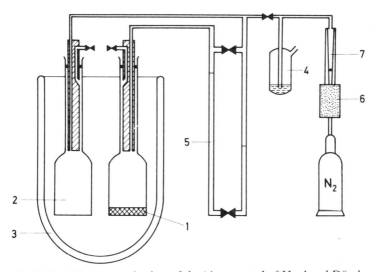

Fig. 2.12 Diagrammatic view of the 'Areameter' of Haul and Dümbgen; 1 sample bulb with sample, 2 reference bulb with glass spheres, 3 Dewar vessel with liquid nitrogen, 4 pressure relief valve, 5 oil manometer, 6 gas dryer, 7 flowmeter

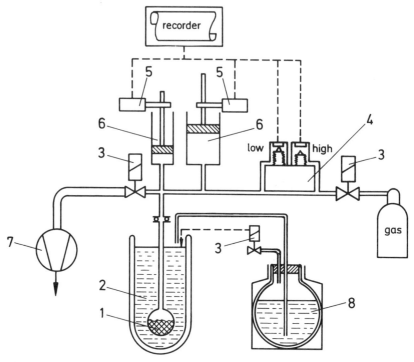

Fig. 2.13 Scheme of an automatic volumetric instrument; 1 sample vessel, 2 liquid nitrogen bath or heater, 3 solenoid valves, 4 pressure gauges and control, 5 step motors, 6 piston burettes, 7 vacuum pump, 8 liquid nitrogen reservoir for level control of the bath (2)

determined by measuring the pressure variations resulting from the adsorption of a known aliquot of nitrogen at 77 K. The 'Sorpty' is equipped with a vacuum pump and heaters for degassing. Nitrogen is injected up to a pressure preset in the BET range by a pressure switch by use of solenoid valves and a piston burette. When this pressure has been reached, an adjustable timer is actuated. If after the preset time no pressure equilibrium is observed, another nitrogen volume is induced, and this procedure can be repeated. The 'Sorptomatic' (Fig. 2.13) functions on the same principle, but it is designed for the stepwise measurement of complete adsorption and desorption isotherms with various gases. The instrument is equipped with two piston burettes and an electronic pressure transducer. Results are presented in digital form for on-line evaluation of the measured isotherm.

Two types of instruments are offered by Micromeritics: a manually operated surface area analyser and an automatic instrument 'Digisorb' for the measurement of complete adsorption and desorption isotherms, both working on a static-volumetric principle with nitrogen at 77 K. Degassing with the surface area analyser is performed with dry nitrogen at elevated temperature. Nitrogen is injected with a motor-activated piston burette up to a preset

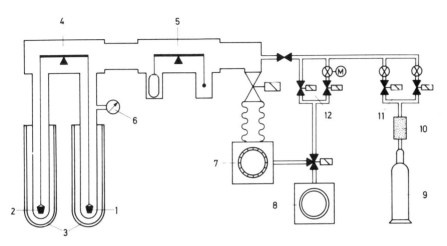

Fig. 2.14 Scheme of the 'Gravimat'; 1 sample pan, 2 counterweight, 3 Dewar vessels or heater, 4 sorption balance, 5 buoyancy pressure gauge, 6 ionization vacuum gauge, 7 turbo molecular pump, 8 rotary vane pump, 9 pressure cylinder for nitrogen or other gases, 10 gas scrubber, 11, 12 pressure controller (combination of solenoid, motor and needle valves

pressure. The movement of the piston to displace the gas is converted directly to surface area coverage and indicated in square meters by digital readout. The 'Digisorb' is equipped with a vacuum aggregate including an oil diffusion pump. Up to five samples can be measured simultaneously and five others meanwhile degassed. A computer is built in for the evaluation of the data.

The unique automatic gravimetric instrument 'Gravimat' (Fig. 2.14) of Sandstede and Robens[44,45] is manufactured by Netzsch. It is equipped with one or more electromagnetic microbalances after Gast[46]. An additional microbalance equipped with a glass ballon serves for the pressure measurement and control by buoyancy. A turbomolecular pump permits the balance case to be evacuated down to 10^{-5} Pa. The gas pressure (nitrogen or other) can be varied in 100 steps between 1 and $2 \cdot 10^5$ Pa. The temperature can be controlled using liquid gases down to 77 K and for degassing the sample up to 2000 K. With this apparatus automatic discontinuous isobaric measurements of adsorption and desorption isotherms are possible, and also thermogravimetric experiments with means of a temperature programme of the heater.

2.4 Comparison of methods for isotherm measurement

Finally, a critical assessment of the three kinds of adsorption isotherm measurement is made. To establish the isotherm we need to know, basically, five measuring quantities: the sample mass, the temperature, the saturation pressure of the adsorptive, and the adsorbed amount (as volume or mass) as a function of pressure. The three methods differ principally in the method of determination of the adsorbed amount.

The advantage of the carrier gas method is the compact and inexpensive equipment which comprises no moving parts except some valves. The handling is easy, and because the measurement is made under streaming gas, temperature equilibrium is established somewhat faster than with both the other methods. All parameters can be measured independently; this is also true for the adsorbed amount. Using a heat conductivity cell, degassing can be controlled. The most serious drawback is the very indirect method of determination of the adsorbed amount by a heat conductivity measurement. Therefore gauging with an absolute method is inevitable. Correction of the sample mass by degassing is difficult to estimate.

To compare the volumetric and the gravimetric method, first the most serious errors of both methods will be compared[47]. In the volumetric measuring method, this is the error involved in the calibration of the dead space in the sample vessel, whereas in the gravimetric method it is the buoyancy error[48-50]. In both calibrations the error is due to unexpected adsorption.

2.4.1 Error due to the calibration procedure for the dead space in the volumetric method

Consider a calibration procedure using helium as an inert gas with respect to the sample material and is for practical purposes not adsorbed at room temperature. In Fig. 2.15 two volumes are shown connected by a tube with a valve where V_b is the volume of the burette from which the sample vessel V_d will be provided with proportioned amounts of nitrogen. The sample vessel, which contains the sample and the dead space, is at first evacuated, whereas V_b is filled with helium at the pressure p_0. Before opening the valve, room temperature T_r is established in both volumes.

After the valve has been opened, the gas pressure in both volumes becomes p. By assuming the conservation of mass, we obtain:

$$\frac{V_b p_0}{RT_r} = \frac{V_b p}{RT_r} + \frac{V_d p}{RT_r} + \mathcal{H} \frac{A_s}{A_{He}} \frac{1}{6 \times 10^{23}} \tag{2.16}$$

where A_s is the surface area of the sample and walls of V_d, A_{He} is the surface area occupied by one helium atom, and $\mathcal{H}$ is the specific covering factor of the

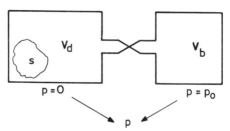

Fig. 2.15 Calculation of the dead space error

surface defined as the number of sites occupied divided by $p \times$ number of available sites. By ignoring the volume of the adsorbed helium, the resulting error δV_b is given by

$$\delta V_b = -RT \mathcal{H}_{He} A_s / A_{He} \cdot 6 \times 10^{23} \tag{2.17}$$

When performing the actual adsorption measurement, gas from V_b at P_0 is added to the sample at temperature T_s using a gas of molecular weight M_w. The adsorbed mass is calculated from the measured final pressure p_f using

$$\frac{V_b p_0}{RT_r} = \frac{V_b p_f}{RT_r} + \frac{V_d p_f}{RT_s} + \frac{m_{ads}}{M_w} \tag{2.18}$$

The error δm_{ads} now satisfies

$$\delta m_{ads} = M_w \frac{p_f}{RT_s} \tag{2.19}$$

and

$$\delta V_d = M_w \frac{T_r}{T_s} p_f \mathcal{H}_{He} \frac{A_s}{A_{He}} \frac{1}{6 \times 10^{23}} \tag{2.20}$$

As an example, for $M_w = 30$; $p_f = 10^5$ Pa; $T_r//T_s = 4$; $\mathcal{H}_{He} = 10^{-1}$ Pa^{-1}; $A_s = 10^2$ m^2; and $A_{He} = 3 \times 10^{-20}$ m^2:

$$V_b = 100 \text{ mm}^3 \text{ and } m_{ads} = 5 \times 10^{-4} \text{ g}$$

The error increases with pressure and cumulates in each step of the incrementally measured isotherm.

2.4.2 Error due to buoyancy in the gravimetric method

Using compensating loads of selected density, the buoyancy force of the balance beam may be cancelled completely. In the same way the buoyancy force of the sample can be compensated by using a counterweight with negligible surface area and similar mean molecular mass[50]. To determine the buoyancy one can perform weight determinations at room temperature under vacuum and under helium, corresponding to the procedure of the volumetric method. As the difference of the force measured we obtain:

$$F_{vac} - F_{He} = V_s g \rho_{He,r} + g \mathcal{H} p \frac{A_s}{A_{He}} \frac{1}{6 \times 10^{23}} \tag{2.21}$$

where g stands for the acceleration due to gravity and $\rho_{He,r}$ for the density of helium at room temperature and pressure p. If the adsorbed amount is ignored, the error δV_s becomes

$$\delta V_s = -RT_r \mathcal{H} \frac{A_s}{A_{He}} \frac{1}{6 \times 10^{23}} \qquad (2.22)$$

This expression surprisingly enough equals the error of the dead space calculated above.

When performing the actual adsorption measurement at temperature T_s, the related error satisfies

$$m_{ads} = M_w T_r p \mathcal{H} / T_s A_{He} \cdot 6 \times 10^{23} \qquad (2.23)$$

which again is identical to the final error in the volumetric case. However, during the measurement of an isotherm, this error *only* increases proportionally to the pressure of the measuring gas. In the volumetric method the error is also accumulated at each step. So attempts to secure detailed shapes of isotherms must become counterproductive because of the cumulative error.

In contrast to the gravimetric method, with the volumetric method the adsorbed amount is measured indirectly and is dependent on the pressure measurement. Nevertheless, using carefully calibrated apparatus no serious deviations have been observed. Because of the cumulative error, the fine structure of the isotherm, however, cannot be resolved. The errors discussed can be reduced by using a measuring device of symmetrical design. Symmetrical beam balances are usual here. Symmetrical volumetric apparatus are also possible, as shown by the example of the Haul–Dümbgen apparatus (Fig. 2.12), which, however, is only designed for surface area determination by a one-point measurement.

For surface area determinations the error becomes insignificant when using krypton as adsorbate. In volumetric measurements krypton is used at 77 K, whereas in gravimetric measurements it is used mostly at 90 K. Both kinds of measurements are twice as sensitive as with nitrogen with regard to the molecular area (and mass) of the krypton atom. Unfortunately, the molecular area of krypton seems to be much more dependent on the sample material than does that of nitrogen. Besides, pore size determinations are not possible because krypton is adsorbed in quasi-solid form.

With krypton it is possible to determine surface areas of some ten square centimetres, which means that even the surface roughness of a smooth sample is detected. Often such a surface is attached to a big bulk. In that case the volumetric method is advantageous because the sample size is unlimited, whereas the sample weight in gravimetry is limited by the maximum load of the balance.

In the applicability for sorption measurements with various gases and in their sensitivity, both methods are comparable. The advantage of the volumetric instruments is the simple and cheaper design and easy handling. A

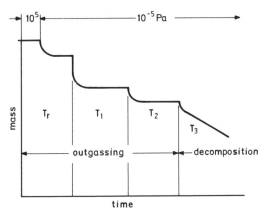

Fig. 2.16 Outgassing curve of material with
hydroxidic surface

drawback of the gravimetric method is the difficulties in adjustment and
measurement of the temperature because unlike the volumetric method the
sample is not in direct contact with the thermostat. However, as discussed in
Part 3, the right temperature can be adjusted by simple means.

A major advantage of the gravimetric method is that outgassing the sample
is facilitated by the much bigger diameter of the connecting tube between
sample and vacuum pump. The volumetric apparatus requires a capillary,
which leads to a much more time-consuming degassing procedure with higher
residual gas pressures over the sample. Attention should be drawn to the fact
that different outgassing procedures may well lead to different pore structures
of the degassed sample.

Furthermore, the degassing process is continuously monitored in
gravimetry, so that the rate and extent of the outgassing procedure can be
controlled. The curve of mass loss versus time may reveal temperature-
dependent reactions of the material or its decomposition. The typical outgassing curve of a material with a hydroxidic surface is shown in Fig. 2.16.
The first temperature rise may already be correlated with a change of the
surface area. A further advantage of the gravimetric method is the possibility
of correcting the sample mass for material lost during outgassing. This correction might easily be as high as 5 per cent and would be very difficult indeed to
estimate when using the volumetric method.

As regards research work, the most interesting aspect is that gravimetric
apparatus is more versatile than the volumetric equipment. When simply
replacing the liquid nitrogen bath by a furnace, one can measure controlled
chemical reactions of the sample with a gas as well as thermal decomposition
and drying, or one can carry out thermogravimetric analysis. Different
investigations can be performed one after the other without having to remove
the sample.

2.5 The classification of adsorption isotherms

Thousands of adsorption isotherms are accumulating, obtained during academic or industrial operations and measured on a wide variety of solids; nevertheless those isotherms which result from physical adsorption may conveniently be grouped into five types, as originally proposed by Brunauer, Deming, Deming, and Teller[51] (BDDT), more commonly referred to as the Brunauer, Emmett, and Teller[52] (BET) classification. These types are shown in Fig. 2.17, although in practice, many of these isotherms show a further upward turn as the saturation vapour pressure is approached.

The various shapes result from the different interactions of the adsorbate molecules with one another and with the adsorbent, and from the pore structure[53]. Type I is characteristic of monolayer adsorption as is involved in chemisorption (Langmuir isotherm). This shape is also observed with highly microporous adsorbents with a much sharper knee at very low relative pressures, because micropores are filled up before a monolayer can be established on the other surface. Types II and III are representative of multilayer adsorption. Type II is obtained if a large net heat of adsorption, $E_{ads} - E_l$, is required

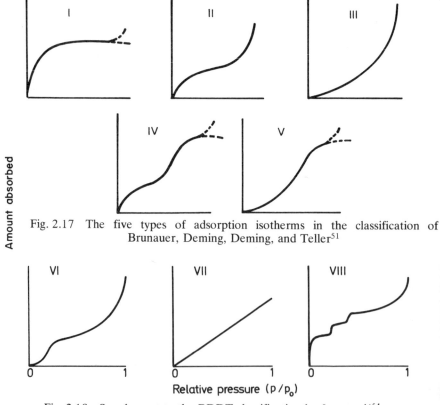

Fig. 2.17 The five types of adsorption isotherms in the classification of Brunauer, Deming, Deming, and Teller[51]

Fig. 2.18 Supplement to the BDDT classification by Jovanović[54]

to convert the sorptive from the liquid state, E_l, to the adsorbed state, E_{ads}. Type III appears at small net heat of adsorption. Isotherms of type IV and V are analogous to types II and III in cases where capillary condensation also occurs. Types II and IV are the most common shapes. Type III isotherms have been observed for the adsorption of bromine and iodine on silica gel.

Undoubtedly this classification does not cover all experimentally obtained isotherms, and, therefore, Jovanović[54] added three more types to them (Fig. 2.18). Type VI sometimes is observed on carbon and graphite[55], type VII on charcoal and silica gel[54]. Type VIII is a stepped isotherm and sometimes many more steps are reported, e.g. on graphitized carbon with krypton[56] and on pyrolysates with nitrogen[57]. Furthermore, there are borderline cases which are difficult to assign to one group or another, as for example the isotherms obtained for the system calcined gibbsite–carbon tetrachloride[58], which partake of the characteristics of types I and IV. Additional irregularities can be observed when measuring an isotherm at a temperature in the vicinity of the (two-dimensional) triple point so that with increasing pressure a phase change may occur.

Many of these isotherms (and in particular type IV isotherms) posses hysteresis loops, in which the desorption branches lie above the adsorption branches. The two commonest forms of hysteresis are those in which the desorption path rejoins the adsorption path at some lower relative pressure, and an open loop in which a measurable amount of material is irreversibly adsorbed. The closed loop is commonly associated with porous materials. The open loop can be due to a mixture of chemisorption and physical adsorption, or it could be due to irreversible changes in the solid adsorbent, as in the swelling–deswelling effects due to adsorption–desorption on layered clay minerals[59,60], and on hardened Portland cement pastes[61].

To understand these effects we will start with a molecular approach of the physisorption process. Figure 2.19(a) shows highly schematically how the potential energy ε of a single molecule varies with its distance r from a plane surface, when approaching that surface[62]. Figures 2.19(b) and (c) show the potential curve for a molecule in pores of different diameters. The minimum of the desorption energy in general is somewhat lower than the minimum of the adsorption process because an orientation of the molecule to the best adsorption site may take place. That means that when desorbing in a vacuum, often a small remainder only can be removed by supplying heat.

In the general case involving a material with pores of every size, the adsorbate is first bound in the micropores at low relative pressure, and every molecule interacts with several wall sites. After the micropores have been filled, adsorption takes place at the external surface and at the mesopore and macropore surfaces. The first adsorbate layer is bonded by the interaction between sorbent and sorbate, while bonding of the molecules of the second and subsequent layers depends on the interaction between the adsorbate molecules. The construction of the layers takes place, however, in a statistical way; this means that molecules in the second and third layer are settled before

a   b   c

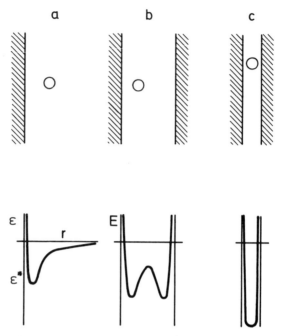

Fig. 2.19 Schematic representation of the dependence of the potential energy of a molecule on (a) its distance from a plane wall; (b) and (c) on its position within pores of different diameter[62]

the first has been completed as shown schematically in Fig. 2.20. It should be noted that a physisorbed molecule will not rest on a distinct place. Even in equilibrium we observe a permanent exchange of molecules with the gas phase and a movement of and within the adsorbate.

Capillary condensation takes place at elevated relative pressure, starting at about 0.35, and in this region often a pronounced hysteresis between the adsorption and the desorption branch of the isotherm is observed. Disregarding processes connected with a change of the pore structure (swelling), two mechanisms explain this behaviour. One is the contact angle hysteresis

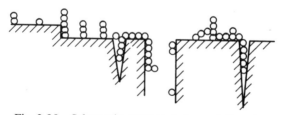

Fig. 2.20 Schematic representation of the structure of an adsorbed 'monolayer'

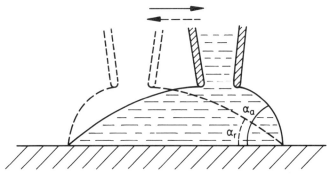

Fig. 2.21 Change of the contact angle when a droplet is moved forward (α_a: advancing) and backward (α_r: receding contact angle)

of a liquid moved on a solid surface. The contact angle on a liquid drop measured within the liquid phase as shown in Fig. 2.21 depends on the movement of the drop with regard to the surface and a stable angle region between the so-called advancing and receding angles can be measured. The same angle region can be measured in a liquid column when the pressure over the liquid is varied (Fig. 2.22). Obviously on account of this effect a pore is emptied at a lower pressure than the filling pressure (Fig. 2.23).

In a complex pore system as shown in Fig. 2.24, according to the Kelvin equation the pressure over a curved surface is lower than over a plane surface. Thus a pore with a bigger diameter behind a small pore neck will be emptied at a lower pressure. Obviously with this pore model the chance that a pore remains filled at lower pressure during the desorption process decreases with increasing complexity. This is in contrast to the 'pore blocking' effect of Doe and Haynes[63] discussed later.

Barrer et al.[64] investigated the shape of the isotherm and of the hysteresis loop to be expected theoretically for different pore shapes as calculated by means of the Kelvin equation in its usual form, for different shapes of the

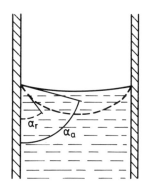

Fig. 2.22 Change of contact angle as result of moving the meniscus by pressure variation

50

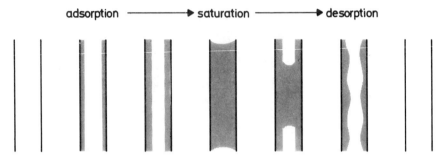

Fig. 2.23   Schematic representation of stages of adsorption and desorption in a cylindrical pore showing capillary condensation[62]

meniscus:

$$RT \ln(p_0/p) = \gamma V_L \cos(\theta) \cdot (1/R_1 + 1/R_2) \qquad (2.24)$$

where R_1 and R_2 are the two main radii of curvature of the meniscus
    γ is the surface tension
    V_L is the molar volume of the liquid phase condensing in the pore
    θ is the contact angle
    p is the vapour pressure of the meniscus
and p_0 is the saturation pressure of the bulk liquid.

Following the reverse procedure, de Boer[65] showed that in practical cases the shape of the hysteresis loop may lead to a more or less detailed picture of the shape of the pores present in a certain solid. De Boer distinguished five

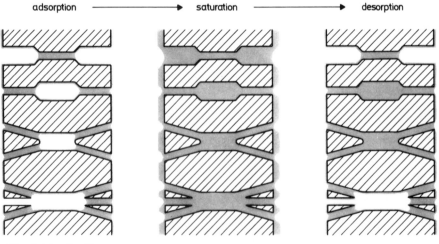

Fig. 2.24   Capillary condensation in a pore system consisting of randomly connected tubes of various diameter[62]

51

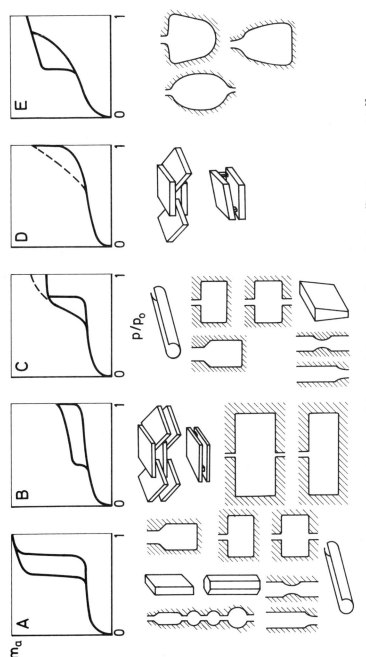

Fig. 2.25   The five types of hysteresis loop according to de Boer[65] with pore models[53]

types of hysteresis loops, as shown in Fig. 2.25, and these have proved of great significance in the interpretation of sorption isotherms. The most common are types A, B, and E.

Type A has two very steep branches and can be related in its simplest form to cylindrical pores open at both ends. The classical explanation in this type of hysteresis has been given by Cohen[66]. If the tubular pores contain widened parts, their isotherms still exhibit A-type behaviour, and in this case it is called a non-ideal A-type behaviour in the sense that the width of the hysteresis loop would be smaller than that for 'ideal' open cylinders. For a more detailed review of the different pore shapes consistent with non-ideal A-type hysteresis loops, the reader is referred to the work by Linsen and van der Heuvel[67].

A hysteresis loop of type B is characterized by a vertical adsorption branch near saturation and a steep desorption branch at intermediate relative pressures. This type of hysteresis may be caused by either ink-bottle structures with very wide bodies and narrow necks or by slit-shaped pores open at all sides.

An E-type hysteresis loop is intermediate between types A and B, with the adsorption branch sloping and the desorption branch steep. This type of hysteresis may be attributed to a distribution of pores with narrow necks of rather uniform diameters, but with wide bodies of different diameters.

It has been ascertained that this theory for the description of real pore systems is insufficient, even qualitatively. This becomes obvious by the pore models shown under the respective isotherms. Taking furthermore into account that most isotherms cannot be attributed clearly to a distinct type, it is indeed very difficult to classify a pore system on the basis of the isotherm shape.

There is as yet no satisfactory quantitative theory of hysteresis and exact interpretation of the shape of the hysteresis loop is complicated by many factors. The most obvious are:

1. The existence of a distribution of pore sizes or of different pore shapes in one and the same adsorbent.
2. In small micropores (ultramicropores) hysteresis is never observed.
3. It is not always easy to separate the pores within particles from the irregular voids formed between particles caused by packing configurations.

Walter[68] concluded that, although it is possible to deduce capillary condensation phenomena from pore structure, it is not possible, unfortunately, to derive a specific pore system from the sorption isotherm. This is easily understood when one considers that the mean radius of curvature depends on two principal radii, r_1 and r_2, of a surface:

$$\frac{1}{r_m} = \frac{1}{2}\left(\frac{1}{r_1} + \frac{1}{r_2}\right) \tag{2.25}$$

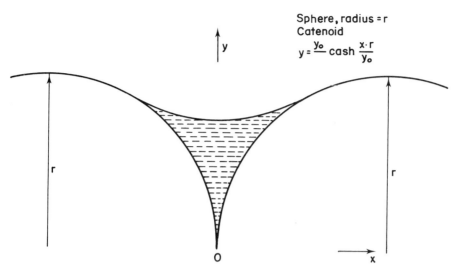

Sphere, radius = r
Catenoid
$$y = \frac{y_o}{r} \cosh \frac{x \cdot r}{y_o}$$

Fig. 2.26 Meniscus between adjacent spheres; mean curvature zero at saturation pressure

which may have different signs. For instance, the pendular condensate rings between two contacting spheres will assume the shape of a catenoid with $r_1 = -r_2$ and, consequently, infinite mean radius of curvature at saturation pressure (Fig. 2.26). Hence, in a porous material loosely composed of strings of spherical particles, capillary condensation will stop before all interior space

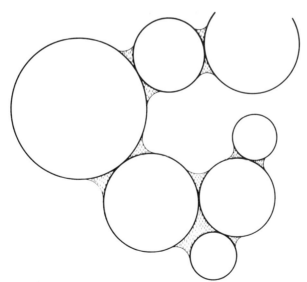

Fig. 2.27 Assembly of spheres; annular capillary condensation of vapour

54

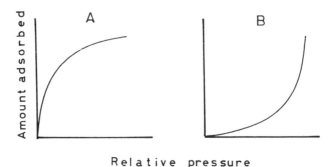

Fig. 2.28   Initial behaviour of adsorption isotherm[69]. (Courtesy Dollimore, Spooner, and Turner)

is filled with condensate, as shown schematically in Fig. 2.27. With assemblies of spheres of closer packing, capillary condensation will occur in all interstices before saturation is reached because the pendular condensate rings merge.

Doe and Haynes[63] calculated probabilistically the influence of the pore network on the shape of isotherms. They pointed out that a 'pore blocking effect' gives rise to a hysteresis independent from the shape of the single pores. This 'net-work hysteresis' in many cases cannot be distinguished from the smaller-scale events of 'pore hysteresis'. Therefore the evaluation of the desorption isotherm becomes very doubtful.

Dollimore *et al.*[69] attempted to classify adsorption isotherms first in terms of low relative pressure behaviour and then in terms of subsequent behaviour at higher pressures. The low relative pressure behaviour can be of two types (Fig. 2.28): type A, a sharply rising initial portion concave to the pressure axis, or type B, an initial portion which only rises slowly as the pressure is increased and which is convex to the pressure axis. Type A is supposed to represent strong interaction between the adsorbate and the adsorbent, and in the original BET theory lateral adsorbate–adsorbate interaction is not considered. It is from this initial portion that the surface area is calculated. Type

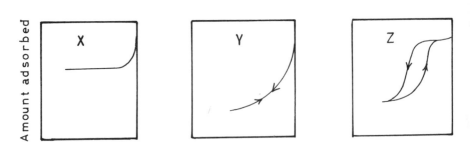

Fig. 2.29   Higher pressure behaviour of adsorption isotherm[69]. (Courtesy Dollimore, Spooner, and Turner)

B is supposed to represent the condition where adsorbate–adsorbate interactions are more important or are of the same magnitude as adsorbate–adsorbent interaction.

Further classification of adsorption isotherm behaviour is then based on the
behaviour at higher relative pressures. Figure 2.29 shows the different patterns proposed in the classification. Type Z represents the behaviour commonly associated with hysteresis. The other two types of behaviour are basi-

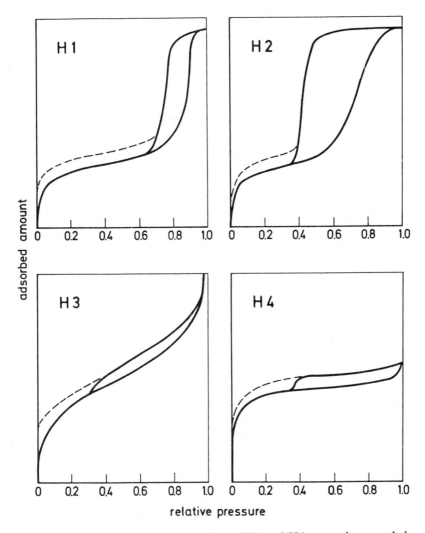

Fig. 2.30 IUPAC classification of isotherms H1 and H4 are to be regarded as
limiting cases due to specific pore systems, whereas H2 and H3 may be due to
mixed pore systems. Dashed lines denote the desorption curves for specific microporous materials

cally the behaviour to be expected for an external surface. In type X the external surface is negligible compared with the magnitude of porosity present, while in the type Y isotherm the external surface is appreciable.

This method of considering the adsorption isotherm in two parts is claimed to be superior to the conventional classification[69]. Thus the type II isotherm in the BET classification is considered to be typical of nonporous adsorbents, with nonspecific interaction between adsorbate and adsorbent, but a consideration of the isotherm in two parts shows that the initial portion could arise because of strong adsorbate–adsorbent interaction, which might arise through the presence of micropores or simple interaction in the monolayer, or a mixture of both. The latter high pressure portion of the isotherm results because the external surface predominates over any microporosity which may be present.

The newest approach is a classification adopted by the IUPAC[70], which is shown in Fig. 2.30. It is assumed that the isotherms H1 and H4 are limiting cases and may relate to specific pore systems, whereas the shapes H2 and H3 are due to mixed pore systems.

An attempt to integrate the existing theories on capillary condensation phenomena has been made by Everett[71]. He started an approach of a fundamental thermodynamic description of adsorption and condensation processes, distinguishing between Laplace equilibrium reached at a constant liquid volume and a Kelvin equilibrium established by a condensation–evaporation process. In this way, for simple geometric situations, one can identify reversible and irreversible processes; for complex pore systems the aid of computer would be required.

2.6 The thickness (t) of the adsorbed layers

Shüll[72] showed that for a number of nonporous solids, the nitrogen adsorption isotherms could be represented approximately by a single curve, if the ratio between the adsorbed volume V_a and the volume of the monolayer V_m were plotted as a function of the relative pressure. With the aid of this function the thickness of the adsorbed layer could be calculated as a function of the relative pressure. Shüll assumed that the thickness of a unimolecular layer is equal to the diameter of the nitrogen molecule. Assuming that each nitrogen molecule of a following layer is situated just on top of a nitrogen molecule of the previous layer, this diameter has a value of 0.43 nm. This, however, does not correspond to closest packing. For the calculation of the t-values, Lippens et al.[15] assigned the same density to the adsorbed layers as to the capillary condensed liquid, which is taken to have the density of normal liquid nitrogen. It is therefore necessary to use, in this case, a statistical thickness which is defined as:

$$t = (V/S) \cdot 10^3 \text{ nm} = (M/V_{sp}/22414)(V_a/S) \cdot 10^3 \text{ nm} \qquad (2.26)$$

where t is the statistical thickness of the adsorbed layer; V is the adsorbed volume in ml of liquid adsorbate; S is the specific surface area of the adsorbent in m^2/g; M is the molecular weight of the adsorbate; V_{sp} is the specific volume of the adsorbate in ml/g; and V_a is the adsorbed volume of the adsorbate in ml gas STP/g of adsorbent.

For nitrogen we obtain:

$$t = 1.547\, V_a S^{-1}\ \text{nm} \tag{2.27}$$

If S is taken to be equal to S_{BET}, with the nitrogen adsorbate assumed to have a close-packed structure, so that $0.1627\ nm^2$ represents the surface area occupied by one molecule, then:

$$S_{BET} = 6.023 \times 10^{23} \times 16.27 \times 10^{-20} \times \frac{V_m}{22414}\ \ m^2/g = 4.371\, V_m\ \ m^2/g \tag{2.28}$$

Introducing Eqn. (2.28) into Eqn. (2.27), we obtain:

$$t = 0.354\, n\ \text{nm} \tag{2.29}$$

where n is the number of adsorbed layers.

From the latter equation it follows that for a unimoleular layer where $V_a = V_m$, the value of t equals 0.354 nm. This value differs considerably from the value of 0.43 nm used by Shüll.

Broekhoff, Linsen and Boer[73] measured some standard multilayer thickness curves (i.e. t against p/p_0) for nitrogen adsorption, on a wide variety of solids, and claimed that all measured isotherms superimpose, indicating that there is no appreciable influence of the nature of the surface on the thickness of the adsorbed layer. According to Pierce[74], the multilayer adsorption of nitrogen on a range of nonporous solids may be represented by the Frenkel–Halsey–Hill (FHH) equation:

$$\log (p_0/p) = k/\theta^r \tag{2.30}$$

where θ is the surface coverage and k and r are constants for a given system and temperature, with $r = 2.75$ and $k = 2.99$. Other theoretical equations have been suggested[75-78].

It seems now well established that the concept of a 'universal' standard isotherm for nitrogen, or for any other adsorbate, is unsatisfactory[79]. Even in the absence of specific adsorbent–adsorbate interactions, the adsorption energy and isotherm character for a given adsorbate are dependent on the adsorbent structure and polarizability. With nitrogen there is the complication of the specific, field gradient quadrupole contribution, which enhances the BET C-value (constant of the equation of Brunauer, Emmett and Teller) and the sharpness of point B (see Chapter 3). It is evident therefore, that even in the absence of any porosity, this factor, which is a 'field-force' factor, requires that a standard isotherm must be established for each gas–solid system. This is of course the ideal situation and other alternatives can be adopted as will be shown later.

Beside this factor, which primarily depends on the chemistry of the solid surface and the adsorbent–adsorbate interaction, a second factor has been discussed in the literature, which also leads to deviations in the t-curve. This is the geometric factor. If the solid is built up of very small nonporous spherical particles, the surface available for adsorption is not constant during adsorption, but is a function of the thickness t and of the average number of particles touching each given particle, i.e. the coordination number of the particle. The thickness measured in this case would be a formal thickness t_f and not the actual thickness t of the adsorbed layer[80]. This factor is based on the general phenomenon that the curvature of a surface has an influence on the adsorption. The thermodynamic treatment of this phenomenon was reported[73], and the effects exerted on the t-values calculated from Eqn. (2.29) by the surface curvature and by the coordination number was quantitatively discussed.

The t-curve is required in pore structure analysis of porous materials, and there are two schools of thought. One advocates the use of a standard isotherm that has been determined on a nonporous substance, chemically similar to the material undergoing examination[81,82]; the second suggest the use of a standard isotherm that gives the same BET C constant as the calculated from the experimental isotherm[83,84].

Nitrogen has high C constant at 77 K on the majority of solids, and the packing of the adsorbed molecule is very seldom influenced by the nature of structure of the adsorbing surface. The assumption of $t = 0.354$ nm for the thickness of one adsorbed layer is probably valid, or very nearly valid, for all porous adsorbents. As will be seen, the situation is much more complicated with other molecules. Even for nitrogen, which is considered to be a simpler case to deal with, several t-curves were proposed and they all differ somewhat from one another. One frequently used t-curve is that of Cranston and Inkley[85]; another is that of de Boer and co-workers[86]. The latter gives smaller t values than the former at relative pressures below 0.7. This might be due to the fact that the adsorbents on which the de Boer t-curve is based had somewhat lower heats of adsorption than those of Cranston and Inkley[85]. In such instances, at a given relative pressure more gas is adsorbed if the heat of adsorption is higher. This is especially noticeable at low relative pressures; the effect of the surface is much weaker in the second adsorbed layer, and hardly noticeable in the third and higher layers. This effect is magnified in the t-curves of nitrogen measured by Mikhail et al.[87] on surfaces associated with low BET C-values ranging between 5 and 30 (low energy surfaces). The results obtained on vermiculite are summarized in Table 2.3 and are compared with the values obtained by Sing et al.[88]

Following the idea that a standard isotherm must be established for each

Table 2.3 Statistical number of layers vs. relative pressure for nitrogen

	V/V_m				
	1	2	3	4	5
p/p_0	$C = 5 - 6$	$C = 8 - 12$	$C = 20 - 30$	$C = 110^*$	Extrapolated
0.01	0.05	0.12	0.20	0.34	
0.025	0.10	0.20	0.35	0.54	
0.05	0.20	0.35	0.55	0.76	
0.10	0.375	0.55	0.775	1.04	
0.15	0.55	0.70	0.90	1.13	
0.20	0.72	0.84	1.00	1.22	
0.25	0.86	0.975	1.10	1.30	
0.30	0.975	1.125	1.20	1.37	
0.35	1.125	1.225	1.30	1.45	
0.40	1.30	1.35	1.425	1.53	
0.45	1.475	1.50	1.55	1.60	
0.50	1.60	1.63	1.70	1.68	
0.55	1.70	1.73		1.76	1.75
0.60	1.80			1.80	1.80
0.65				1.97	1.95
0.70				2.11	2.10
0.75				2.25	2.25
0.80				2.48	2.45
0.85				2.76	2.78
0.90				3.66	3.60
0.95				5.65	6.10

*Reference 87

gas–solid system, Sing and co-workers[82,88–91] introduced several t-curves for nitrogen, argon, carbon tetrachloride, and other adsorbates on a range of well-defined nonporous solids.

The nature of the surface plays an important role in the adsorption of polar molecules, and especially with water vapour. In the first place, hydrophobic substances do not adsorb water in appreciable amounts at low relative pressures; consequently, only hydrophilic substances can be used for the determination of t-curves. This means that only ionic solids can be used, which introduces further difficulties. The ionic surface may be composite, i.e., partly hydrophobic, partly hydrophilic. The ions of the surface cause orientation of the dipoles of the water molecules, and the area occupied by a water molecule on the surfaces of different adsorbents is different. The first t-curves for water were introduced by Hagymassy, Brunauer, and Mikhail[92], and they showed that the thickness of the adsorbed film at a given pressure depends on the heat of adsorption; consequently, the t-curve to be used is that which matches the heat of water on the adsorbent to be analysed. The authors used the C-constant of the BET equation as an adequate measure of the heat of adsorption. Several t-curves are offered, depending on the C-constants. The

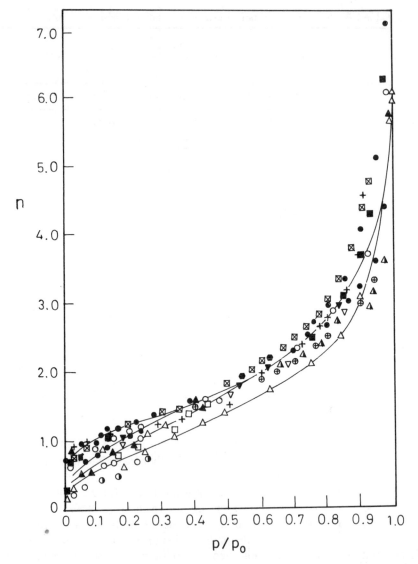

Fig. 2.31   *t*-Curves for pore structure analysis by water vapour adsorption[92]. The following symbols are used for the experimental points: zirconium silicate (*C* = 4.2) ◑◐; rutile (*C* = 5.2) △ △; silica (*C* = 7) ○ ○; silica gel, Davidson 81 (C = 10) □ □; zirconium silicate (*C* = 14.5) ▲ ▲; silica gel, Davidson 59 (C = 23) ▽ ▽; quartz (C = 23) ● ●; anatase (*C* about 50) ■ ■; anatase (*C* about 60) ⊕ ⊕; calcite (*C* about 70) ⊠ ⊠; barium sulphate (*C* about 120) ▼ ▼; barium sulphate (*C* about 160) ◕ ◕; quartz (*C* about 200) + +

experimental curves obtained by the authors are shown in Fig. 2.31, and the statistical number of layers vs. relative pressure are summarized in Table 2.4. The authors also suggested that 0.30 nm appears to be a reasonable value for the thickness of a monolayer.

Several n-curves were measured for the adsorption of organic molecules on nonporous solids. This includes benzene, cyclohexane, carbon tetrachloride, isopropanol, as well as methanol[93]. An example is given in Fig. 2.32 for the n-curve of benzene measured on several nonporous oxides[93]. With organic molecules, a difficulty is encountered in converting the n-values into t-values, especially when the latter are to be applied for porous substances. The difficulty arises when considering the effects of pore narrowing on various parameters of the adsorbed molecule, and Mikhail *et al.*[93] have shown that pore narrowing might affect the area occupied by a single molecule on the surface, which in turn will affect the calculated statistical thickness t on the surface. For nonspherical molecules, such as benzene and cyclohexane, adsorption in micropores might lead to a change in the orientation of the molecule on the surface from flat to vertical orientation in the limit of one to three layers. For benzene the sectional areas occupied in the two orientations are 0.42 and

Table 2.4   Statistical number of water layers vs. relative pressure

p/p_0	C = 50 to 200	C = 23	C = 10 to 14.5	C = 5.2	C = 10 to 200
			V/V_m		
0.010	0.54	0.45	0.30	0.20	
0.025	0.63	0.54	0.40	0.30	
0.05	0.87	0.63	0.49	0.41	
0.10	1.03	0.79	0.64	0.56	
0.15	1.13	0.94	0.78	0.68	
0.20	1.22	1.08	0.92	0.79	
0.25	1.31	1.21	1.04	0.89	
0.30	1.39	1.33	1.17	0.99	
0.35	1.47	1.46	1.29	1.10	
0.40	1.56	1.56	1.41	1.21	
0.45	1.64	1.64	1.57	1.31	
0.50	1.75	1.75	1.72	1.43	1.75
0.55				1.54	1.88
0.60				1.67	2.00
0.65				1.82	2.16
0.20				1.96	2.33
0.25				2.11	2.53
0.80				2.30	2.78
0.85				2.55	3.11
0.90				3.03	3.54
0.925				3.45	3.80
0.950				4.00	4.15
0.975				4.68	4.68
0.99				5.72	5.72
1.00				6.06	6.06

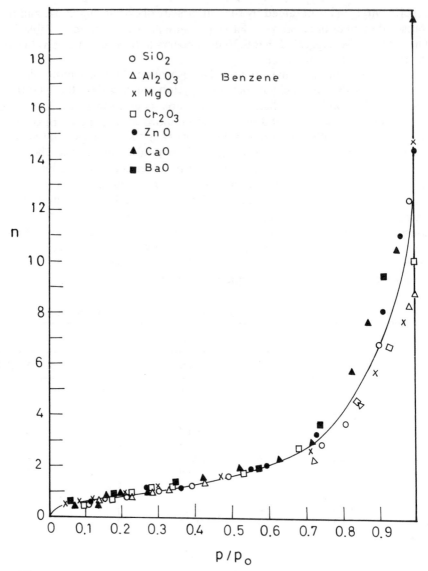

Fig. 2.32   Number n of layers adsorbed as a function of the relative vapour pressure for benzene on nonporous solids[93]

0.25 nm^3 [92], and for cyclohexane the sectional areas in the two orientations are 0.39 and 0.30 nm^2 [94,95], respectively. From the sectional areas a (nm), the volume adsorbed per square centimeter can be obtained from the equation

$$\frac{M}{a \times 10^{-14} \times A} \times \frac{1}{\rho} \quad cm^3 \qquad (2.31)$$

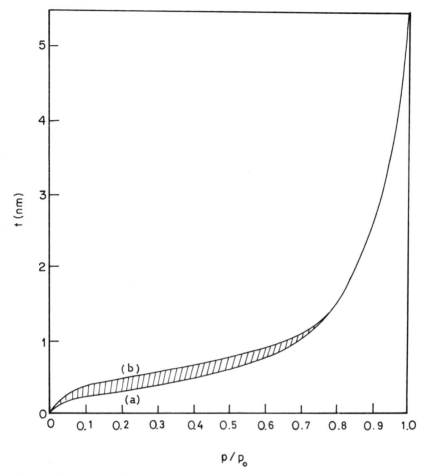

Fig. 2.33 *t*-Curves for benzene vapour adsorbed on nonporous and on porous oxides; (a) on plane and mesoporous adsorbents, (b) on micro- and mixed pore adsorbents

where M is the molecular weight of the adsorbate, A is Avogadro's number, and ρ is the density of the bulk liquid. In this equation it is assumed that the adsorbed layer has the normal density of the bulk liquid. Since the area in question is 1 cm^2, this is the required thickness of a molecular layer in nanometers. This equation leads to computed statistical thickness (t) of 0.36 and 0.59 nm for benzene with a flat hexagonal model and standing on edge respectively; and to values of 0.46 and 0.60 nm for cyclohexane in the same two orientations. As already pointed out, the *n*-curves are experimentally measured curves, and the *t*-curves calculated for benzene and cyclohexane are shown in Figs 2.33 and 2.34, where curve 2.33(a) and 2.34(a) represent the cases of flat orientation, i.e. t = 0.36 and 0.46 nm respectively; and curves 2.33(b) and 2.34(b) are obtained by varying the thickness of the adsorbate

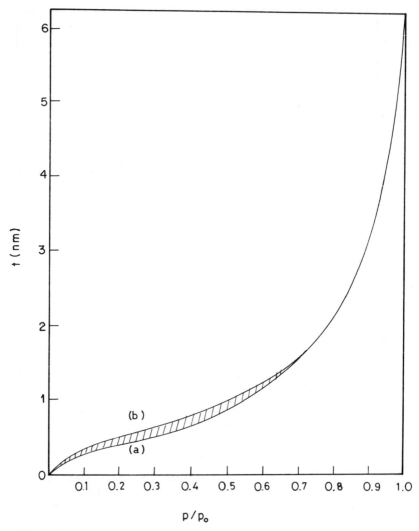

Fig. 2.34 *t*-Curves for cyclohexane vapour adsorbed on nonporous and on porous oxides; (a) on plane and mesoporous adsorbents, (b) on micro- and mixed pore adsorbents

molecules, in the low-pressure end, to account for the vertical orientation, namely 0.59 at 0.60 nm for benzene and cyclohexane respectively. Vertical orientation is probably acquired in micropores, while in mesopores or on a plane surface the molecules are most likely to lie flat on the surface. It is not possible to assess the exact orientation of the molecules in micropores, and the authors believe that the shaded areas in Figs 2.33 and 2.34 represent the areas of 'uncertainty' in computing the *t*-values for these molecules at the low-pressure end of the isotherm. Even for nearly spherical molecules, such

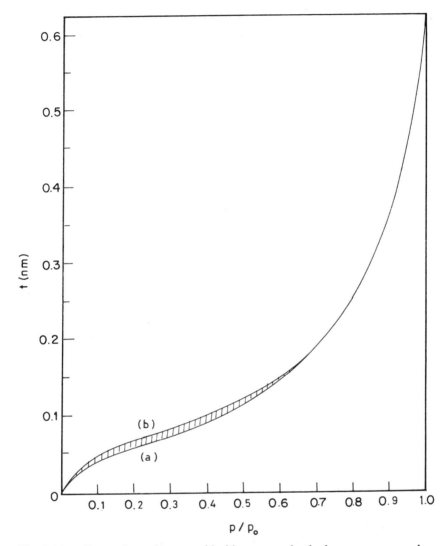

Fig. 2.35 *t*-Curves for carbon tetrachloride vapour adsorbed on nonporous and on porous oxides; (a) on plane and mesoporous adsorbents, (b) on micro- and mixed pore adsorbents

as carbon tetrachloride, this 'uncertainty' in computing the *t*-values arises from changes in the degree of packing in micropores which has been shown to be different from packing on a plane surface. Figure 2.35 represents this situation. Also for methanol, which predominantly interacts specifically with most solid surfaces, and particularly oxides, this uncertainty exists due to changes in the 'apparent' areas occupied by a single molecule on the surface[90], and Fig. 2.36 represents the situation with methanol.

From the foregoing presentation, it is evident that although the situation

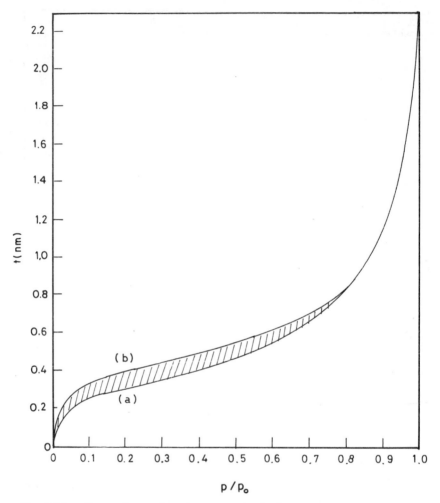

Fig. 2.36 *t*-Curves for methanol vapour adsorbed on nonporous and on porous oxides assuming specific interaction on the surface; (a) molecular area 0.25 nm² (b) molecular area 0.18–0.25 nm²

with measuring a certain *t*-curve for a particular adsorbate on a nonporous solid seems to be a straightforward operation, major problems are involved in the subsequent applications and use of the *t*-curve, particularly in pore structure analysis. These problems are associated with the type of adsorbent–adsorbate interaction and (related also to this effect) the size and shape of the adsorbate molecule, and the location of the solid surface, particularly in narrow pores.

2.7 The comparison of adsorption isotherms

For the purpose of detecting the porosity of solids, it is usual to make a comparison between the adsorbate–adsorbent system under study and a reference system in which the same adsorbate is used and the adsorbent is judged to possess a nonporous character. Ideally, the two solids should have similar chemical structure, which in most cases would mean that the BET C-value is the same in both cases. Conversely, if the BET C-values are the same in both cases, this will indicate that roughly the same type of solid–adsorbate interaction is operating in both systems. However, the argument is still continuing whether it would be enough to use the BET C-value as a sufficiently satisfactory evidence[83,84,93,] or rather to ensure the chemical identity of the two surfaces[81,82].

Methods of making a comparison between isotherms fall into three categories[69]:

(a) direct comparison;
(b) methods in which the adsorption isotherm is referred to unit area of surface; and
(c) methods in which the point of reference is the monolayer or some other suitable point in the isotherm.

The method of direct comparison due to Gregg[96] is most revealing and very simple. The ordinate f is calculated as the ratio of the ordinates of the two adsorption isotherms, one the isotherm under study, the other a reference isotherm, taken at a series of values of relative pressure p/p_0 and then plotted against p/p_0. Figure 2.37 demonstrates the use of this method. In the case of system A it can be seen that capillary condensation is involved on the adsorption branch of the hysteresis loop, while in another system (B), capillary

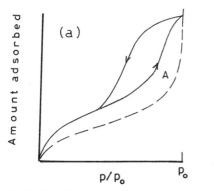
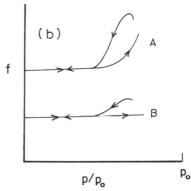

Fig. 2.37 Schematic representation of Gregg's f plots[94]: (a) typical isotherm showing hysteresis. The broken line indicates nonporous reference isotherm; (b) f-plots: system A indicates capillary condensation upon adsorption; system B indicates no capillary condensation upon adsorption. (Courtesy S. J. Gregg)

68

condensation is not occurring on the adsorption branch. Gregg quotes specific examples of these two classes of behaviour. Evidently, in the early stages of the isotherm the ratio f indicates the ratio of surface areas.

Methods in which the adsorption isotherm is referred to unit area of surface produce plots which are sometimes referred to as the absolute (or reduced) adsorption isotherms[97]. Such a method has been utilized by Mikhail et al.[98,99] to show the effects of pore narrowing on the adsorption of organic molecules[98] or water vapour[99], on nonporous and porous silica gels of various porosities. It has been shown that when the interaction is predominantly physical (dispersion forces), as for example adsorption of carbon tetrachloride or cyclohexane on silica gel, pore narrowing leads to an increase in the amount adsorbed due to enhancement of the adsorption potential in micropores. On the other hand, when the interaction is predominantly specific, as with benzene (π-bonding), or methanol (H-bonding), pore

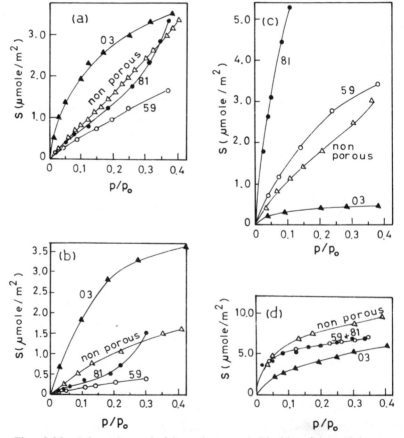

Fig. 2.38 Adsorption of (a) carbon tetrachloride, (b) cyclohexane, (c) benzene, and (d) methanol on microporous (Davidson 03), mesoporous (Davidson 59 and 81), and on nonporous silica gels[98]

narrowing leads to a decrease in the amount adsorbed[98] which is also the case with water vapour adsorption[99]. Figure 2.38 shows some of these reduced isotherms.

This method has also been used by Clough et al.[100] to show that, for adsorption of polar molecules on alumina impregnated with various quantities of nickel and uranium, the changes in the ionic nature of the surface are reflected in an enchanced interaction between the adsorbed phase and the adsorbent. These effects are, however, absent in the adsorption of nonpolar adsorbates.

In the third group of methods of making a comparison between isotherms, reference is made to a point on the isotherm, which is normally the monolayer capacity V_m, which in turn is most commonly determined by the BET method. De Boer and his associates developed a method of comparing adsorption isotherms, to be known later as the t-method, and a review of this method is given by Broekhoff and Linsen[73]. As already pointed out, the volume adsorbed on a nonporous reference sample (V) and the monolary capacity (V_m) gives the number of layers $(V/V_m = n)$ as a function of the relative pressure p/p_0, from which it is possible to evaluate the thickness as a function of the relative pressure. A plot of V for an unknown sample against the value of t corresponding to the common relative pressure of the standard adsorption isotherm (obtained on the nonporous solid) produces a straight line passing through the origin for nonporous materials, from the slope of which the surface area may be calculated from the relation:

$$S_t = 10^{-3} \frac{V_l}{t} \tag{2.32}$$

where S_t is the surface area evaluated from the t-plot, V_l is the volume adsorbed in ml/g of adsorbent, and t is measured in nanometers. If S_t differs from the BET calculation, this is due to differences that may also exist in the other parameter of the BET equation, the BET C-constant. An upward deviation from linearity in the multilayer range indicates capillary condensation in mesopores, and a downward deviation from linearity indicates micropore filling by the adsorbed layers, and therefore their surface is cut from any further adsorption.

Lippens and de Boer[101] assumed that monolayer adsorption takes place on the walls of micropores in essentially the same manner as on the mesopore walls. This approach was critized by Dubinin[102] and Sing[103], and the t-method was modified by Day and Parfitt[104] and Sing[105] to take into account micropore filling and to provide an assessment of the micropore volume. This modification, however, can only apply when the solid is totally microporous and devoid of any mesoporosity.

The most serious limitation of the t-method it that it is basically dependent on the BET evaluation of the monolayer capacity since t is itself calculated from V/V_m. To avoid this difficulty, Sing[105,106] replaced t by V/V_s, termed α_s,

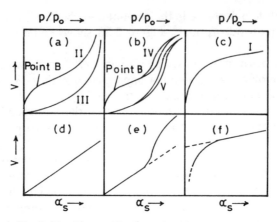

Fig. 2.39 Types of adsorption isotherms and α_S plots, after Sing[106]. (Courtesy K. S. W. Sing)

where V_S is the amount adsorbed at a selected relative pressure (standard state). The reduced isotherm on the nonporous reference solid is therefore arrived at empirically and not via the BET monolayer capacity. With a number of systems, it has been found convenient to place $\alpha_s = 1$ at $p/p_0 = 0.4$, which represents an insensitive part of the adsorption isotherm before capillary condensation can occur. Three hypothetical α_s-plots were given by Sing[106], and these are shown in (d), (e), and (f) of Fig. 2.39, with the corresponding isotherms in (a), (b), and (c). Values of surface area, S_s, are readily calculated from the slopes of the linear regions of the α_s-plots in (d), (e), and (f) by using a proportionality (or normalizing) factor, which is obtained from the standard isotherm on the nonporous reference material of known BET surface area. For nitrogen the surface area could be calculated by using the relation

$$S_s = 2.87\, V/\alpha_s \qquad (2.33)$$

where V is the volume of nitrogen adsorbed, expressed in cm^3 (stp), and the factor 2.87 has been obtained by calibration against the BET area of Degussa aluminium oxide C, taken as the nonporous reference solid. Other factors were also given by Sing[106] for the adsorption of carbon tetrachloride and neopentane on silica. So far the α_s-method has been employed for the analysis of argon, carbon tetrachloride, and neopentane isotherms on various forms of alumina, chromia, silica, titania, nickel oxide and iron oxides[79]. The significance of the α_{ss}-method lies in its independence of the BET surface area. The choice of the reference relative pressure, however, is not based on definite criteria which can be used to justify that choice.

Beside the t-method of de Boer et al. and the α_s-method of Sing, other methods utilize the number of adsorbed layers n, thus avoiding the assumption of the thickness t. A method was offered by Mikhail and Cadenhead[107]

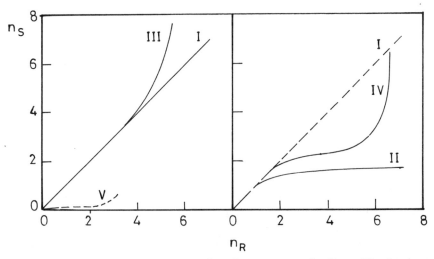

Fig. 2.40 Typical schematic n_S–n_R plots. I, nonporous adsorbents; II, micropores only; III, mesopores only; IV, micro- and mesopores; V, speculated specific interaction[107]

which they called the n_S–n_R method, where the subscript S stands for the sample under test and the subscript R stands for the reference nonporous solid. A plot is constructed of n_S versus n_R, each value being at the same p/p_0. Typical schematic n_S–n_R plots are shown in Fig. 2.40.

For a nonporous sample, an n_S–n_R plot should give a straight line passing through the origin, and having a slope equal to unity (curve I, Fig. 2.40). In addition, deviations similar to those obtained with t-plots will take place. Thus, the presence of micropores can be detected by a downward deviation from the straight line (curve II), the presence of mesopores by an upward deviation from the straight line (curve III), and the presence of both micro- and mesopores by an early downward deviation followed by an upward deviation (curve IV). If adsorption was initially limited to specific sites on the adsorbent the expected curve would resemble curve V. These plots are all similar to the corresponding de Boer t-plots, but this approach has some advantage over the t-method:

1. It eliminates the assumptions of the thickness (t) for the adsorbed layer. The use of t can bring serious complications if its value in micropores differs from that on a plane surface. Also there are problems with organic molecules, if the order of packing or orientation in micropores is different from that on a plane surface[93]. The thickness t in the t-method is an absolute value, whereas the number of layers n in the n_S–n_R plot is an 'internal' value, with each n value being determined from its own particular isotherm. The value n thus includes all the variables, and permits an improved comparison between nonporous and porous substances. Similar objections to the use of t have been made by others[108].

2. A straight line, passing through the origin, with a slope of unity, provides a reference for comparison between porous and nonporous solids provided the nature of the adsorption on the two samples is similar. The de Boer t-plot for a nonporous reference will also exhibit a straight line. Its slope, however, is impossible to predict without making further assumptions.

3. In certain cases specific interactions can govern the adsorption process, primarily during the building up of the first layer. The t-method is unable to detect such effects because an average t-value is calculated at a particular coverage on a plane surface, and this is compared to a volume adsorbed on the test sample. In the proposed plot, n_S provides the first step in a more direct analysis. Thus, for the adsorption of any molecule, the volume V adsorbed can be related to its own V_m value, or to the V_m obtained by another vapour, such as nitrogen, which is known to be physically adsorbed. It is also possible to use a completely independent value obtained by such a method as low angle X-ray scattering. Thus, the proposed method need not depend on the BET treatment.

In summary, the n_S–n_R plot appears to combine the better features of the de Boer[73] and Pierce[108,74] approaches.

In the three empirical methods mentioned in this section, namely the t-method, the α_S-method and the n_S–n_R method, it is worth re-emphasizing that a correct choice of the reference isotherm is essential for the correct analysis to be made of the sample under test. As already pointed out, the debate whether the two isotherms should have identical heat of adsorption (or more correctly free energy of adsorption) or that the two isotherms should have common chemical identity is not yet solved. Nevertheless, it is a common experience that this difficulty arises only when the solid contains micropores and is less demanding when the size of pores increases so that the solid becomes totally mesoporous, macroporous, or nonporous.

References

1. W. Delle, *Beiträge zur 3. Internationalen Kohlenstofftagung*, CARBON '80, Jül-Conf-36, KFA, Jülich, 1980
2. W. Delle, *Possibilities and limitations in porosity determinations on graphite and carbon.* Carbon '80, Baden-Baden, 1980
3. K. Frye *et al.*, *KFA Report*, KFA, Jülich, 1980
4. J. M. Haynes, *Matériaux et constructions*, **6**, (33), 169 (1973)
5. J. Van Kuelen, *Matériaux et constructions*, **6**, (33), 181 (1973)
6. A. S. Joy, *Vacuum*, **3**, 254 (1953)
7. P. H. Emmett, *Advan. Colloid Sci.*, **1**, 3 (1942)
8. M. R. Harris and K. S. W. Sing, *J. Appl. Chem.*, **5**, 223 (1955)
9. B. C. Lippens, B. G. Linsen, and J. H. de Boer, *J. Catalysis*, **3**, 32 (1964)
10. S. J. Gregg and K. S. W. Sing, *J. Phys. Chem.*, **56**, 388 (1952)
11. K. S. W. Sing and J. D. Madeley, *J. Appl. Chem.* **3**, 552 (1953)
12. E. G. Schlosser, *Chem. Ing. Tech.*, **31**, 779 (1959)
13. K. S. W. Sing and D. Swallow, *J. Appl. Chem.*, **10**, 171 (1960)
14. B. C. Lippens and M. E. A. Hermans, *Powder Metall.*, **7**, 66 (1961)
15. B. C. Lippens, B. G. Linsen, and J. H. de Boer, *J. Catalysis*, **3**, 32 (1964)

16. M. A. Alario Franco, F. S. Baker and K. S. W. Sing, in: S. C. Bevan, S. J. Gregg and N. D. Parkyns (eds.), *Progress in Vacuum Microbalance Techniques*, Vol. 2, Heyden, London, 1973, p. 51
17. D. Dollimore, G. Rickitt and R. Robinson, *J. Phys. E. Sci. Instrum.*, **6**, 94 (1973)
18. British Standard 4359: *Methods for the Determination of Specific Surface of Powders*, Part 1. Nitrogen adsorption (BET method), British Standard Institution, London, 1969
19. R. A. W. Haul, *Angew. Chemie*, **68**, 238 (1956)
20. G. G. Litvan, *J. Phys. Chem.*, **76**, 2584 (1972)
21. M. J. Jaycock in: M. J. Groves (ed.), *Particle Size Analysis*, Heyden, London, 1978, p. 308
22. J. Dollimore, G. R. Heal, and D. McIlquhan, *Chem. ind.*, 742 (1969)
23. R. A. Beebe, J. B. Beckwith and J. M. Honig, *J. Amer. Chem. Soc.*, **67**, 1554 (1945)
24. D. W. Aylmore and W. B. Jepson, *J. Sci. Instrum.*, **42**, 821 (1965)
25. J. P. W. Houtman and J. Medema, *Ber. Bunsenges. Phys. Chem.*, **70**, 489 (1966)
26. J. Medema and J. P. W. Houtman, *Analytical Chemistry*, **41**, 209 (1969)
27. K. A. Kini, R. M. Manser and A. S. Joy, *J. Phys. Chem.*, **72**, 2127 (1968)
28. K. Watanabe and T. Yamashina, *J. Catalysis*, **17**, 272 (1970)
29. P. Chènebault and A. Schürenkämper, *J. Phys. Chem.*, **69**, 2300 (1965)
30. A. J. Juhola, *Kemia-Kemi*, **4**, 543 (1977)
31. E. Robens, *Archiv Techn. Messen* V1285-1/2, Lfg. 386, p. 45; Lfg. 387, p. 69.
32. E. V. Ballou and O. K. Doolen, *Analyt. Chem.*, **32**, 532 (1960)
33. E. G. Schlosser, *Chem. Ing. Techn.*, **31**, 799 (1959)
34. N. Hansen and W. Littmann, *Z. Instrumentenkde.*, **71**, 153 (1963)
35. Th. Kraus in: *Physik und Technik von Sorptions- und Desorptionsvorgängen bei niedrigen Drücken*, Dechema, Frankfurt am Main, 1963, p. 245
36. Th. Kraus and E. Zollinger, *Vakuum-Technik*, **23**, 40 (1974)
37. L. S. Ettre, N. Brenner and E. W. Cieplinski, *Z. Phys. Chem.*, **219**, 17 (1962)
38. W. Gellert, D. Baresel and G. Schulz-Ekloff, *Bosch Techn. Ber.* **4**, 245 (1974)
39. W. Gellert, D. Baresel and G. Schulz-Ekloff, *Bosch Techn. Ber.,* **5**, 127 (1975)
40. A. P. Karnaukhov and N. E. Buyanova, in: D. H. Everett and R. H. Ottewill, *Surface Area Determination*, Butterworths, London, 1970, p. 165.
41. S. Lowell, *Introduction to Powder Surface Area*, Wiley–Interscience, New York, 1979
42. R. Haul and G. Dümbgen, *Chem.-Ing.-Techn.* **32**, 349 (1960)
43. R. Haul and G. Dümbgen, *Chem.-Ing.-Techn.* **35**, 586 (1963)
44. E. Robens and G. Sandstede, *J. Sci. Instrum.* **2**, 365 (1969)
45. H. Fischer, E. Robens, G. Sandstede, R. Sieglen and G. Walter, in: T. Gast, E. Robens (eds.), *Progress in Vacuum Microbalance Techniques*, Vol. I; Heyden, London (1972)
46. Th. Gast, *Vakuum-Tech.*, **14**, 41 (1965)
47. E. L. Fuller, J. A. Poulis, A. W. Czanderna and E. Robens: *Thermochimica Acta*, **29**, 315 (1979)
48. A. W. Czanderna in: S. P. Wolsky and E. J. Zdanuk (eds.), *Ultra Micro Weight Determination in Controlled Environments*, Wiley, New York, 1969, p. 41
49. R. A. Pierotti in: A. W. Czanderna (ed.), *Vacuum Microbalance Techniques*, Vol. 6; Plenum, New York 1967, p. 1
50. E. Robens and Th. Gast, *J. Vac. Sci. Techn.*, **15**, 805 (1967)
51. S. Brunauer, L. S. Deming, W. S. Deming, and E. Teller, *J. Amer. Chem. Soc.*, **62**, 1723 (1940)
52. S. Brunauer, P. H. Emmett, and E. Teller, *J. Amer. Chem. Soc.*, **60**, 309 (1938)
53. E. Robens and G. Walter in F. Korte (ed.), *Methodicum Chimicum*, Vol. 1, Part B, Academic Press, New York 1974, p. 678.

54. D. S. Jovanović, *Kolloid Z., Z. Polym.*, **235**, 1214 (1969)
55. S. J. Gregg and K. S. W. Sing, *Adsorption, Surface Area and Porosity*, Academic Press, London, 1967
56. C. H. Amberg, W. B. Spencer, and R. A. Beebe, *Can. J. Chem.*, **33**, 305 (1955)
57. H. Behret, H. Binder and E. Robens *Thermochimica Acta*, **24**, 407 (1978)
58. S. J. Gregg and K. S. W. Sing, *J. Phys. Chem.*, **55**, 597 (1951)
59. R. Sh. Mikhail, N. M. Guindy, and S. Hanafi, *Surface Technology*, **7**, 201 (1978)
60. R. Sh. Mikhail, N. M. Guindy and S. Hanafi, *J. Colloid and Interface Sci.*, **70**, 282 (1979)
61. R. Sh. Mikhail and A. M. Youssef, *Cement and Concrete Research*, **4**, 869 (1974)
62. E. A. Boucher, *J. Materials Sci.*, **11**, 1734 (1976)
63. P. H. Doe and J. M. Haynes in: S. J. Gregg, K. S. W. Sing and H. F. Stoeckli (eds.), *Characterisation of Porous Solids*, Soc. Chemical Industry, London, 1979, p. 253
64. R. M. Barrer, N. McKenzie, and J. S. S. Reay, *J. Colloid Sci.*, **11**, 479 (1956)
65. J. H. de Boer, in: D. H. Everett and F. Stone (eds.), *The Structure and Properties of Porous Materials*, Butterworth, London, 1958, p. 68
66. L. H. Cohen, *J. Am. Chem. Soc.*, **60**, 433 (1938)
67. B. G. Linsen and A. van der Heuvel, in: E. A. Flood (ed.), *The Gas Solid Interface*, Vol. II, p. 185, Marcel Dekker, New York, 1967.
68. G. Walter and E. Robens in: E. Drauglis and R. I. Jaffee (eds.), *The Physical Basis for Heterogeneous Catalysis*, Plenum, New York, 1975
69. D. Dollimore, P. Spooner, and A. Turner, *Surface Technology*, **4**, 121, (1976)
70. *IUPAC Manual of Symbols and Terminology of Colloid Science*, Butterworths, London, 1982
71. D. H. Everett, in: S. J. Gregg, K. S. W. Sing and H. F. Stoeckli (eds.), *Characterisation of Porous Solids*, Soc. Chemical Industry, London, 1979, p. 229.
72. C. G. Shüll, *J. Am. Chem. Soc.*, **70**, 1405 (1948)
73. J. C. P. Broekhoff and B. G. Linsen, in: B. G. Linsen (ed.), *Physical and Chemical Aspects of Adsorbents and Catalysts*, Academic Press, London and New York, 1970
74. C. Pierce, *J. Phys. Chem.*, **72**, 3673 (1968)
75. A. Wheeler, *Advan. Catalysis*, **3**, 249 (1951)
76. J. O. Mingle and J. M. Smith, *Chem. Eng. Sci.*, **16**, 31 (1960)
77. J. B. Butt, *J. Catal.*, **4**, 685 (1965)
78. A. V. Kiselev and A. P. Karnaukov, *Russ. J. Phys. Chem.* **34**, 21 (1960)
79. K. S. W. Sing, *Specialist Periodical Report*, Colloid science 1, p. 1, The Chemical Society, London, 1973
80. I. C. P. Broeckhoff, and J. H. de Boer, *J. Catalysis*, **9**, 15 (1967)
81. T. G. Lamond and C. G. Price, *J. Colloid Interface Sci.*, **31**, 104 (1969)
82. M. R. Bhambhani, P. A. Cutting, K. S. W. Sing, and D. G. Turk, *J. Colloid Interface Sci.*, **38**, 107 (1972)
83. S. Brunauer, in: D. H. Everett and R. H. Ottewill (eds.), *Surface Area Determination*, p. 63, Butterworths, London, 1970
84. R. Sh. Mikhail, S. Brunauer, and E. E. Bodor, *J. Colloid Interface Sci.*, **26**, 45 (1968); **26**, 54 (1968)
85. R. H. Cranston and F. A. Inkley, *Advan. Catalysis*, **9**, 143 (1957)
86. J. H. de Boer, B. G. Linsen, and Th. J. Osinga, *J. Catalysis*, **4**, 643 (1965)
87. R. Sh. Mikhail, N. M. Guindy, and S. H. Hanafi, *Egypt. J. Chem.*, Sp. Issue, Tourky, **53** (1973)
88. J. D. Carruther, P. A. Cutting, R. E. Day, M. R. Harris, S. A. Mitchell and K. S. W. Sing, *Chem. and Ind.*, 1772 (1968)

89. D. A. Payne, K. S. W. Sing, and D. H. Turk, *J. Colloid Interface Sci.*, **43**, 287 (1973)
90. P. A. Cutting and K. S. W. Sing, *Chem. Industry*, 268 (1969)
91. J. D. Carruthers, D. A. Payne, K. S. W. Sing, and D. H. Turk, *J. Colloid Interface Sci.*, **36**, 205 (1971)
92. J. Hagymassy, Jr., S. Brunauer, and R. Sh. Mikhail, *J. Colloid Interface Sci.*, **29**, 485 (1969)
93. R. Sh. Mikhail, S. A. Selim and F. Shebl, *Egypt. J. Chem.*, **19**, 405 (1976)
94. R. M. Barrer and J. S. S. Reay, *Proc. Second Intern. Congr. Surface Activity*, London, Butterworths, **2**, 79 (1957)
95. R. N. Smith, C. Pierce, and M. Cordes, *J. Am. Chem. Soc.*, **72**, 5596 (1950)
96. S. J. Gregg, *J. C. S. Chem. Comm.*, 699 (1975)
97. A. V. Kiselev, in: D. H. Everett and F. S. Stone (eds.), *Structure and Properties of Porous Materials*, Academic Press, New York, 1958, pp. 195–226.
98. R. Sh. Mikhail and T. El-Akkad, *J. Colloid Interface Sci.*, **51**, 560 (1975)
99. R. Sh. Mikhail, S. Nashed, and K. S. W. Sing, in: Pore structure and properties of materials *Proceedings International Symposium*, RILEM/IUPAC, Prague, 1973, Academic Press, Vol. IV, p. C–157
100. P. S. Clough, D. Dollimore, and T. Nicklin, *J. Appl. Chem. Biotech.*, **21**, 137 (1971)
101. B. C. Lippens and J. H. de Boer, *J. Catalysis* **4**, 319 (1965)
102. M. M. Dubinin, in: D. H. Everett and R. H. Ottewill (eds.), *Proceedings of International Symposium Surface Area Determination*, p. 123, Butterworths, London, 1970
103. K. S. W. Sing, *Chem. and Ind.*, 829 (1967)
104. R. E. Day and G. D. Parfitt, *Trans. Faraday Soc.*, **63**, 708 (1967)
105. K. S. W. Sing, *Chem. Ind.*, 1520 (1968)
106. K. S. W. Sing, in: D. H. Everett and R. H. Ottewill (eds.), *Proceedings of International Symposium Surface Area Determination*, p. 25, Butterworths, London, 1970
107. R. Sh. Mikhail and D. A. Cadenhead, *J. Colloid Interface Sci.*, **55**, 462 (1975)
108. C. Pierce, *J. Phys. Chem.*, **72**, 3673 (1975)

Chapter 3

Methods of Surface Area Determination

The general subject of surface area determination has received much attention[1-4] since it was reviewed by Emmett[5] in 1954, and updated in 1968 by Innes[6]. In this chapter the reviews are extended to methods other than physical adsorption. The practical use is emphasized and the discussion of the fundamentals updated.

Distinction will be made, whenever possible, between two limiting cases, namely determination of surface area of nonporous solids on one hand, and of microporous solids on the other. This distinction, though somewhat artificial, considers adsorption in larger size pores—mesopores and macropores—to be practically indistinguishable, prior to capillary condensation, from adsorption on a nonporous adsorbent since the curvature of the adsorbent surface no longer exerts any appreciable effect on adsorption. Methods other than physical adsorption will also be briefly described.

3.1 Physical adsorption methods

The most important methods for specific surface area analysis of solids are based on adsorption. The following two assumptions are made[7]:

1. It is possible to determine the quantity of adsorbate required for complete coverage of the substrate surface by a monolayer.
2. The cross-sectional area of an adsorbed molecule is known and independent of the substrate (adsorbent).

Strictly speaking, these two requirements contradict each other on physical grounds: in the case of strong interactions of the substrate with the adsorbate we obtain an isotherm with a pronounced plateau at complete coverage with a monolayer; the effective area of an adsorbate molecule, however, depends on the atomic structure of the surface. In the case of weak interactions between substrate surface and adsorbate where the interaction energy is comparable with the interaction between adsorbate molecules themselves, multilayer adsorption is obtained before the monolayer is complete. The isotherm does not have a distinct plateau, and the monolayer has to be calculated from the isotherm on the basis of model concepts. Still, numerous investigations have shown that the measurement of physisorption isotherms is the most reliable method, although the theoretical basis of model concepts is still unsatisfactory.

When a molecule is physi- or chemisorbed on the surface of a solid, the molecular electrons interact with those determining the surface state of the solid[8]. Physisorption is the binding with correlated motion of the electrons in these respective states. The sorption heat released is of the order of the heat of condensation of the adsorbed gas. Physisorption is a reversible process in so far as the adsorbate can be almost completely removed by application of a vacuum. Chemisorption, on the other hand, depends on overlap between the electron distribution of surface molecules and that of adsorbed molecules, including electron exchange. These overlap and exchange interactions produce a stabilization. The chemisorption heat released is of the order of chemical reaction energies. Chemisorption is a distinctly activated process; desorption requires the supply of heat or energy.

The transition between the two types of binding is not sharp, however, and it is even further blurred by the heterogeneity of real surfaces. In fact, the desorption of a physisorbed layer also is more or less an activated process. The frequently quoted upper limit of 40 kJ mol^{-1} for the physisorption heat, therefore can be regarded only as an approximate value. A survey of the binding conditions is given by the potential energy curves in Fig. 3.1.

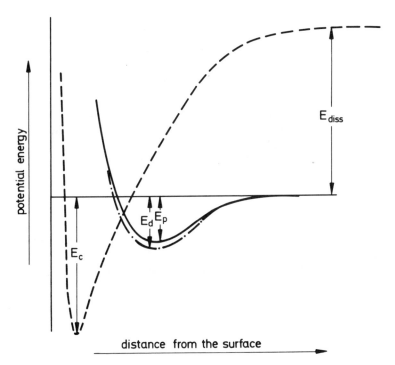

Fig. 3.1 Potential energy diagram for molecule undergoing an activated physisorption and a desorption from micropores or a dissociative chemisorption; E_p isosteric heat of physisorption ($\lesssim$40 kJ mol^{-1}), E_d activation energy for desorption, E_c heat of chemisorption ($\gtrsim$40 kJ mol^{-1}), E_{diss} dissociation energy of molecular adsorbate

3.1.1 Nonporous solids

Henry's law region

According to Henry's law the amount adsorbed V_a in cm³ per gram sample mass is related to the pressure p and the area S by the equation

$$V_a = 10^{-3} k_H p S \qquad (3.1)$$

if p is in bar, S in square metres per gram, and k_H in nanometers per bar. The Henry's law constant k_H can be regarded as the equivalent penetration into the solid of gas at 1 bar. Since the adsorption of gases on the majority of adsorbents conforms to Henry's law at low coverage ($p/p_0 < 0.01$), the surface area can be calculated from a single adsorption point in the low coverage region. Since most adsorption equations also conform to Henry's law at very low surface coverage, Innes[6] related Henry's law constant k_H to the constants of the other adsorption equations as follows:

$$k_H = V_m C \times 10^3/p_0 \qquad (3.2)$$

where V_m and C are the BET equation constants,

$$k_H = V_L a \times 10^3/S \qquad (3.3)$$

where V_L and a are the Langmuir equation constants
$\quad V_L$ is the volume of the monolayer in cm³/g computed by the
$\quad\quad$ Langmuir equation
$\quad a \quad$ is the isothermal adsorption constant for the Langmuir equation
$\quad\quad$ (bar⁻¹);

$$k_H = V_b \times 10^3/KS \qquad (3.4)$$

where V_b is the volume of the monolayer in cm³/g computed by van der
$\quad\quad$ Waals' equation
$\quad K \quad$ is the isothermal constant for the adsorption equation correspond-
$\quad\quad$ ing to the van der Waals' equation (bar).

The temperature coefficient of k_H is only modified slightly by a nonuniform surface at elevated temperature, that is, by the second term in the equation

$$q_{st} \atop \theta \to 0 = -RT^2 \left(\frac{d \ln k_H}{dT} \right) + \frac{1}{2hRT} \qquad (3.5)$$

where q_{st} is the isosteric heat of adsorption (kcal/mole) and h is the heterogeneity parameter (cal/mole)⁻², given as γ by Ross and Olivier[9].

Henry's law could be applied for surface area determination by two methods, namely gas chromatography and gas pycnometry.

1. Surface area by gas chromatography at low relative pressure. In this method the surface area can be obtained from the retention time t_e of an adsorbed species carried by a nonadsorbed carrier gas such as helium, hydrogen, argon, or nitrogen[10,11], and using the relation given by Ross and Olivier[9]

$$k_H = 2.73 \times 10^6 \ (t_e/S)(F_c/\rho_b V_c T_c) \tag{3.6}$$

where F_c is the column flow rate, V_c and T_c are the column volume and temperature, and ρ_b is the adsorbent bulk density. Obviously k_H must be known to utilize the equation to determine S.

2. Surface area by gas pycnometry. This method utilizes precise measurement of volume of a gas-solid system at elevated temperature to determine surface area[12,13]. For a nonadsorbed gas, such as helium at high temperatures, k_H yields negative values, which arise because there is a limit on how close such a molecule can approach a solid surface. Steele and Halsey[14] showed that these negative k_H values could be used as a measure of surface area if the distance of closest approach, D_c, were known. Others also have pointed out that helium skeletal densities should take this effect into account[15]; that is,

$$V(\text{apparent adsorption}) = V(\text{actual adsorption}) - SD_c \times 10^4 \tag{3.7}$$

or

$$k_H(\text{measured}) = k_H(\text{adsorbed}) - D_c \tag{3.8}$$

The apparent adsorption is calculated by the usual means; that is,

$V(\text{apparent adsorption}) = $ total volume of gas present in the geometric volume (volume of container less computed volume of the solid)

Thus by taking measurements at, or extrapolation to, conditions where the actual V_{ads} tends to become zero, it is possible to determine D_c. Since D_c, which is assumed to be temperature independent, can be theoretically estimated, surface areas have been computed by this method[16].

This method requires high-precision volume determinations, and Innes[6] questioned some of its postulates, and he suggested that the most significant factor to consider is that the measured Henry's law constants might need to be corrected by about 0.2 nm in utilizing them for surface area measurement. A simple device has been described by Innes.

Another gas pycnometer method for surface area measurements involves a commercial unit for rapidly measuring volumes of solids up to 50 cm^3 to within 0.1 cm^3. It can be used to measure adsorption as well as skeletal densities[15]. Surface area can be determined when k_H and the volume of the solid are known. Skeletal volume can be obtained from weight and known skeletal density or from direct measurement with helium.

Calculation of Henry's law constant. It should be possible, in principle, to calculate k_H if the attractive and repulsive force fields between adsorbate and surface are known. This has been attempted by Steele[17], Barker and Everett[16], Harlon and Freeman[18], Freeman and Kolb[12,13], Halsey[19,20], and Wolf and Sams[21]. The authors make use of the known 3–9 force-field relation of Lennard–Jones that assumes attraction falls off as the inverse cube of separation distance and that repulsive forces vary with the inverse ninth power. Some of the computed data[15] are given in Table 3.1. The distance of closest approach between adsorbent and adsorbate atom is D_c and ε^* is the potential energy of interaction. The term D_c can be calculated from atomic spacings, and ε^* can be evaluated from q_{st} (isosteric heat of adsorption (cal/mole), and the kinetic energy changes on adsorption)[18,9]. If q_{st} is known, K_H and S can be calculated from a single adsorption point. Reasonable k_H and S values are obtained occasionally, but the S values deviate markedly from the monolayer computed values and vary with different gases in some other cases[16].

Early adsorption studies and most gas chromatographic work using solids does not give S, so that k_H values cannot be calculated. However, some results are accumulating which should have value in characterizing solid surfaces as well as being useful for future Henry's low surface area determinations[22,23,15,9,24].

Table 3.1 Relation of energy of adsorption to k_H/D_c

ε^*/RT	k_H/D_c
0.38	−0.5
0.78	0.0
1.53	1.5
2.3	4.0
3.46	12.4
6.14	131
7.70	527
10.00	4484
11.55	19157

Monolayer region

The commonly used methods for surface area determination involve adsorption when it starts to level out around the monolayer region. The various methods differ in the criteria for the completed monolayer, as well as in the method of calculation of the packing of the adsorbate molecules on the surface.

Estimation of the monolayer capacity. The Langmuir equation for monolayer adsorption, which was derived by equating adsorption rate, taken as proportional to uncovered surface and pressure, to desorption rate, taken as proportional to covered surface, gives

$$\theta = ap(1 - \theta)$$

or
$$p/V_a = 1/aV_L + p/V_L \tag{3.9}$$

where V_a is the volume of gas adsorbed, a the isothermal constant, and $\theta = V_a/V_L$ the fraction of surface covered.

The Langmuir equation was one of the first methods used to evaluate the monolayer. Plotting p/V_a against p enables V_L to be evaluated from the slope of the resultant straight line at $p/p_0 < 0.20$.

The most commonly used theory is the BET theory[25]. This results in the following equation which describes the isotherm:

$$\frac{p/p_0}{V_a(1 - p/p_0)} = \frac{1}{V_m C} + \frac{C - 1}{C} \frac{p/p_0}{V_m} \tag{3.10}$$

Where V_a is the volume adsorbed at pressure p and absolute temperature T; p_0 is the vapour pressure of the gas at temperature T; V_m is the volume of gas adsorbed when the adsorbent surface is covered with a unimolecular layer and is termed the monolayer. This term is an empirical quantity and not a physical reality (compare Fig. 2.20) as the BET theory implies that the surface is never completely covered until the saturated vapour pressure is reached. The constant C is mathematically related to the heat of adsorption. If the function $(p/p_0)/V_a(1 - p/p_0)$ is plotted against p/p_0, a straight line should result, the slope and intercept of which give the values of V_m and C, respectively.

Methods of using BET theory to determine surface characteristics other than by the linear plot already described have been mentioned in Chapter 2. These include comparison of the adsorption isotherm of the material under investigation with that of a standard material.

The BET equation represents an extension of the Langmuir theory of adsorption in which adsorption is restricted to a monolayer, but in the BET theory this restriction is removed. The BET theory concentrates on the forces binding the adsorbate to the adsorbent surface. The existence of such forces, however, implies that they should also attract the adsorbate molecules laterally. One of the reasons for the success of the BET adsorption theory is that an equation of the same algebraic form may be derived by alternative treatments based on different models. The same also holds for the Langmuir equation.

It is widely accepted that an efficient way of relating the assumptions of a molecular model to thermodynamic properties is through the application of statistical mechanics.

The theoretical treatment of monolayer adsorption is mainly concerned with two-dimensional arrays of interacting molecules. It is therefore necessary to approximate the general statistical mechanical results, which are concerned with moving atoms over a three-dimensional potential surface, to be applied to two-dimensional network.

Most theoretical treatments are limited to the two extreme cases of perfectly mobile films and completely localized films, involving a simplified assumption that only nearest-neighbour interactions are important. In the case of a perfectly mobile film the properties of the adsorbent do not appear explicitly in the calculation for the mobile film since the two-dimensional properties of the adsorbed film are determined by the nature of the adsorbate molecules. On the other hand, in completely localized films the two-dimensional lattice gas model is strongly affected by the nature of the adsorbent surface.

The localized model gives the Langmuir adsorption isotherm, which ignores the important factor of attractive lateral interaction between the adsorbate molecules. In this model the theoretically derived enthalpies of adsorption are found to be independent of surface coverage, which is rarely observed experimentally. More realistic theories have been developed, which utilize less precise statistical mechanical arguments; for example, the adsorption isotherms derived by applying lattice gas approximations to a localized monolayer such as the Bragg–Williams approximation and the Fowler isotherm. The effect of lateral interaction of the properties of the lattice gas has been more accurately developed in the treatment of Rushbrooke and Scoins[26]. Some of the techniques and results relevant to this matter have been reviewed by Domb[27] and by Clarke[28].

Among the most accurate calculations based on the theory of the perfectly mobile monolayer, mention should be made of the paper by Alder and Wainwright[29], and of Barker and Henderson[30], who refined the theory and applied it to three-dimensional fluid systems. There are also a number of three-dimensional theories of liquids that can be used to transpose two-dimensional analogues to give adsorption isotherms[31]. Graphitized carbon blacks are most conveniently used to obtain a completely mobile model for monolayer adsorption. Deviations from the basic model are negligible for gases adsorbed on these materials, and the only serious problem in interpreting such data lies in deciding on the precise point at which multilayer adsorption starts to take place at surface coverages above about 0.8. The potential barriers to free translation across the surface are quite small, and Steele[32] has treated these barriers as perturbations to the perfectly mobile layer equation.

One of the major unsolved problems in solid state physics is exactly how to define a heterogeneous Surface[33]. This is unfortunate since most high-area solids and catalysts have highly heterogeneous surfaces.

These methods can be extended to multilayer adsorption. Since the adsorbate–adsorbent interaction energy for nonpolar molecules decays with distance, and since interaction in the second and higher layers is between adsorbate molecules, it can be predicted that there will be a pressure range where multilayer formation competes with adsorption in the first layer. There is a fair balance between the entropy and energy terms in the expression for the free energy of the adsorbate, and calculations can be made of the amount adsorbed in a complete monolayer. This quantity allows one to derive the surface area of the adsorbent. The BET theory[25] provides Eqn. (3.10), which matches the initial and low pressure region and yields estimates of surface areas which are considered most acceptable[34]. In this connection, the reader should refer to the detailed mathematics of this treatment given by Steele[33].

The statistical derivation of the BET equation treats the adsorbed phase as a lattice gas in which the molecules are located at specific sites in the second and higher layers, as well as in the first, and that each pile of molecules of an adsorption site forms an independent statistical system. Basic approximations are that the probability for site occupation in the nth layer is zero unless all sites in the lower layers are occupied, and that only the partition function for a molecule in the first layer differs significantly from that for a molecule in the liquid.

The surface heterogeneity associated with high-area solids has stronger effect on the shape of the isosteric enthalpy–surface coverage curves than on the shape of the isotherm. The modifications necessary to include heterogeneity in the statistical BET theory are similar to those made in introducing heterogeneity in the Langmuir model, and a detailed treatment is given by Steele[33].

In practice many systems fit the BET theory, but only over a limited range. For nitrogen at 77 K, the theory is often satisfied up to a relative pressure of about 0.35, with values of C in the range 10–100. This corresponds to surface coverages of one to two layers.

The criticisms raised against the BET model are:

(1) the lack of consideration of lateral interaction between the adsorbate molecules;
(2) the lack of mobility in the adsorbed layer;
(3) the assumption that all adsorption sites are equivalent;
(4) lack of agreement with the heat of adsorption calculated from other methods;
(5) the possible isolated nature of molecules in the outermost layer; and that
(6) the equation requires adsorption to approach the saturation pressure asymptotically indicating an infinite number of layers adsorbed at that pressure. This may not always be the case.

In most practical cases, at a relative pressure of unity, the adsorbed film is about five to six molecules thick. Brunauer et al.[35] modified the original BET equation (3.10) to take the form

$$\frac{K_1 p}{V(p_0 - K_1 p)} = \frac{1}{V_m' C'} + \frac{C' - 1}{V_m' C'} \frac{K_1 p}{p_0} \tag{3.11}$$

where the constant K_1 is introduced into the BET equation and has a value below unity, and the modified equation alters the monolayer capacity to V'_m and the BET constant to C'. The use of this equation results in values of V_m and of surface area which are higher than those obtained from the normal BET equation[34].

In a different approach altogether, the assumption is made that the adsorbed layer may be treated as a uniform slab of liquid similar to the bulk phase. This is the Frenkel–Halsey–Hill (FHH) theory[36–40]. As pointed out by Steele[40], this theory should be regarded as complementary to the BET theory and not competitive. The BET theory is most accurate for statistical layers from $\frac{1}{2}$ to 2 while the FHH theory gives a good description of the isotherm above 2 layers coverage.

Tests of the correctness of the monolayer capacity. According to the simple BET model, the differential heat of adsorption q should show a sudden change from E_1 to E_L at the point of completion of the monolayer. Due to certain complications in actual systems[4], it is difficult to predict in detail the shape of the curve of q against the degree of coverage θ, but there is little doubt that in the neighbourhood of the monolayer coverage ($\theta = 1$), the value of q should change rapidly, especially in those cases where the process of completion of the first layer and commencement of the second layer do not overlap to a large extent. A number of experimental measurements of the heat of adsorption on various solids are available for testing this prediction, and therefore for testing the validity of the BET-calculated monolayer coverage. The differential heat of adsorption may be measured calorimetrically (q_{cal}), or may be calculated by the application of the Clausius–Clapeyron equation, known as the isosteric heat of adsorption (q_{st}). Some of the most striking evidence in the present connection has been obtained with graphitized carbon black[41]. Figure 3.2 shows the variation of the heat of adsorption (q_{cal} and q_{st}) of nitrogen adsorption on graphitized carbon black, where the heat varies only slightly with coverage, showing a small minimum probably caused by some surface heterogeneity, followed by a slight maximum caused by the lateral interaction of adsorbate molecules (which is ignored in the BET model). This is followed by a large diminution in the value of q_{cal} and of q_{st}, which starts at a coverage slightly below the monolayer, approaching a value near to the latent heat of condensation of the adsorbate.

Similar results using graphitized carbon blacks have been obtained for the isosteric heat of adsorption of argon[42,43], butane[44], and ethane[45], and also for the calorimetric heat of adsorption of benzene[46], hexane[46, 47], pentane[47], and octane[47]. Some of these results are shown in Fig. 3.3, where the differential heat falls sharply in the vicinity of the monolayer coverage.

With crystalline inorganic substances the effect of surface heterogeneity on the variation of the heats of adsorption with surface coverage is particularly marked. With copper in the form of electropolished single crystals, the heat of

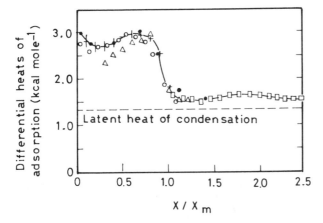

Fig. 3.2 Adsorption of nitrogen on carbon black, graphitized by heating at 2970 K. The differential heat of adsorption was determined calorimetrically at $-195°$ (O, ●), and also isosterically (+, △, □)[41]. (Courtesy Joyner and Emmett)

adsorption for nitrogen reaches a maximum in the vicinity of the monolayer coverage[48]; this behaviour is shown in Fig. 3.4.

Young *et al.*[49] obtained a minimal value for the heat of adsorption corresponding to completion of the monolayer of water vapour on graphitized carbon black. In this case V_m amounts to only about 1/1500 of the value expected from the surface area. Ballou and Ross[50] also obtained a minimal value for benzene and water vapour adsorption on molybdenum disulphide.

In general, data on heats of adsorption support the conclusion that in systems where the isotherm shows a well defined knee (point B, Fig. 3.14) and where the degree of surface heterogeneity is not so great, the value of V_m calculated from the BET equation is, within 10%, equal to the monolayer capacity[4]. It must be mentioned, however, that the interpretation of the heat data cannot yet determine the exact location of the V_m.

Additional evidence for the validity of the BET monolayer capacity is provided from calculations of entropies of adsorption. Hill[38,51] and Everett[52] have shown thermodynamically that the isosteric heat of adsorption gives directly the differential entropy of adsorption,

$$q_{st} = T(S_G - \bar{S}_s) \tag{3.12}$$

where S_G is the molar entropy of the gas at temperature T and $\bar{S}_s$ the differential entropy of adsorbed phase, $(\partial S/\partial n_s)_{s,T}$.

Figure 3.5 shows the main features of an entropy curve for nitrogen adsorption on graphitized carbon black[53], in which a certain minimum in the curve of

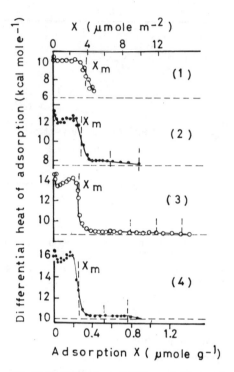

Fig. 3.3 Variation of differential heat of adsorption (q) with amount adsorbed (X)[47], for: (1) n-pentane, (2) n-hexane, (3) n-heptane, (4) n-octane, adsorbed on graphitized carbon black. The monolayer capacity, X_m, is marked on each curve.
(Courtesy Kiselev)

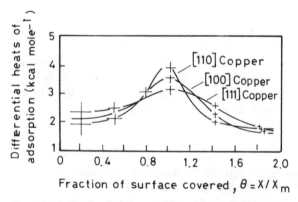

Fig. 3.4 Differential heat of adsorption of nitrogen on the (110), (100), and (111) single crystal faces of copper at different surface coverages[48] (after Rhodin)

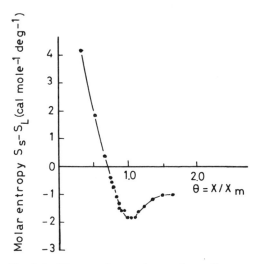

Fig. 3.5 The molar entropy for nitrogen adsorbed on graphitized carbon at $-189.3°$ C, as a function of the amount adsorbed. S_s = molar entropy of adsorbed nitrogen; S_L = molar entropy of liquid nitrogen[53] (after Hill, Emmett and Joyner)

molar entropy appears at the V_m value. Only changes in configurational entropy have been considered[54]. Although many systems follow this general trend[42,44,49,55,56], with some systems, the position is more complicated[4], to the extent that in some systems no minimum at all was found in the S_s plot[43,55]. At present, therefore, entropy calculations seem to be of limited value in identifying monolayer capacities, and it would appear that the most direct test for the validity of the V_m values is to compare their respective calculated surface areas with the surface areas calculated by completely independent methods, as will be shown later.

Molecular cross-section and the calculation of specific surface. The second step in the application of the BET method is the calculation of the surface area, S_{BET} ($m^2 g^{-1}$) from the V_m value using the relation

$$S_{BET} = \frac{V_m}{22\ 414} N\sigma 10^{-18} \qquad (3.13)$$

where V_m is expressed in cm^3 (STP) g^{-1}, N is Avogadro's number (6.023×10^{23} molecules $mole^{-1}$), and σ is the average area occupied by the adsorbate molecule in a completed monolayer, known as the cross-sectional area (nm^2).

Emmett and Brunauer[57] assumed that the packing of the adsorbate molecules in the completed monolayer is the same as in the bulk condensed phase, normally liquid, and they calculated the cross-sectional area from the relation

$$\sigma = 1.091 \ (M/Nd)^{2/3} \times 10^6 \qquad (3.14)$$

where M and d are the molecular weight and density (liquid or solid) of the adsorbate. With nitrogen as the adsorbate, assuming the liquid density, this calculation gives $\sigma = 0.162$ nm^2 at 77 K.

After considerable data of this nature had accumulated, Livingston[58] proposed the more general relation

$$\sigma = F(M/Nd)^{2/3} \times 10^6 \qquad (3.15)$$

He attempted to arrive at the best values of the factor F for various adsorbates apart from affects resulting from interaction with the adsorbent or incomplete penetration because of fine pore structure. On the basis of achieving the best agreement between surface areas with various adsorbates, the differences in F were primarily attributed to differences in packing between the three- and two-dimensional phases which can explain variations in F over the range 0.87–1.09. More recently, the problem has been considered by Pierce[54], Hansen[59], Kodera and Onishi[60], Brennan et al.[61], and Ross and Olivier[9].

The value of σ_{N_2} appears to be nearly constant and close to 0.162 nm^2 in the overwhelming majority of adsorbents. Exceptions to this value have been given for the adsorption of nitrogen on graphitized carbon[62,63] and on α-alumina[64], with values of σ_{N_2} of around 0.20 nm^2 and 0.18 nm^2, respectively, and it is suggested that the nitrogen monolayer is localized on these surfaces.

Argon has been used occasionally for surface area determination, and Kiselev[65] showed that on silica gel, nitrogen adsorption was influenced by specific interactions between the nitrogen quadrupoles and the surface hydroxyls, while argon–hydroxyl interactions were essentially nonspecific; consequently argon offers an advantage over nitrogen for the routine surface area determination. This conclusion received support from other investigators[64,66,67]. However, it has been pointed out by Mikhail and Brunauer[68] that the greatest difficulty with argon adsorption is that the area covered by an argon atom is determined primarily by the adsorbent–adsorbate interaction, with a negligible adsorbate–adsorbate interaction between the argon atoms. Various investigators reported areas occupied on different adsorbent surfaces by an argon atom ranging from 0.137–0.182 nm^2 at 77 K[69–71].

Krypton (at 77 K) has been used extensively for the determination of the specific surface of low-area materials. Deitz and Turner[72], using pristine glass fibre of geometric area 4.6 m^2, found σ_{Kr} to be 0.204 nm^2, in excellent agreement with the value of 0.202 nm^2 reported by Troy and Wightman[73] for stainless steel of geometric area 47.5 cm^2, and close to that obtained by Krowles and Moffat[74] for krypton on boron phosphate, namely 0.215 nm^2.

Trials using water vapour in surface area determination are numerous[4], but comparisons of the water areas with the nitrogen areas present a very complicated picture. This is mainly associated with the high degree of specificity in the interactions of water with solid surfaces. McClellan and Harnsberger[69] have recommended a value of 0.125 nm^2 for σ_{H_2O}, but in fact this value can be considerably larger (e.g. on graphitized carbons or dehydroxylated silica), or much smaller (e.g. on certain alumina or chromia gels, or hardened Portland cement pastes).

The cross-sectional area σ (molecules/m^2) can be calculated also from the van der Waals' constants in the two-dimensional equation of state which takes the form[9]

$$(\pi + \alpha/\sigma^2)(\sigma - \beta) = kT \tag{3.16}$$

where π is the spreading pressure (Nm^{-1}), and α and β are the van der Waals' constants; $\alpha(N$m$^{-1}/($no. of molecules m$^{-2})^2)$ and β (m^2/molecule). The other terms have their usual meaning. The constant of β corresponds to the area occupied by the molecules themselves. If mutual interaction between adsorbate molecules is the same as for the gas phase, it should be possible to calculate β from the three-dimensional constant b[9]. Computed values, designated with the subscript c, are given by the relation

$$\beta_c = 0.96 \ (b/N)^{2/3} \tag{3.17}$$

β_c is largely temperature independent, and both the sectional areas calculated from liquid or solid molar volume and from the van der Waals' constants were found to agree within 7%[6]. A table of cross-sectional areas is included in Appendix C.

Post monolayer region

If the adsorbate is essentially equivalent to the corresponding liquid surface and is of the same area as the adsorbent, the net energy released on further uptake from the actual vapour pressure to the saturation point p_0 (i.e. wetting) should be related to the surface area (S) and surface tension of the liquid (γ) or the corresponding heat term (U) by the two equations:

$$\Delta F(p_0 - p) = S\gamma \times 2.39 \times 10^{-4} \tag{3.18}$$

$$\Delta H(p_0 - p) = SU \times 2.39 \times 10^{-4} \tag{3.19}$$

This relation has been utilised by Harkins and Jura[75] to calculate 'absolute' surface area of a nonporous titanium dioxide pigment. Harkins and Jura measured the heat of immersion of a solid sample which had been exposed to saturation vapour of the adsorbate, assuming that the thick film of the adsorbate would present a liquid surface which would be removed by immersion in the same liquid. This approach has been criticized on the grounds of the likelihood of interparticle capillary condensation leading to a reduction of the film area at saturation. As has been shown by Clint *et al.*[76], it is not essential, however, to condense a liquid film at saturation in order to obtain the liquid-like properties. It was found that pre-coating graphitized carbon black with hydrocarbon vapour of a statistical coverage of only 1.5 already decreased the heat of immersion to a value close to the surface enthalpy of the liquid hydrocarbon. In the case of carbon tetrachloride on nonporous silica, Diano and Gregg[77] found that a coverage of about 0.1 was sufficient to bring the reduction of the heat of immersion to the surface enthalpy of the liquid.

Lafitte and Rouquerol[78] and Letoquart *et al.*[79] have discussed the thermodynamic and practical significance of the heat of immersion in the context of physisorption, and they stressed the useful information which can be gained from this study regarding the texture or chemical nature of the surface, and also the variation of the differential enthalpy as an essential parameter in the study of the surface properties.

Clearly, application of the heat of immersion method is restricted to nonporous and mesoporous solids. When micropores are present, complications might arise in the evaluation of the heat term per unit area of the solid[80]. Gregg and Sing[4] list experimentally determined heats of immersion per unit area of various solids in a number of liquids. In general the values show a considerable variation in different samples of similar materials. Obviously a lot of work is needed to standardize heat of immersion data in order for it to be used for direct routine measurement of surface area.

3.1.2 Porous solids

The methods presented so far can be applied to nonporous solids or to porous solids which are predominantly macro- or mesoporous. The occurrence of adsorbent with a large component of microporosity presents two main obstacles to the evaluation of specific surface from the adsorption isotherm, arising respectively from the likelihood of activated entrance of molecules through narrow constrictions of molecular size, and from the obstruction of multilayer formation in micropores and the possibility that pore filling will occur even at very low pressures. A number of attempts have been made to avoid these complications, and they involve the analysis of the adsorption isotherm mainly in the region of low pressures.

Henry's law region

Bond and Spencer[81] measured the adsorption of neon at room temperature on various coals or cokes, and because of the small size of the adsorbate molecule and the high temperature of measurement compared to the boiling point of neon (27 K), it is considered that the rate of passage through the constrictions should be high, and the amount adsorbed is so small that the measured isotherm falls wholly within the region of Henry's law. The method is a relative one, and it involves calibration against a nonporous reference solid of known surface area. The reference solid should have a surface of almost the same properties as the experimental solid, a requirement which severely restricts the scope of the method. The authors used carbon black as reference substance. It is assumed that the adsorption per unit area is the same at a given pressure on coal or coke as on the reference substance, and it can be easily shown that the specific surfaces of the coal or coke (S_c) and of the reference (S_r) are related by the equation

$$S_c = \frac{k_c}{k_r} S_r \qquad (3.20)$$

where k_c and k_r are the Henry's law proportionality constants of the two solids. It is not necessary to compare the actual adsorption values at a given pressure but only the slopes of the linear portions of the isotherms. In spite of the several limitations of the method[4], it is certainly one of the most realistic attempts to date.

Another method concerned with Henry's law region of the isotherm, is based on the work of Halsey et al.[82], and which was put in a suitable form by Everett[16]. The model put by Everett leads to a Henry's law isotherm in which the proportionality constant is given by

$$k_0 = \frac{SI}{RT} \qquad (3.21)$$

in which S is the surface area which can be calculated from k_0 if the integral I can be evaluated. Such evaluation requires the variation of the potential energy of a gas as a function of the distance r from the surface, and therefore it requires a detailed knowledge of the potential energy curve. Curves of this kind have been so far calculated for relatively simple systems, such as the argon–graphite system, and only for substance which are nonporous or have very wide pores. The results of specific surface are markedly dependent on the kind of gas–solid interaction and on the nature of the adsorbate. Everett regarded the adsorbed phase as a two-dimensional gas, taking into account the forces between the adsorbed molecules, and arrived at specific surface values close to those calculated from particle size determination by electron microscopy. However, the computation procedure is laborious, and no independent check can be made on the various parameters involved.

In fact, the Halsey–Everett method is only a relative one. One has to assume that the potential energy curve, and consequently the integral I is the same for a series of solids in order to be able to determine the surface area. If one of the substances is chosen to be a reference solid whose area is known, the areas of the 'unknown' solids can be evaluated. In reality the method is identical to that of Bond and Spencer[81], but with the advantage that it makes clearer assumptions on the nature of the gas–solid interaction.

A third method for the evaluation of the Henry's law constant k_0 was put forward by Zwietering and van Krevelin[83] which is based on the concept, emphasized by De Boer[84], of the average time of sojourn τ_1 of an adsorbed molecule on the surface. In their treatment, Zwietering and van Krevelin calculated the Henry's law proportionality constant as equal to

$$k_0 = 5.8 \times 10^{-1} \tau_0 \left(\frac{M}{T}\right)^{1/2} \exp(E_1/RT) \cdot S \qquad (3.22)$$

where τ_0 is the time of a single oscillation of an adsorbed molecule in a direction normal to the surface, E_1 is the heat of adsorption, and M and T are the molecular weight and the absolute temperature of the adsorbate.

The difficulty in applying Eqn. (3.22) is that of evaluating τ_0. In practice, the oscillation frequency of the adsorbed molecules ($1/\tau_0$) is usually assumed to be of the same order as the frequency of vibration of the atoms or ions of the solid lattice, which can be assessed with some accuracy, for example from the melting point of the solid (Lindemann) or from the temperature variation of the heat capacity (Einstein). If an average value of $b \times 10^{-13}$ sec is inserted for τ_0 in Eqn. (3.22), where b is a small number, between 1 and 10, the equation will be reduced to

$$k_0 = 5.8 \times 10^{-14} \left(\frac{M}{T}\right)^{1/2} \exp(E_1/RT) \cdot S \qquad (3.23)$$

This equation contains E_1, the differential heat of adsorption, which is assumed to be the same for all parts of the surface; an assumption which obviously is not justified. If E_1 can be evaluated, either calorimetrically or isosterically, then the specific surface can be calculated from the slope of the isotherm in the Henry's law region by Eqn. (3.23). In microporous solids, the value of E_1 may vary from place to place, due not only to the surface heterogeneity but also to the overlap of the potential field from the walls of the pores of different sizes.

Obviously, the major point of weakness of the method lies in the estimation of τ_0 which is of an uncertain order of magnitude, and therefore, as an 'absolute' method it gives surface areas with a several-fold uncertainty. On the other hand, as a relative method, for comparing the values of specific surface for a series of related solids, the uncertainty is reduced.

Essentially, the three methods mentioned so far are the same, and differ only in their approaches to estimating Henry's law constant.

The micropore filling region

It has been established[85–89,4] that micropores tend to fill with adsorbate at low relative pressures ($p/p_0 < 0.3$), an effect which is often attributed to enhanced dispersion forces resulting from the proximity of the pore walls. Dubinin et al.[90-92,85] have directed attention to this low-pressure region of the isotherm for the investigation of micropore structure, and have extended the Polanyi potential theory of adsorption to give their 'theory of volume filling of micropores'. Dubinin's treatment has been modified by Kaganer[93] to yield a method for the calculation of specific surface from the isotherm.

Two principal assumptions are involved in Dubinin's treatment:

1. The characteristic curves for different adsorbates on the same adsorbent can be superimposed by using an affinity coefficient β, and

$$\Delta G = RT \ln \left(\frac{p_0}{p}\right) = \beta f(W) \tag{3.24}$$

where ΔG is the differential molar free energy change of adsorption, taking the bulk liquid as the standard state, and W is the volume of adsorption space filled with adsorbate.

2. The equation of the characteristic curve for the adsorption of vapours on microporous solids takes the form:

$$\frac{W}{W_0} = \exp\left(\frac{-k \, \Delta G^2}{\beta^2}\right) \tag{3.25}$$

which is known as the Dubinin–Radushkevich (D–R) equation[94]. In this equation k is a constant and W/W_0 is the fraction of the total adsorption volume (W_0) filled at any value of ΔG.

The D–R equation can be expressed in the linear form

$$\log W = \log W_0 - D \log^2(p_0/p) \tag{3.26}$$

Where $D = 2.303 \, k \, R^2T^2/\beta^2$. Dubinin et al. presented experimental data to show that Eqn. (3.26) describes, over a wide pressure range, the adsorption data of many adsorbates onto a wide variety of microporous carbons. It has also been shown[95-97] that many adsorption isotherms of vapours on nonporous solids can be linearized, in the submonolayer region, by Eqn. (3.26). It would appear, therefore, that the D–R equation is of wide applicability. However, deviations from linearity can be observed at low values of $\log^2 (p/p_0)$ owing to capillary condensation in mesopores, or multilayer formation on the walls of micropores[91,94], and the plot deviates upwards with increased slope.

The D–R equation is empirical in origin and predicts that there is a distribution of free energies with adsorption of the form

$$f(\Delta G) = \frac{-2k \, \Delta G}{\beta} \exp\left(\frac{-k \, \Delta G^2}{\beta^2}\right) \tag{3.27}$$

94

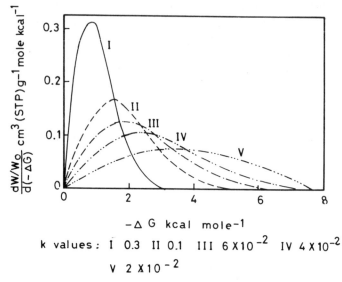

Fig. 3.6 Distribution of W with ΔG from the Dubinin–Radushkevich plots[98] (after Marsh and Rand)

This is known as the Rayleigh distribution. Marsh and Rand[98] have shown that only when this distribution is present in microporous solids will a completely linear D–R plot result. Figure 3.6 shows the slope of this distribution obtained from linear D–R (Fig. 3.7), and the effect of the constant k in

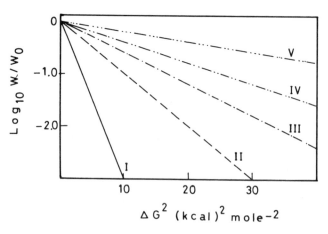

Fig. 3.7 Idealized Dubinin–Radushkevich plots[98] (after Marsh and Rand)

governing the distribution, taking $\beta = 1$. The distribution is seen to be skewed towards high values of $-\Delta G$. On the other hand, Gregg and Sing[4] and Sutherland[99] consider that the apparent wide applicability of the D–R equation arises because the plot of log W vs. $\log^2 (p/p_0)$ is inherently insensitive and the distribution of adsorption free energy with volume need not be of the Rayleigh type. Marsh and Rand[98] have shown, however, that nonlinear D–R plots result when Gaussian, Poisson, and log-normal distributions are assumed (Figs. 3.8–3.10). If only high values of $-\Delta G$ are considered, the Poisson distribution with values of greater than or equal to 3 can be linear in the D–R coordinates. It therefore does not appear to be justifiable to assume that the D–R equation is insensitive to the type of distribution. The important factor is that the range of pressures investigated should cover the whole distribution of free energies.

In principle, the method makes it possible to calculate the micropore volume from the low-pressure part of the isotherm, the region where the adsorption is still much below the plateau value. This is most readily achieved by the application of Eqn. (3.26), in which the micropore volume (W_0) is evaluated from the intercept of the line on the adsorption axis (where $\log_{10}(p/p_0) = 0$ or $p/p_0 = 1$); this intercept is $\log_{10} W_0$. The difficulty in testing this method is of a general nature in practice, namely the difficulty of obtaining an independent check in the value of the micropore volume[4].

The treatment of Dubinin has been modified by Kaganer[96] to yield a method for the calculation of the specific surface from the isotherm. He utilized the monolayer region, and assumed Gaussian distribution of adsorption over the sites on the surface, which can be represented by the equation

$$\theta = \exp(-k_1 \varepsilon^3) \tag{3.28}$$

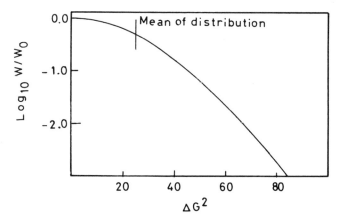

Fig. 3.8 D–R plot of Gaussian distribution of W with ΔG[98]
(after Marsh and Rand)

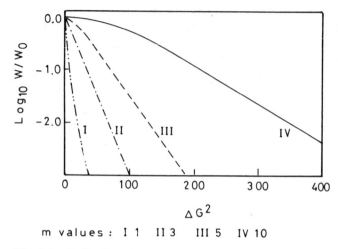

Fig. 3.9 D–R plot of Poisson distribution of W with ΔG^{98} (after Marsh and Rand)

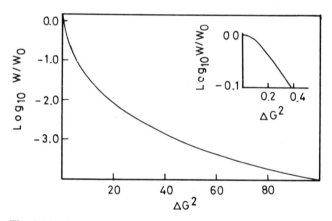

Fig. 3.10 Dubinin–Radushkevich plot of log-normal distribution of W with ΔG^{98} (after Marsh and Rand)

where θ is the fraction of the monolayer occupied and k_1 is a constant which characterizes the Gaussian distribution; ε is the adsorption potential as given by Dubinin,

$$\varepsilon = RT \ln\left(\frac{p_0}{p}\right) \tag{3.29}$$

Combining Eqns. (3.28) and (3.29) gives

$$\theta = \exp\left[-k_1\left(2.303RT \log_{10}\frac{p_0}{p}\right)^2\right] \tag{3.30}$$

Putting $\theta = V/V_m$,

$$\log_{10} V = \log_{10} V_m - D_1 \left(\log_{10} \frac{p_0}{p}\right)^2 \qquad (3.31)$$

where

$$D_1 = 2.303 k_1 R^2 T^2 \qquad (3.32)$$

Equation (3.31) is identical to Eqn. (3.26), and a plot of $\log_{10} V$ against $(\log_{10} p_0/p)^2$ should give a straight line, but the intercept is now equal to the logarithm of the monolayer capacity rather than to the logarithm of the pore volume. In testing the method, one again encounters the difficulty of finding suitable adsorbents of known area, which can be used as reference materials to check the method. Kaganer measures the adsorption of nitrogen[96] and argon and krypton[100] on a variety of solid adsorbents, and compared the monolayer capacity calculated with the aid of Eqn. (3.31) with the value obtained by the BET method, and he found that both values agreed within ±3%. This agreement was used by Kaganer as evidence for the correctness of the validity of his method, but this evidence is subject to criticism, since the BET method itself is based on a nonporous model as already indicated in this chapter. Actually, the agreement between the Kaganer and the BET values gives more support to the applicability of the BET method to microporous solids than to the correctness of the values evaluated by the Kaganar method, assuming that the latter gives more reliable values for microporous solids than does the BET method.

The criticisms levelled against the D–R equation can be equally levelled against Kaganer equation (both combined are known as the DRK equation), and both are actually empirical in nature. The assumption of a certain type of distribution of site energies is arbitrary in nature, and the constant k_1 cannot be independently checked by any means. The DRK equation can, therefore, be regarded as an extrapolation formula. On theoretical grounds, the D–R or the DRK equations offer no attempt to elucidate the mechanism of micropore filling or surface coverage.

3.1.3 Routine surface area determination using the adsorption method

The most commonly used evaluation methods are summarized by Unger[102,104] and illustrated in Fig. 3.11. Today, the general routine determinations are based on the measurement of the nitrogen isotherm at 77 K. All commercially available instruments use this method and the evaluation has been standardized in some countries[105–106]. For samples with surface areas below 0.1 $m^2 g^{-1}$ krypton may be preferred, in volumetry at 77 K, and in gravimetry at 90 K.

Volumetric measurement

The experimental procedure described in this section is suitable for use with the apparatus as described in Figs. 2.6–2.8. For other apparatus the instruc-

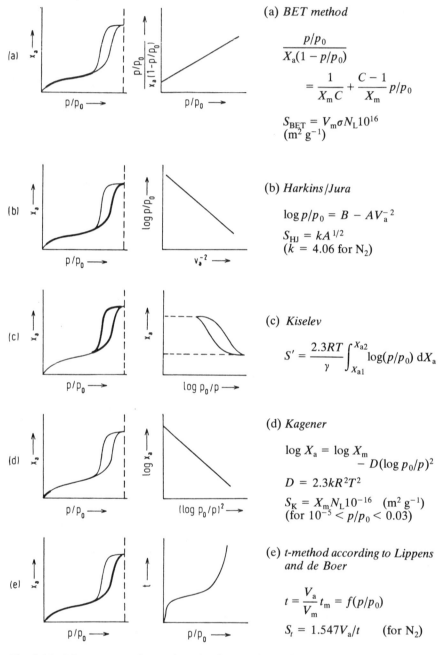

(a) *BET method*

$$\frac{p/p_0}{X_a(1 - p/p_0)}$$

$$= \frac{1}{X_m C} + \frac{C - 1}{X_m} p/p_0$$

$$S_{BET} = V_m \sigma N_L 10^{16}$$
$$(m^2\,g^{-1})$$

(b) *Harkins/Jura*

$$\log p/p_0 = B - A V_a^{-2}$$
$$S_{HJ} = k A^{1/2}$$
$$(k = 4.06 \text{ for } N_2)$$

(c) *Kiselev*

$$S' = \frac{2.3RT}{\gamma} \int_{X_{a1}}^{X_{a2}} \log(p/p_0)\, dX_a$$

(d) *Kagener*

$$\log X_a = \log X_m$$
$$\qquad - D(\log p_0/p)^2$$

$$D = 2.3kR^2T^2$$

$$S_K = X_m N_L 10^{-16} \quad (m^2\,g^{-1})$$
$$(\text{for } 10^{-5} < p/p_0 < 0.03)$$

(e) *t-method according to Lippens and de Boer*

$$t = \frac{V_a}{V_m} t_m = f(p/p_0)$$

$$S_t = 1.547 V_a/t \qquad (\text{for } N_2)$$

Fig. 3.11 Most commonly used evaluation methods for the specific surface area according to Unger[102]; X_a adsorbed amount (mol g^{-1}), X_m monolayer capacity (mol g^{-1}), V_a adsorbed amount (ml gas g^{-1}), V_m monolayer capacity (ml gas g^{-1}), σ molecular cross-sectional area (nm^2/molecule), t_m monolayer thickness (nm), t statistical thickness of one adsorbed layer, γ surface tension of the adsorbed liquid, B constant of the Langmuir equation, R gas constant, T temperature (K)

tions should be modified accordingly. Prior to the measurements the volumes of the burette and that of the sample bulbs have to be calibrated, using dry nitrogen or helium. Then the apparatus has to be cleaned by evacuation or flushing with dried nitrogen of high purity (not less than 99.9 per cent). Leak tightness has to be checked carefully. After a period of 15 minutes, a vacuum of less than 10^{-3} Pa should be reached. If the apparatus has not been used for some time all taps (except those of the gas reservoirs) should be regreased. Greasing of taps and connections should always be carried out with very little grease.

The sample to be tested should have a total surface area in the range of 20 to 200 m^2, preferably in the region of 50 m^2. Wet samples should be dried before being introduced into the sample bulb. The sample bulb should preferably be of such a size that it is approximately two-thirds full. The bulb must be weighed empty, filled with the sample before and after outgassing and/or after the measurement of the isotherm when warmed up again. The specific surface area should always be normalized to the mass of the degassed sample.

Outgassing starts with desorption in vacuum at room temperature. To avoid scattering of the sample the pressure in the sample bulb should be reduced slowly by small adjustments of the tap to the vacuum line. In general, a vacuum of 10^{-3} Pa and a temperature of 130 °C is sufficient, whereas some organic compounds tolerate only lower temperatures. For stable adsorbents (activated carbon, molecular sieves) a temperature of 300 °C can be applied. Alpha-aluminia in a quartz bulb (glass can safely be heated only up to 400 °C) can be degassed at 1000 °C, whereas an 'active' oxide prepared by precipitation from solution (e.g. iron oxide) may sinter appreciably at 100 °C. With highly porous samples a 10-hour treatment will be necessary. To avoid damaging the sample surface by sintering or decomposition, degassing should be done as quickly as possible and thus at a temperature as high as possible. These optimal conditions can only be obtained by treatment of the sample at stepwise higher temperatures and successive measurement of the specific surface area after each step.

To determine the dead space, the sample bulb is cooled down to room temperature and dry helium (which is scarcely adsorbed) is introduced into the gas burette, which is levelled to the calibration mark, and the pressure H_1 is recorded to at least 0.1 mm Hg. Then the helium is allowed to expand into the sample bulb and the bulb is immersed in liquid nitrogen to a standard depth. After that, the final pressure H_2 is recorded. Subsequently the bulb is warmed and evacuated.

To measure the isotherm in the BET range $p/p_0 = 0.05$ to 0.35 (90 to 250 mm Hg), the sample bulb is cooled down again in liquid nitrogen. The nitrogen level must be kept stable. Nitrogen is introduced into the burette from the reservoir, levelled and the pressure recorded (P_1), and it is then allowed to expand into the sample bulb. After equilibrium has been reached (after about 10 to 20 min.; longer with microporous samples) the burette again is levelled and the pressure recorded (P_2). This cycle is repeated at least five times using increasing pressures.

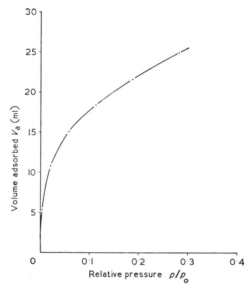

Fig. 3.12 Sorption isotherm for the volumetric BET surface area determination

Finally the bulb is warmed in a warm water bath to a temperature above room temperature and the bulb is filled with nitrogen gas to atmospheric pressure. The bulb is removed from the apparatus, the connection degreased, and the bulb with sample weighed to obtain the weight of the dry sample.

V_m is obtained by determining the volume of gas adsorbed V_a at a series of relative pressures p/p_0 in equilibrium as described above, and can be plotted as an isotherm (Fig. 3.12). The data are interpreted by means of the two parameter BET-equation (3.10).

The plot of $p/V_a(p_0 - p)$ against p/p_0 (Fig. 3.13) should be a straight line of slope $C - 1/V_mC$ and intercept $1/V_mC$, from which V_mC and C and hence V_m can be calculated. In general, the linearity is restricted to the range of $0.05 \leqslant p/p_0 \leqslant 0.35$. If the curve is not straight the range can be shortened and if the intercept is negative a line through zero can be approximated. Such results, however, indicate either an error of measurement or that the BET method is not applicable for the material under investigation.

Using

$$S = \frac{V_m \sigma N_L}{V_0 m} = \frac{4.35 V_m}{m} \tag{3.33}$$

for nitrogen (molecular area = 0.162 nm^2), the specific surface area can be calculated where N_L is Avogadro's number, $V_0 = 22.41$ l (the ideal gas volume), and m is the sample mass.

The computation of the specific surface area can be facilitated using the

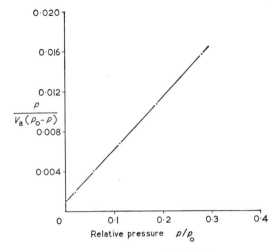

Fig. 3.13   Volumetric BET-plot

calculation scheme[105] shown in the example (Table 3.2). In this calculation, which can easily be performed using a computer, no correction has been made for nonideality of nitrogen at low temperature. The error is negligible for BET calculations but must be considered when calculating the pore size distribution (Chapter 4).

Gravimetric measurement

Since microbalances are generally used in gravimetric measurements[8,107,108] the sample size is between a few milligrams and a few grams. The specific surface area for nonporous powder samples can be estimated using Figs. 3.38–3.40. In comparison with the volumetric method, degassing of the sample is easier because the connections to the vacuum line are wider, and therefore the evacuation is more effective and the final vacuum better. Furthermore, the degassing can be observed, and thus the optimal degassing can be observed, and thus the optimal degassing conditions and the end of the degassing process can be determined more easily.

On the other hand, some sources of error, discussed in Part 3, must be avoided. For example, effects by thermomolecular flow require a final vacuum of lower than 10^{-3} Pa and a temperature equilibrium has to be reached (requiring a time delay of about 0.5 h) in order to pinpoint the zero point.

B-point. The stepwise-measured mass values must be corrected by subtracting the zero point and the (pressure-dependent) buoyancy to obtain the adsorbed mass m_a as a function of the relative pressure p/p_0. It is advisable to plot the isotherm $m_a = f(p/p_0)$ (Fig. 3.14). A rough estimate of the surface area can be made using the 'B point'. This point marks the lower end of the linear part

Table 3.2 Calculation of the specific surface area according to British Standard 4359 (simplified method)

Date	14 April 66		Outgassing time	1 h
Sample	Phthalocyanine blue		Outgassing temperature	130 °C
Reference	—		Outgassing pressure	10^{-3} Pa

mass of bulb $= 6.9248$ g

mass of bulb + sample $= 8.2177$ g

mass of sample, $m = 1.2929$ g

$p_0 = 760$ mmHg

$T = 291.5$ K

$T_N = 77.3$ K

$H_1 = 136.0$ mmHg

$H_3 = 63.0$ mmHg

$v = 23.42$ cm^3

$A = \dfrac{v}{T} \times \dfrac{273.2}{760} = 0.02888$

$u = \dfrac{H_1 - H_3}{H_3} = 1.1587$

$Q = A \times u = 0.033\ 46$

Slope $(s) = 0.052\ 18$ Intercept $(i) = 0.000\ 95$ $s = \dfrac{4.35}{m(s+i)} = 64.4$ m^2/g

D	E	G	H	J	K	M	X	N	Y
		$D - E$	$A \cdot G$	ΣH	$E \cdot Q$	$J - K$	E/p_0	$(1-X)M$	X/N
$\leqslant P_1$	$*P_2$	ΔP	ΔV	$\Sigma \Delta V$	$P_2 \cdot Q$	V_a	P_2/p_0	$(1-p/p_0)V_a$	$\dfrac{P_2}{(p_0 - p_2)V_a}$
192.3	2.1	190.2	5.4930	5.4930	0.0703	5.4227	0.0028	5.4075	0.000 52
219.2	15.3	203.9	5.8886	11.3816	0.5120	10.8696	0.0201	10.6511	0.001 89
223.9	43.9	180.0	5.1984	16.5800	1.4690	15.1110	0.0578	14.2376	0.004 06
247.9	85.0	162.9	4.7046	21.2846	2.8444	18.4402	0.1118	16.3786	0.006 83
323.8	143.2	180.6	5.2157	26.5003	4.7919	21.7084	0.1884	17.6185	0.010 69
412.9	213.9	199.0	5.7471	32.2474	7.1577	25.0897	0.2814	18.0295	0.015 61

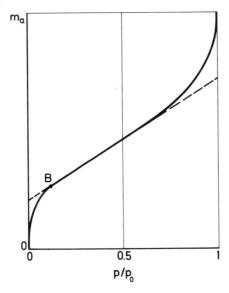

Fig. 3.14 Surface area determination
using the B-point

of the isotherm which is observed in general between $0.05 \leqslant p/p_0 \leqslant 0.5$ and was previously considered to be the point at which the monolayer is complete and from which the second layer is built up. Using this value as m_m, the specific surface area S can be drawn from the diagram (Fig. 3.15) or calculated using

$$S = \frac{m_m \phi}{m} \qquad (3.34)$$

with m the sample mass and $\phi = 3480 \text{ m}^2 \text{ g}^{-1}$ for N_2 at 77 K or 1540 for Kr at 90 K. ϕ results from

$$\phi = s_M N_L / M \qquad (3.35)$$

where N_L is the Loschmidt number $= 6.02 \cdot 10^{23}$ molecules per mole, s_M the cross-sectional molecular area, and M the molecular mass. Values of s_M and ϕ are tabulated in Appendix C.

BET method. To evaluate the isotherm (Fig. 3.16) by the BET method we use the BET equation in the form

$$\frac{p}{p_0} = \frac{C-1}{Cm_m} \cdot \frac{p}{p_0} + \frac{1}{Cm_m} \qquad (3.36)$$

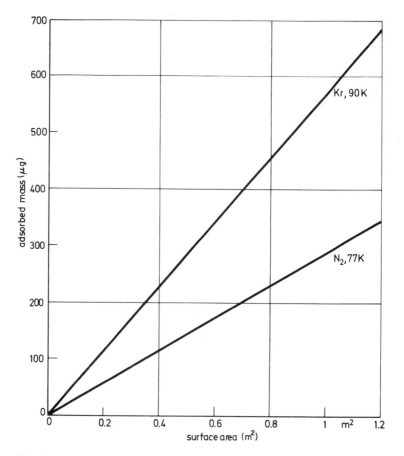

Fig. 3.15 Surface area as a function of the adsorbed monolayer mass of nitrogen at 77 K and krypton at 90 K

with p/p_0 the relative pressure, C the BET constant, and m_m the monolayer mass. The values m_a as a function of p/p_0 are taken either from the isotherm plot or directly from the recorded measuring points preferably at fixed p/p_0 values 0.05, 0.1, 0.15, 0.20, and 0.25. Transforming Eqn. (3.36) to

$$y\left(\frac{p}{p_0}\right) = \frac{p/p_0}{m_a(1 - p/p_0)} \qquad (3.37)$$

the corresponding values of $y(p/p_0)$ are calculated as shown in Table 3.3. Thus the first columns of Table 3.3 are predetermined. When using this table it is not necessary to plot the isotherm. From this table the BET chart $y(p/p_0)$ versus p/p_0 can be plotted (Fig. 3.17).

The easiest way to calculate the amount of monolayer sorbate is to take the

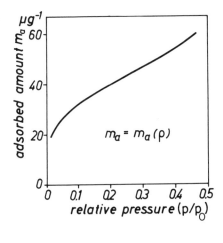

$$y_p = \tfrac{p}{p_o} / m_a (1 - \tfrac{p}{p_o})$$
$$m_m = 0.1 / (y_{0.1} - 0.9 y_0)$$

Fig. 3.16 Sorption isotherm for the gravimetric BET surface area determination

values of $y(p/p_0)$ for $p/p_0 = 0$ and $p/p_0 = 0.1$ from the BET diagram. With these values the amount of monolayer sorbate is determined from Eqn. (3.37) to be

$$m_m = \frac{0.1}{y(p/p_0)_{0.1} - 0.9y(p/p_0)_0} \tag{3.38}$$

Using Eqn. (3.38), the amount of monolayer sorbate yields the specific surface area of the sample.

For orienting measurements and for production controls in which devia-

Table 3.3 Calculation of the specific surface area measured gravimetrically

p (Pa)	p/p_0	$\dfrac{p/p_0}{1 - p/p_0}$	m_a (g)	$\dfrac{p/p_0}{m_a(1 - p/p_0)}$ (g^{-1})
5 550	0.050	0.0526	0.001 16	45.3
11 100	0.100	0.1111	0.001 30	85.4
16 650	0.150	0.178	0.001 44	124
22 200	0.200	0.250	0.001 56	160
27 750	0.250	0.333	0.001 68	198

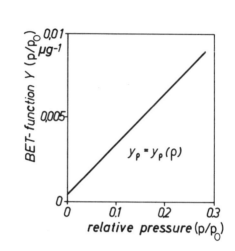

$$\text{surface } S = m_m \underbrace{F_M N_L/M}_{}$$
$$= 34.8\,cm^2/\mu g$$
$$(N_2, 77\ K)$$

Fig. 3.17   Gravimetric BET-plot

tions from a standard rather than absolute values of the surface area are of interest, the measuring time can be considerably reduced by application of a 'single-point method'. In many cases the BET constant C of Eqn. (3.36) is much greater than 1. Under this assumption the amount of monolayer sorbate in Eqn. (3.37) can be approximated by

$$m_m = m_a\left(1 - \frac{p}{p_0}\right) \tag{3.39}$$

Hence the amount of sorbate needs to be measured only at a single pressure within the range of the relative pressure $p/p_0 = 0.05$ to 0.35. To calculate p/p_0 a fixed value can be used for the saturation vapour pressure (see Part 3).

If the sample is not porous or is only slightly so, it need not be completely degassed. In this case it is sufficient to evacuate the balance at room temperature with a high-vacuum pump until the sample weight is approximately constant. Then the Dewar vessels filled with liquid nitrogen are placed below the sample and the counterweight and, after having been switched to zero, the balance is set to a pressure of about 10^4 Pa. After about 10 minutes the weight of the sorbate can be read. The specific surface area determined by the single-point method in general is 10 per cent smaller than that obtained from the complete BET equation.

In some cases the difference between differently treated samples is of greater interest than the absolute values. An example for the measurement

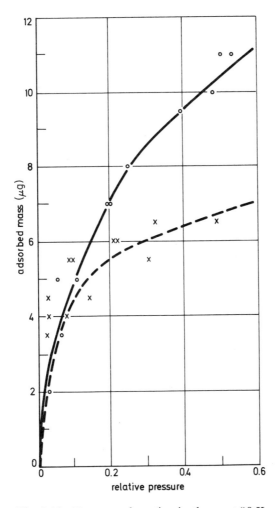

Fig. 3.18 Krypton adsorption isotherm at 90 K
on 2 g aluminium sheets. Full line: difference
between adsorption on a polished and an etched
sheet. Dashed line: difference between adsorption on a sandblasted and an etched sheet

of the difference of surface areas is presented in Fig. 3.18. The samples are
aluminium sheets, polished, sand blasted and etched. Samples of 2 g have
been placed on each side of the balance. The full line of the krypton isotherm
at 90 K designates the difference of the adsorbed amount of the polished and
the etched sample; the dashed line the difference between the sandblasted
and the etched sample. From these measurements a difference of 20 cm^2
between the etched and the sandblasted surface was determined.

The specific surface area can be calculated, as described in Chapter 2, by comparison of the isotherm to be evaluated with an isotherm measured on nonporous materials of the same chemical type with known surface area.

t-method. In the so-called *t*-method, the adsorbed amount is transformed into the layer thickness *t* using the density of the bulk liquid. When plotting the amount adsorbed on the sample at different pressures versus *t* determined at the same pressures on the standard (Fig. 3.19), a straight line is obtained if the two materials have a similar surface structure. The slope gives the ratio of the surface area of the sample to that of the standard. The surface area S_t of the sample, using nitrogen as adsorbate at 77 K, is then found to be $S_t = 1.24 \, dm_a/dt$. If m_a is expressed in mg, and t in nm, the unit of S_t is m^2.

The *t*-method depends strongly on the BET method because the monolayer capacity from which the layer thickness is calculated is determined by the BET formalism. Furthermore, it depends strongly on the validity of the standard isotherm for a certain temperature which cannot be used for another group of materials nor for another adsorbate. For such another system, the reliable standard isotherm first has to be chosen. Brunauer *et al.*[109] proposed using averaged isotherms with the same BET constant *C*.

To be able to do without the BET theory, Sing[110] normalized the standard isotherm at a variable relative pressure and used as abscissa the dimensionless value α_s. He found that if the isotherm is normalized at the relative pressure of 0.4, many isotherms will coincide in a better way than if it is normalized at the BET monolayer capacity. The α_s method as well needs relevant standard isotherms normalized to a specific surface area determined by another method which, however, need not be the BET method.

An advantage of the comparison methods is that the slope of the curve may be measured at any point. In this way, the influence of micropores on the value of the specific surface area, for example, can be excluded.

Cumulative method. For that part of the isotherm where, within porous materials, multilayer adsorption and capillary condensation occur simultaneously,

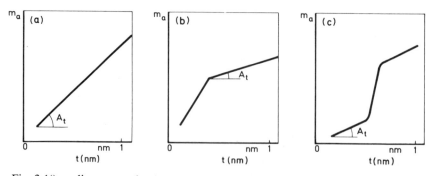

Fig. 3.19 *t*-diagrams: adsorbed mass versus layer thickness. The angle for surface area determination is recorded

i.e. between the relative pressures 0.35 and 1, and where a hysteresis loop often is observed, Kiselev[65] established the general thermodynamic equation $\sigma ds = \Delta\mu \, dn$, where σ is the surface tension of the liquid adsorbate, ds is the decrease of the surface area when covered by capillary condensation, $\Delta\mu$ is the change in chemical potential as a result of the transition from the gaseous adsorptive to the liquid bonded adsorbed state, and dn is the increase in moles of the adsorbate. The change in chemical potential equals the decrease in the differential free energy of adsorption

$$A_a = -\Delta\mu = -RT \ln x \qquad (3.40)$$

where T is the absolute temperature and R the gas constant. From this the surface area of the sample can be calculated:

$$S = \frac{RT}{\sigma} \int_{n_h}^{n_{max}} \ln x \, dn \qquad (3.41)$$

where n_h and n_{max} are the numbers of moles adsorbed at the beginning and at the end of the hysteresis loop (saturation point), respectively. In the case of hysteresis, two sets of experimental dn values can be used for the analysis. In general, the adsorption isotherm should be used for the calculation because the desorption process and the causes of hysteresis are not yet clearly understood[111]. In the case of cylindrical pores, the adsorption branch seems to be closer to the equilibrium state than the desorption branch[112].

The resulting surface area is not the surface area of the pore walls but that of the core of the pores covered with adsorbate. For more exact calculations, the thickness of the adsorbate has to be taken into account, assuming suitable pore model. The area of the outer surface of porous materials can be neglected in general.

Other cumulative surface area determinations are described in Chapter 4.

3.2 Chemisorption methods

Chemisorption involves a sharing of electrons between the adsorbate and the surface and a chemical or valency bond which is formed between the adsorbed molecule and the adsorbent (compare Fig. 3.1). Chemisorption is therefore characterized by strong and selective bonding between surface and adsorbate molecules, but interaction of adsorbate molecules by lateral forces is usually unimportant[113]. The exception is chemisorption on metals in which electron transfer results in a change in the character of the substrate due to adsorption on neighbouring sites.

With chemisorption, there is little question that the chemisorbed layer cannot exceed a single molecule in thickness, and that adsorbate spacing depends primarily on surface sites. Monolayer coverage is characteristically reached at low p/p_0 values so that monolayer criteria are unrelated to p_0. As

110

chemisorption involves bond formation rather than enhanced condensation, it frequently occurs at temperatures much higher than the critical temperature at which physical adsorption is small. The Langmuir equation was originally derived for this type of adsorption assuming uniform surface sites and no interaction between neighbouring adsorbate molecules.

The surface area of adsorbing sites S_s can be calculated from the Langmuir equation by the relation

$$S_s = \frac{V_L \sigma_s \times N \times 10^{-18}}{N_s \times 22\,400} \tag{3.42}$$

Where σ_s is the area per site (nm²), V_L the Langmuir equation constant (monolayer adsorption), N the Avogadro number, and N_s the number of molecules adsorbed per site for a monolayer, which is usually 1.00. In chemisorption, adsorption at fixed pressure on the flat part of the isotherm normally serves as an adequate approximation to V_L.

Chemisorption, unlike physical adsorption, may be complicated by the slow rate of activated adsorption, particularly at low temperatures. Gradual transfer of physical adsorption to chemisorption on raising temperature is common, and measurements should be carried out at temperatures high enough so that physical adsorption can be neglected. This state of affairs can be represented by the hypothetical isobar shown in Fig. 3.20.

Studies with clean metal wires and evaporated films have shown that chemisorption is not invariably an activated process, and is sometimes rapid even at low temperatures[113]. It is also found in some cases that a rapid chemi-

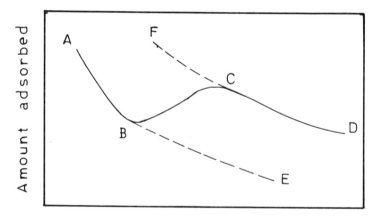

Fig. 3.20 Hypothetical isobar. The curve ABE represents the equilibrium isotherm for physisorption, while the curve FCD represents chemisorption. ABCD is the measured isobar, while BC is the activated region

sorption is followed by a slower uptake. An example is oxygen chemisorption on metals[114], which could be explained on the basis of the formation of a thin layer of bulk oxide on the surface of the metal. However, this phenomenon is sometimes found with other gases also, such as hydrogen or carbon monoxide on tungstun or iron. In the case of hydrogen on evaporated metals, the slow process was assumed to be due to a penetration into fine cracks and fissures, or even into the lattice itself[115].

Where active surface sites are heterogeneous, calculation of a meaningful surface area is more difficult, since the Langmuir equation itself may not approximate the data. A reasonable estimate of the total site area is still attainable at pressures high enough for complete site coverage.

Chemisorption, because it is normally selective on active sites, is a particularly useful tool in determining the active surface in a multicomponent system, e.g. metal catalysts on a carrier matrix. It was used, for example, by Spenadel and Boudart[116] to obtain the area of platinum black calculated from the physical adsorption of argon. In order to convert the amount of hydrogen adsorbed into a surface area of platinum, it was assumed that the average density of sites on the (100) and (110) planes is 1.12×10^{15} cm^{-2}, corresponding to area of 0.0089 nm^2 per atom of platinum. This assumption supposes that the (100) and the (110) planes are equally exposed. If each atom of metal is attached to one atom of hydrogen, then the effective area per hydrogen atom is 0.89 nm^2. The calculations lead to a surface area of platinum black of 0.54 m^2 g^{-1}, which is in good agreement with the value of 0.55 m^2 g^{-1} from the BET method.

In a later work by Adams et al.[117], the average area per chemisorbed hydrogen molecule on platinum was calculated to be 0.224 nm^2, so that the site area per atom of metal is 0.112 nm^2. This is in reasonable agreement with the assumption that the (110) plane predominates in the surface of platinum black, with the site density of platinum atoms in this plane being 0.93×10^{15} cm^{-2}. From the saturation adsorption on the supported platinum catalyst (reached above 10 Pa even at 273 K), the specific surface of platinum was calculated to be 2.04 m^2 g^{-1}. The differences between the areas found by Spenadel and Boudart[116] and by Adams et al.[117] can be attributed to differences in the particle size of the platinum crystallites or to the differences in the baking temperatures of the catalysts which might cause sintering of the metal even at low temperatures by migration over the surface of the support[118].

Infrared studies[119] reveal both strong and weak chemisorption of hydrogen on supported platinum. The strongly bound hydrogen atom is attached to two platinum atoms, while the weakly bound hydrogen atom is attached to one platinum atom only. If the interpretation is correct, then the average area of chemisorbed hydrogen may vary considerably from one sample to another depending on the crystallinity and degree of dispersion of the catalyst which are functions of the method of preparation.

The chemisorption of oxygen on metals is expected to be far more complicated than the chemisorption of hydrogen in view of the fact the the chemisorption of oxygen is normally the first step in the oxidation of metal, leading to the formation of a large oxide bulk on the surface[114]. The thickness of this layer depends on both the temperature and the nature of the metal, but even at room temperature, it is rarely less than 2 to 3 nm thick[4]. The work of Brennan, Hayward, Graham, and Trapnell[120,121] is particularly interesting in this connection; they were able to calculate the ratio of the number of atoms of chemisorbed oxygen to the number of metal atoms in the surface, and this ratio was 6.00, 3.39, and 2.45 for titanium, iron, and niobium respectively, while for other metals it was close to unity. The ratios far above unity indicate bulk rather than surface uptake. Morrison and Roberts (see ref. 121) have suggested that on cobalt and nickel at 77 K the chemisorbed layer of oxygen is confined to the surface, whereas at 273 K an oxide layer is formed.

Not only metals, but also some metal oxides are able to chemisorb oxygen, and if the metal is capable of existing in a higher valency state, the uptake of oxygen may exceed the amount required to form a monolayer. An example is provided by Garner, Stone, and Tiley[122] for the chemisorption of oxygen by cuprous oxide, in which case oxygen ions are joined in the surface by cuprous ions which have migrated there from the interior, leaving behind 'positive holes' in the lattice. In this case an extension of the lattice is thus built up.

The chemisorption of oxygen has been used for the determination of the specific surface of oxides, and Bridges, MacIver, and Tobin[123] tried to find the specific surface area of chromia in chromia–alumina catalysts by this method. Potassium, which serves as a promoter for the catalyst, was found to depress the chemisorption of oxygen to an extent proportional to the potassium content, due to the formation of a complex with the Cr^{6+} produced by the oxygen[124].

It is clear, therefore, that for the chemisorption of oxygen on metals, the mechanism may vary from metal to metal, and even for the same metal. This consideration does not always apply, and the mechanism may vary at different temperatures. On oxides, the same observation seems to hold, and hopefully, as our detailed knowledge of the adsorptive behaviour of the various constituents accumulates, some more general picture will eventually develop.

Chemisorption of carbon monoxide has also recieved considerable attention, and Beeck et al.[125] came to the conclusion that the chemisorption of this gas on nickel occurred through a 'single site' mechanism, and that each molecule of carbon monoxide was attached to a single atom of nickel. A single-site mechanism is believed to occur also on palladium. On molybdenum and rhodium carbon monoxide proved to be attached to two metal atoms[126], while the results with iron and tungsten indicated the presence of a mixed one-site and two-site mechanism[127]. The existence of two modes of attachment was revealed by Eischens and his co-workers[128,129] in their pioneering work on infrared spectroscopy of adsorbed molecules.

The chemisorption of carbon monoxide can be regarded as an established method for the estimation of the surface area of dispersal metals, particularly

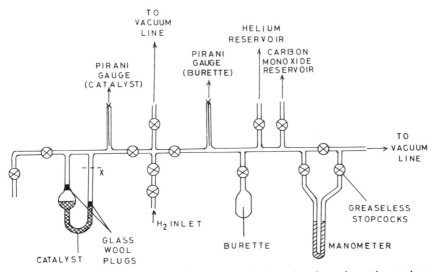

Fig. 3.21 Determination of metal areas by selective chemisorption using carbon monoxide (or hydrogen) by the volumetric method[130] (after Moss)

in supported catalysts. Not yet solved is the problem of deciding the average area occupied by the carbon monoxide molecule, because of the possibility of one-site and two-site modes of attachment, a state which may vary from metal to metal, and also with temperature and with surface coverage.

The quantity of chemisorbed gas, e.g. hydrogen or carbon monoxide, is commonly measured by volumetric methods using a fixed-volume apparatus. An example is shown in Fig. 3.21 for the apparatus used by Moss[130]. It is based on the use of miniature Pirani (thermal conductivity) gauges for pressure measurement and greaseless stopcocks. The gas burette has a known volume and the 'dead-space' correction is made with helium. The whole apparatus is thermostated. A sample of about 1 g or less of catalyst is reduced *in situ* in a stream of hydrogen, purified by diffusion through palladium, and then outgassed. For the metal surface determination, the burette is filled with the adsorbate (e.g. carbon monoxide) and doses admitted to the catalyst section with duc regard to the time of equilibrium. A support 'blank' is usually also required.

Gravimetric techniques and flow techniques are also attractive alternatives for the determination of metal areas[130].

The chemisorption of other gases and vapours such as ammonia, amines, and basic vapours has been investigated in connection with studies of surface acidities of oxide catalysts, and this topic will be discussed in Part 2.

3.3 Calorimetric methods

The measurement of isosteric heat of adsorption h_{ads} is another approach for determining the contribution of specific interactions between adsorbate molecules and the surface. This may be done for example by comparing the heat effects with different adsorbates[102,131] one exhibiting a specific interaction with the surface and the other not. As shown by Ross and Olivier[9], h_{ads} can easily be determined by means of gas chromatographic measurements. The adsorbent under investigation is packed into a column and the corrected retention volume V_r of the corresponding adsorbate is measured at various column temperatures T_c. The plot of V_r versus T_c^{-1} yields a straight line of slope $h_{ads}/2.303 R$. Elkinton and Curthoys[132] made a study based on this technique in comparison to infrared spectrum analysis on porous silica.

The heat effects, of course, are all dependent on the specific area of the sample and therefore provide the possibility for surface area determination. For this the heat evolved usually is measured when the outgassed solid is immersed in a pure liquid. This quantity of heat is known as heat of immersion. Of particular importance is the HJ method based on Harkin's and Jura's work[75,76]: before immersion the substance is covered with two or more layers of the immersant, thus avoiding the scattering-specific interactions of the liquid with different solids.

This method thus can be used to compare surface areas of various samples; or to obtain absolute surface areas if the heat of immersion of the solid per unit area is known. Heats of immersion are also useful for establishing estimates of the average polarity of solid surfaces using various monofunctional organics as the immersional liquids. Another important use is the study of solution adsorption at solid/solution interfaces. The method is suitable for low vapour pressure liquids and for measurements at quite low coverages. This represents an advantage over measuring isosteric heats. It is noteworthy that the heats of interaction can be established even if the adsorption is irreversible; chemisorption indeed usually produces higher heat evolutions than physical adsorption. When entropy changes are evaluated from one isotherm and heats of immersion, the results are usually more precise than those calculated from multi-temperature isotherms[133].

A description of the various types of calorimeters and some of the difficulties in the measurement and interpretation of heats of immersion have been discussed by Zettlemoyer and Chessik[134,135]. Manufacturers of commercial instruments are included in the list in Appendix D. Certain important precautions have to be taken into account in the construction of a calorimeter including:

1. A steady and efficient stirring rate to ensure good mixing with minimum heat generation.
2. Precise measurements of both temperature changes and calibration of the heat capacity of the calorimeter.
3. Attainment and maintenance of a steady rating period.
4. A reproducible method of sample bulb breaking.

A thermistor calorimeter developed by Zettlemoyer et al.[136] is shown in Fig. 3.22 which fulfils these requirements, and is sensitive to heat effects of

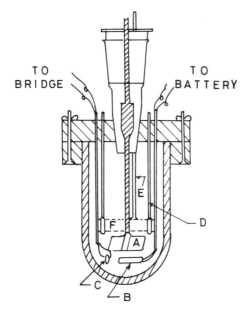

TO
BRIDGE

TO
BATTERY

Fig. 3.22 Thermistor calorimeter developed by Zettlemoyer et al.[136] for measurement of heat of immersion. A, stirrer; B, heater; C, thermistor; D, sample holder; E, breaking rod; F, sample tube. A sensitive resitance bridge such as the Mueller bridge and a galvanometer of sensitivity of the order of 10^{-10} A allows the determination of heats of the order of 0.01 cal. The calorimeter is placed inside an air thermostat. Evolution of heat up to about 10 min can be followed using a simple arrangement of this type

the order of 0.01 cal, and is adequate for the study of solids with surface areas greater than 5 m^2/g. Microcalorimeters are used in the case of solids with low surface areas. Calorimeters of this type are capable of measuring heat effects of the order of 0.001 cal and can be employed for solids of surface areas as low as 0.1 m^2/g [137]. Berghausen[138] has shown that slow heat effects (up to 2000 min) can be followed with differential adiabatic calorimeters.

One of the important sources of uncertainty in immersional calorimetry is the heat evolved during bulb breaking plus accessory events. Several procedures have been used to minimize the uncertainties in heat of bulb breaking, and these are summarized by Zettlemoyer and Narayan[133]. Also, extreme care has to be exercised in preparing powders for measurement, especially polar solids which readily pick up contaminants from the atmosphere, and further, outgassing at high temperature can cause reduction. Special pre-

116

cautions also have to be taken to ensure the purity of immersional liquids, especially when dealing with polar surfaces and relatively nonpolar solvents. It has long been established[139] that the presence of trace quantities of water are sufficient to raise the heat of immersion nearly to that of water itself. Whalen[137] has suggested breaking several bulbs of Linde sieves in the liquid until the heat evolved upon the introduction of successive buckets reaches a constant level. The use of the adsorbent itself as a 'getter' for traces of water has also been successful[140].

The heat of immersion isotherm describes the variation of heat of immersion at a given temperature with precoverage. Typical known types of heat of immersion isotherms have been discussed by Zettlemoyer and Narayan[133], and are shown in Fig. 3.23, and other types of immersion curves predicted from adsorbing data, but not yet experimentally observed, are also presented by Zettlemoyer and Narayan[133].

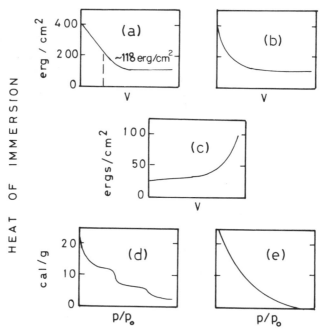

Fig. 3.23 Known types of heat-of-immersion isotherms, i.e., heat of immersion vs. coverage at a constant temperature[133] (a) Homogeneous surfaces, (b) heterogeneous surfaces, e.g. water on most oxide surfaces, (c) wetting of a hydrophobic surface with a few hydrophilic sites, e.g., water on graphon, (d) swelling of clay or stratified mineral with internal surface area, e.g., water on Wyoming bentonite. The adsorbate penetrates through platelets of the mineral at definite relative pressures, (e) gradual filling of pores, making a large part of the surface inaccessible for the wetting liquid, e.g., benzene on graphitized black (after Zettlemoyer and Narayan)

Heats of immersion were found to depend also on the temperature of outgassing and some relationships have been discussed elsewhere[133]. Among the factors which have been introduced, is the presence of micropores which can have a significant effect as demonstrated by Mikhail et al.[141] for magnesia

Table 3.4   Heats of immersion (h^i) of various solids in a number of liquids

Solid	Activation temp. (°C)	Liquid	h^i (J m^{-2})	Ref.
TiO$_2$ (anatase)	100–400	hexane	0.095–0.142	144
	120–750	benzene	0.110–0.137	145
	500	water	0.41	145
	750	water	0.53	145
	100	water	0.510	146
TiO$_2$ (rutile)	200	hexane	0.074–0.134	144
	400	hexane	0.069–0.137	144
	—	water	0.55	147
α-Alumina	100–450	hexane	0.142–0.155	144
	100–450	water	0.372–1.076	144
	1200	benzene	0.165	148
	1200	water	0.773	148
γ-Alumina	100–450	hexane	0.081–0.089	144
	600	benzene	0.231	148
	550–900	carbon	0.100–0.115	149
		tetrachloride	0.100–0.115	149
SiO$_2$ (quartz)	160	water	0.850	150
SiO$_2$ (aerosil)	—	water	0.165	151
SiO$_2$ (aerosil)	—	n-heptane	0.120	151
Gel		carbon		
		tetrachloride	0.012	152
		heptane	0.050–0.075	153
	300–500	benzene	0.1	154
SiO$_2$–Al$_2$O$_3$	160	water	0.70	150
		n-hexane	0.15	150
GeO$_2$ (hydrons)	25	water	0.20	155
ZrO$_2$	400–600	water	0.60	139
		benzene	0.19	139
BaSO$_4$	400–600	water	0.40	139
		benzene	0.14	139
chrysotile	25	water	0.41	136
asbestos	450	water	0.85	136
bentonite	25	water	1.59	156
muscovite	25	water	0.63	157
kaolinite	25	water	0.49	157
montmorillonite	25	water	0.14	157
graphite	400–600	water	0.048	140
		n-heptane	0.125	140
graphon	25	water	0.032	158
		n-heptane	0.11	158
tetrafluorethylene	25	water	0.006	159
		n-heptane	0.06	159

in cyclohexane. With this hydrocarbon where dispersion forces only are involved, it has been shown that the presence of micropores beyond a certain fraction of the total pores present, could lead to an *increase* in the heat of immersion. In contrast to cyclohexane, water possesses permanent dipoles, and it has been shown that for the system water–silica gel, pore narrowing could lead to a *decrease* in the heat of immersion[142,143].

The integral heat of adsorption, and with it the heat of immersion, are proportional to the surface area, according to the simple relation

$$\Delta H^i = h^i S \tag{3.43}$$

where h^i is the heat of immersion per unit area of the solid in the given liquid, S is the specific surface of the solid, and ΔH^i is the heat of immersion per gram of solid. If, therefore, the value of h^i is known for a particular solid–liquid pair, the absolute value of S for a given sample of the solid can at once be calculated from the heat of immersion. The fact that the applicability of the heat of immersion method to surface area determination depends on the availability of a value of h^i for the solid–liquid pair in question rather restricts its scope. Some typical values are collected in Table 3.4. Many values in the literature are unreliable because outgassing conditions were not carefully specified, or because surface areas were not determined, or because the role of the pore structure is not mentioned. As already indicated, the value of h^i is needed for absolute surface area measurement. The experimental and theoretical limitations must be borne in mind in determining the h^i value for a given solid–liquid pair. On the other hand, for the comparison of the areas of a number of specimens of the same chemical nature in the same liquid, the value of h^i may be assumed to remain constant, and the method becomes convenient even when the absolute values of h^i are uncertain.

3.4 Adsorption from the liquid phase

Prior to the introduction of nitrogen as adsorbate, it was customary to determine the specific surface area by adsorption from solutions[113,131,160]. This method can be applied only with reservations. In the case of adsorption from solutions solute and solvent compete in the adsorption, whereas normally only one parameter, i.e. the concentration of the solute, can be determined. Using the following designations for a two-component system:

n_0 number of moles of solute (A) and solvent (B) prior to adsorption
n_A^s number of moles of solute adsorbed
n_B^s number of moles of solvent adsorbed
X_A mole fraction of solute after adsorption in equilibrium with the adsorbate
ΔX_A change in mole fraction of the solute due to adsorption;

the following equation applies:

$$n_0 \Delta X_A = n_A^s(1 - X_A) - n_B^s X_A \qquad (3.44)$$

It must be noted that the quantity $n_0 \Delta X_A$, which can be measured, is not identical with n_A from which the specific area should be calculated; n_B^s is unknown.

If X_A is small, Eqn. (3.44) is simplified to

$$n_0 \Delta X_A = n_A^s \qquad (3.45)$$

If Eqn. (3.45) is extended to cover larger X_A values, negative adsorption may apparently be encountered.

With some adsorbates in low concentration, a saturation value is reached, resulting in an isotherm shape corresponding to a type I shape isotherm (Fig. 2.17). In this case the behaviour can be represented fairly accurately by a Langmuir equation. Thus it is possible to determine the point of monolayer capacity by the isotherm equation or by the B-point method. The conversion of the monolayer capacity into the specific surface is then carried out with the aid of the relationship quoted in connection with gas adsorption, and here the area occupied by one molecule of the solute in a close-packed film on the surface must be known.

On practical grounds, however, the situation is much more complicated, and the evaluation of both the monolayer capacity (X_m), and the area occupied by one molecule on the surface (A_m) are complicated by two main factors: first, the competitive adsorption between the solute and the solvent molecules, and second, the solute molecules are often large and complicated in shape[4].

When both the solute and the solvent compete for the surface, it becomes more appropriate to express results of adsorption measurements in terms of mole fractions rather than concentrations. The isotherm of 'apparent' adsorption of the solute A is then the curve of ΔX_A against X_A, where ΔX_A is changed in mole fraction of component A in the solution when adsorption occurs, and X_A is the mole fraction of A in the solution which is in equilibrium with the solid C. Figure 3.24 shows such an isotherm for the adsorption of benzene from its solution in methanol on charcoal[161]; the apparent adsorption of benzene, $n_A X_A/m$, is plotted against the mole fraction of benzene in solution and equilibrium, X_A. n_A is the number of moles of benzene originally present, ΔX_A is the change in mole fraction of benzene by adsorption, and m is the weight of the solid. The curve is S-shaped, with negative values of the apparent adsorption at the right-hand side of the curve. Negative apparent adsorption of one component merely implies that this component is being adsorbed to a lesser extent than is the second component in that part of the concentration range.

For the determination of specific surface it is necessary to have the

120

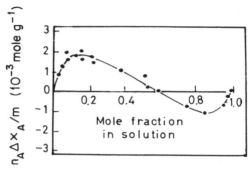

Fig. 3.24 Composite isotherm for adsorption of benzene from its solution in methanol. The abscissae represent the mole fraction of benzene in the solution[161] (after Innes and Rowley)

isotherm of an individual component, e.g. component A, and the separation of the composite into two individual isotherms becomes possible when both of the components are volatile. In such cases the solid will adsorb the same amount of each component as it will adsorb from the solution itself if it is exposed to the vapour in equilibrium with the solution. The procedure for such calculations has been summarized by Gregg and Sing[4], and need not be repeated here. Calculations of this kind have been carried out by many workers in the field and in particular by Kipling[162,163]. An example of the composite isotherm being separated into two individual isotherms is shown in Fig. 3.25, which shows that the composite isotherms differ markedly in appearance from the individual isotherms.

Even when the individual isotherm of the solute is calculated, there still remains the difficulties in selection of 'point B', and of assigning a value to the cross-sectional area of the adsorbate molecule. In some practical cases, the presence of the solvent may lead to the complete disappearance of a point B, or even more, the shape of the individual isotherm is found to depend markedly on the nature of the solvent. It is obvious, therefore, that for a reliable estimation of surface areas from adsorption from solution, the value of molecular area of the solute must be known, and the point corresponding to monolayer completion must be clearly identifiable. In this respect difficulties may arise if the adsorbate assumes different orientations (with different space requirements) relative to the surface at different concentrations and a mixed monolayer consisting of solvent and solute is encountered upon saturation.

Another consideration is the surface uniformity, especially in the kind of studies where competition between the two species for adsorption sites is involved. The orientation of the solute molecules relative to the surface depends on their interaction with the surface. Fatty acid molecules, for example, have been observed to orient themselves perpendicularly to oxide surfaces and parallel to graphite surfaces. Varying orientations have been observed with dye molecules which are used frequently because their concen-

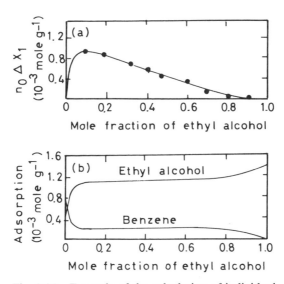

Fig. 3.25 Example of the calculation of individual isotherms from the measured isotherm. (a) Measured isotherms for the adsorption, of ethyl alcohol from its solution in benzene, on activated alumina, (b) individual isotherms of ethyl alcohol and of benzene, calculated from the measured isotherm[162,163]

tration can be determined readily. On account of the large size of the dye molecules and their complicated shape, pores may possibly not be accessible. Formation and adsorption of micelles may increase the amount adsorbed. Adsorption on organic substances (e.g. fibre and pigments) may involve dissolution in the solids.

Giles and his co-workers[164,165] examined the shape of a very large number of published isotherms, and have divided them into four main types, with subdivision of each type (Fig. 3.26). The main types are S, L, H, and C, characterized by the curvature of the isotherm near the origin. The authors discussed the various isotherms in terms of the solid–solute, solid–solvent, and solute–solute interactions, and also in terms of the orientation of the solute molecule on the surface. They concluded that the choice of a solute for reliable measurement of specific surface is very restricted, and thus it became clear that the dyestuff method must be limited to those cases where a clear plateau is obtained, with full attention paid to other factors, namely: (a) the shape and size and consequently the molecular area must be known; (b) the orientation on the surface must be known; (c) since dyestuffs are liable to form colloidal micelles in solution, it is essential to know the degree of association of the molecules adsorbed on the surface[166]. Since these factors are not easy to determine, many authors consider the adsorption of dyestuffs to be a secondary method only, and that a calibration by reference to a sample of the solid of known area is essential.

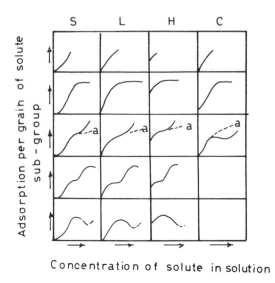

Fig. 3.26 Classification of isotherms of adsorption from solution, according to Giles *et al.*[164,165]

Despite these limitations, the method is a useful tool for checking and comparing the specific surface area of chemically identical solids, especially if these can be measured *in situ*, provided a comparison with the gas adsorption method has been made. Conventional adsorbates include dyes, fatty acids, and phenol.

3.4.1 Dye tests

Dye tests were practical means to characterize the activity of adsorbents like charcoal before methods to obtain objective parameters like specific surface area and pore size distribution were known. Their application today in industry is still in use and some have been standardized by the administration (ASTM, DIN, AFNOR) in many countries[167-176]. Conventional tests are performed with alizarin red, Bismarck brown, crystal violet, caramel, iodine, methylene blue, methyl orange, molasses, Ponceau red, and potassium permanganate. As solvents, water and ethanol are in use; typical concentrations are given in Table 3.5. Because many adsorbents contain small amounts of acid or alkaline constituents, it is advisable to buffer the test solution with non-adsorbable agents such as mono- and di-sodium phosphate to avoid colour change by pH. The procedure is as follows: To 100 ml of the solute in a 200 ml Erlenmeyer flask, portions of the weight sample are introduced to give a 60 to 99% removal of the solute originally present. At 298 K the contents of the flask are agitated for 10 to 60 minutes. Then the mixture is filtered, stirred, and the dilution is measured calorimetrically or by titration.

Table 3.5   Solutions for dye tests

Solvent	Solute	Concentration $(g\ l^{-1})$	Buffered to pH
water	methylene blue	0.80	
ethanol	methylene blue	0.50	
water	malachite green	0.91	
ethanol	malachite green	0.43	
water	alizarin red	0.73	6.2
water	Ponceau red	1.09	7.0
water	molasses	20–60	6.5
water	caramel	4–6	
water	iodine	2.7	
water	$KMnO_4$	79	

Methylene blue

The methylene blue number is defined as the milligrams of methylene blue adsorbed by one gram adsorbent with a solution of methylene blue at a concentration of $1.0\ mg\ l^{-1}$. To perform the test, a representative sample is micronized and sieved. According to Hassler[167], 4–8 g (depending on the activity of the sample) are added to a 400 ml beaker, 80 ml of methylene blue solution $(20\ g\ l^{-1})$ are added to the sample, and subsequently the mixture is stirred at fast speed. After that the sample is filtered by means of suction. The first 10 to 15 ml are discarded and the remainder is measured using a Nessler tube. Norit[169] recommends a 100 mg sample of dry carbon with 25 ml methylene blue solution $(1.2\ g\ l^{-1})$ in 5% by volume acetic acid, diluted 1:200. Lurgi[168], in concordance with the DAB[175], measures how much of a 0.15% methylene blue solution is cleared within 5 minutes by 100 mg of dried carbon as the methylene blue factor.

The concentration of dyes can be determined photometrically by comparing the light transmittance of the sample with that of a reference solution. The change of the extinction coefficient serves as a measure for the decrease of the concentration. For methylene blue a wavelength of 445 or 665 nm should be used and a concentration range of about 0.2 before and 0.1% after the adsorption. Commercial instruments for this optical concentration measurement are available.

Methylene blue concentration can also be determined by means of cation exchange[177-179] using NH_4, Ca, or Na ions. Another possibility is the iodometric titration or titration with titanium chloride[177,180]. One mole of methylene blue is reduced by two moles of titanium chloride. To avoid photo-oxidation of the $TiCl_3$, the titration should be carried out in a CO_2 atmosphere.

The molecular area of methylene blue is determined to be between 1.30 to $1.35\ nm^2$. The area covered by 1 mg of methylene blue is reported to be $1.46\ m^2$ for graphitized carbon black and 2.45 for non-graphitized carbon black[181], and to $2.44\ m^2 mg^{-1}$ on mercury[182].

Molasses

The molasses test is a rather practical test with regard to sugar refining[167]. Because it is a natural product, batches from different sources vary considerably in depth of colour and in the adsorbability of colour. Thus the concentration depends on the type of molasses. Suitable concentrations are 20 to 60 g l^{-1} of solution in water together with 30 g of disodium phosphate. Phosphoric acid is added to give a pH of 6.5. The solution should be filtered. In a refrigerator the solution will usually be stable for 4 to 8 hours, the stability being controlled with standard carbon. To a 50 ml portion of the solution in a 150 ml beaker, 0.5 g of the adsorbent (usually active carbon) is added and stirred. Then the mixture is boiled and filtered. The colour of the filtrate is measured. The procedure is repeated with other weights of adsorbent until an adsorption range between 70 and 90% removal of the original colour is reached. The adsorption may be calculated using the Freundlich isotherm

$$\left(\frac{m_a}{m}\right)_T = k \cdot c^n \tag{3.46}$$

where m_a is the amount adsorbed
   m the sample mass
   c the equilibrium concentration of the adsorptive in the solution
   k, n are constants
   T the constant temperature.

The amount adsorbed, related to unit mass, is plotted against the relating residual concentration on the abscissa on log/log paper. There the Freundlich isotherm should give a straight line. The adsorption (in percentage by weight) at 1 mg l^{-1} residual concentration is the required value.

Caramel

In similar way, the caramel test[167] (today seldom used because of its little relevance for decolorization) is carried out. Usually 4 to 6 g l^{-1} in water gives a satisfactory solution.

Iodine

For the iodine test[167] a stock solution with 2.7 g iodine and 4.1 g potassium iodide per litre of water is prepared. The solution can be stored in dark bottles kept cool. According to Norit, 1 g of finely ground carbon should be boiled with 10 ml of 5% HCl for 30 seconds. After cooling, 100 ml of 0.1 N iodine solution (potassium iodide/iodine: 1.5/1) is added. The solution is filtered, discarding 20 ml. Then 50 ml of the remainder is titrated with 0.1 N sodium thiosulphate with starch as an indicator[173,176].

Potassium permanganate

Potassium permanganate, with 0.5 N $KMnO_4$, may be used to test activated carbons.

3.4.2 The phenol test

The phenol test originally was developed to evaluate carbons for the removal of tastes and odours from potable water supplies. The amount of activated carbon to reduce the phenol concentration in 1 l water from 0.10 to 0.01 ppm is known as the phenol number. The test used by waterworks is standardized in some countries[167,169–174]. For the test, some carbon suspensions, e.g. 100 to 500 mg/990 ml, are prepared and 10 ml phenol solution 1 g l^{-1} (tenable for one month) is added. The mixture is agitated for three hours at ambient temperature, and subsequently filtered. Discarding the first 200 ml, to 100 ml of the filtrate are added 5 ml of buffer solution (20 g ammonium chloride in about 800 ml of water to give pH 10), 2 ml of 4-amino phenazone solution (2% w/v in water), and 2 ml of potassium ferricyanide solution (8% w/v in water). The extinction is measured against a reagent blank after 15 minutes at 510 nm, and the phenol concentration determined from a calibration graph which has been previously determined by treating phenol solutions of known concentration in the same way. The adsorbed amount related to unit mass of adsorbent is plotted versus the relation residual concentration on the abscissa on log/log paper. This Freundlich isotherm should give a straight-line plot.

For hydrophobic material the adsorption of phenol from aqueous solution, and for hydrophilic from carbon tetrachloride solution, is a suitable method for rough surface area determination[180]. Another solvent is decane. Molecular cross-sectional areas of 0.402 to 0.412 nm^2 and areas of 2.64 to 3.2 m^2 mg^{-1} are reported. The solvent capacity for phenol must be sufficient but less than 10 g/100 ml. The change of concentration can either be measured by bromatometric titration or interferometrically (not with carbon tetrachloride).

The surface area can be calculated according to the BET equation. A sufficient estimate is a one-point measurement and (in case of $K \gg 1$) the calculation[180] gives

$$S \approx \sigma \, \frac{x}{m} \, \frac{c_0 - c}{c} \left(\frac{c}{c_0} + \frac{1}{K} \right) \tag{3.47}$$

with
$$K \approx \exp[(E_A - E_L)/RT] \tag{3.48}$$

σ the area required by 1 mg phenol
x/m the adsorbed phenol in mg per g adsorbent
c equilibrium concentration
c_0 saturation concentration (3.75 g phenol per 100 ml decane)
E_A heat of adsorption in the first layer
E_L heat of adsorption in subsequent layers = heat of solution

Measurements of the adsorption of fatty acids have been made by several authors[183-187]. Mainly they used stearic acid dissolved in benzene or methanol. The adsorption isotherm is of the Langmuir type. Reaction of the adsorbate with the surface is a serious source of error.

3.5 Electrochemical methods

In special cases these methods are advantageous to characterize electrodes *in situ*. The work was started by Bowden and Rideal[188], and aimed at the determination of the area of a metal surface by measurement of the electrical capacity of the interface when it was immersed in an electrolyte. These measurements showed that the 'real' area, which is accessible to hydrogen ions and to water molecules of a smooth metal surface, was appreciably greater than its apparent area.

Berndt[189] investigated electrodes of sintered carbonyl nickel powder in alkali solution using a method described by Wagner[190]. A positive potential jump from $U = 4$ to 28 mV results in an increase of the current up to about 30 mA, followed by a decrease within about 1 second to a remaining small Faraday current. The area under the current curve $\int i\ \mathrm{d}t$ down to the Faraday level is found and the differential capacity of the generated double layer calculated using the equation

$$C = \frac{\int i\ \mathrm{d}t}{\Delta U} \tag{3.49}$$

C is proportional to the surface area, and the area can be calculated in comparison with the capacity measured on a plane sample of the same size (regarding the surface roughness).

Berndt observed very good agreement with the BET values for those samples exhibiting a coarse pore system but remarkably smaller electrochemical active surface areas in comparison with BET of commercially manufactured PbO_2 electrodes with many small pores. It is to be suspected that in small pores the double layer is bridged and their surface for the electrocatalytic action is not available.

Binder *et al.*[191] investigated platinum electrodes for fuel cell catalysts with methanol added to 3 N H_2SO_4. In the arrangement shown in Fig. 3.27 a voltage up to 0.6 V is fed to the electrode sample. The potential first is linearly increased and then decreased periodically at a rate of 0.7 mV s^{-1} (triangle method). In Fig. 3.28 a periodic potential/current curve is shown. For the determination of the specific surface area the production of the hydrogen adsorbate (hatched section in Fig. 3.28) is used. The oxygen adsorption is hardly reproducible on account of the slow diffusion of oxygen into the platinum lattice.

The amount of hydrogen adsorbate is determined by direct counting of the charge amount or can be calculated by integration of the area below the

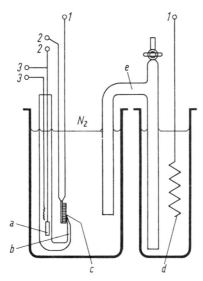

Fig. 3.27 Half-cell device for
potentiodynamic measurements; a
H_2 reference electrode, b Lugin
capillary, c working electrode, e
counter electrode, 1–1 current
resulting from the potential fed in,
2–2 feed potential, 3–3 current for
hydrogen production for the H_2
reference electrode

respective curve. In Fig. 3.28 at 298 K the charge amounts cathodically to
11.6 A s and anodically to 11.5 A s. The slight difference is accounted for by
the solution of some hydrogen in water which in general is negligible, because
the electrolyte is saturated with hydrogen. From the whole charge amount the
charge necessary for changing the potential of the double layer must be
substrated. In the case of graphic integration only the dashed part of the
right-hand side area between 400 and 600 mV is used. Provided each
platinum surface atom will adsorb one hydrogen atom, the charge measured
can be transferred to hydrogen coverage using Table 3.6. Disregarding areas
with higher index numbers an arithmetic mean of 200 μC cm^{-2} is calculated.
Comparison with BET measurements provides good agreement and that
means that despite the fact that the electric field cannot penetrate far into the
pore system, the total surface area of the electrode is engaged in the reaction,
because the hydrogen atoms after being decharged at the outer surface diffuse
into the pore system to cover the internal surface.

Similar results have been obtained in perchloric acid, whereas in potassium
hydroxide the amount of hydrogen adsorbed was about 15% lower. It is
suspected that adsorbed potassium ions impede the generation of a complete
hydrogen monolayer. In neutral electrolyte only a little hydrogen is adsorbed.

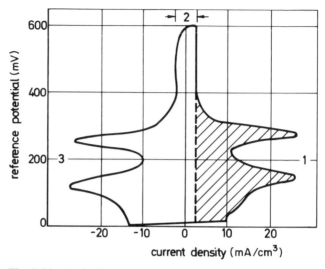

Fig. 3.28 Periodic voltage/current curve of a platinum electrode in 3N H_2SO_4. Triangle method with $dU/dt = 40$ mV min^{-1}; 1 anodic oxidation of the hydrogen adsorbate, 2 charge reversal of the double layer, 3 cathodic reduction of the oxygen adsorbate

Table 3.6 Specific number of atoms and specific charge of platinum surface under the supposition of one elementary charge per surface atom

Crystal face	Atoms cm^{-2}	μC cm^{-2}
(111)	$1.5 \cdot 10^{15}$	240
(100)	$1.3 \cdot 10^{15}$	208
(110)	$0.92 \cdot 10^{15}$	147

3.6 Radioactive Isotope Methods

In these methods several approaches have been utilized for surface area determination, and these include Hahn's emanation technique, adsorption from solution and gas adsorption.

3.6.1 Hahn's emanation technique

In this method, radium, thorium, actinium[192-195] or tellurium 132[196] are incorporated in the solid during preparation, and the emanation of radon, thoron, actinon or iodine 132 is measured. The radioactive emanation gives a measure of the surface since only the surface radioactive material can decay into the gas phase.

The desirable properties of such a radioactive system are a relatively long half-life for the parent so that decay during the experiment is not serious, while the volatile daughter should have a short half-life so that radioactive equilibrium with the parent is rapidly attained when the equilibrium is seriously disturbed.

The incorporation of the radionuclides can be done in various ways, for example during precipitation, crystallization, or by adsorption during the generation of a high-surface precipitate. The measurement of the emanation per unit time can be made in the usual manner after sampling the gas in a vessel, or continuously, by using a carrier gas. Ionization chambers of scintillation counters are used as detectors.

3.6.2 Adsorption from solution

The radioactive isotope indicator method of Paneth and Vorwerk (see 195–197) involves the adsorption of a radioactive component from a solution. The amount of radioactive isotope adsorbed from solution is determined, and surface areas can then be determined if the area per site can be computed from crystal dimensions[198].

3.6.3 Gas adsorption

This method uses direct measurement of adsorption of radioactive-labelled compounds. A suitable gas should have a rather long half-life, and emit an easily detectable radiation which is not absorbed by the sample and its container. The last point excludes carbon-14. The use of xenon-133 has been proposed[199–201]. Though the γ-yield of this isotope is high, the γ-energy (81 keV) and the half-life (5.3 days) are rather low. Only krypton-85 (half-life 10.6 years) seems to meet the requirements, though its low γ-yield is a relative disadvantage. An example is the adsorption by graphite of krypton containing Kr^{85}. The γ-radiation from the adsorbent can be related to krypton adsorption, and surface area can be computed from the isotherm. The method is claimed to be usable in the range $0.001–100 \ m^2/g$[202–204].

Houtman and Medema[205,206] designed an apparatus (Fig. 3.29) which has been commercially available for some time. It consists basically of a krypton storage vessel (a) filled with high specific area Al_2O_3, and for suction of the krypton at the end of the measurement cooled with liquid nitrogen. With a mercury valve (2) which acts as well as a manometer, the Kr-vessel could be sealed. The sample vessel (3) is cooled with liquid nitrogen. Two Geiger-Müller tubes (4) are arranged near the sample by a connecting tube. For the vacuum measurement a MacLeod gauge (5) is built in. A rotary vane pump is connected via a liquid nitrogen operated cold trap (6) to generate a vacuum of better than 0.1 Pa.

Radioactive isotope methods are somewhat specialized, in the techniques, in the equipment, and in the precautions involved. Because of restrictions in new laws, such instruments only can be used in authorized laboratories. It seems that there is no way to judge the sensitivity of the method in an

130

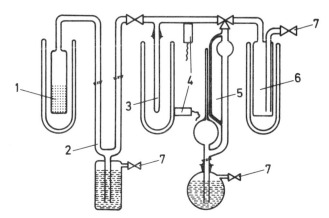

Fig. 3.29 Krypton-85 BET-apparatus according to Houtman and Medema; 1 krypton supply bottle filled with Al_2O_3,
2 mercury valve and monometer, 3 adsorption measuring cell,
4 Geiger–Müller tubes, 5 Macleod gauge, 6 cold trap, 7 to
atmosphere and vacuum pump respectively

absolute sense, since in almost every case studied, the results were compared
with the gas adsorption method.

3.7 Flow Rate and Diffusion Methods

The resistance to a flow of a gas or a liquid through a porous system depends
on the specific surface area related to the volume of the sample. In the
methods based on this principle, differentiation should be made between
forced flow through packed beds and diffusive flow through small pores. For
the forced flow, both viscous (Poisseuille) and diffusive (Knudsen) flow can
occur. Both types occur in gases, while liquid flow gives viscous flow only.

For gases, in which both types occur, their relative importance depends on
the Knudsen number

$$Kn = \bar{\lambda}/d \qquad (3.50)$$

with ratio of mean free path $\bar{\lambda}$ to pore size[207]. The mean free path can be
calculated from the kinetic gas theory using

$$\bar{\lambda} = \frac{1}{\pi\sqrt{2}n(2r)^2} \qquad (3.51)$$

with n number of molecules per cm^{-3}, and r the molecule radius. For 293 K at
ambient pressure, the mean free path of nitrogen is 61 nm; for other gases see
the gas kinetic diagram in Appendix C. That means that for nitrogen in pores
with a diameter of 61 nm, the Knudsen number is 1. Thus, in mesopores and
micropores we have to reckon with Knudsen diffusive flow, whereas in
macropores (e.g. most compacted nonporous powders) we have viscous flow.

In the viscous flow region we have to distinguish furthermore between laminar and turbulent flow. For surface area determinations only laminar flow is used. In this region d'Arcy's law[208] governs permeability calculation. From that the Carman–Kozeny equation[209] can be derived:

$$\Sigma^2 = k_2 \frac{\Delta p \; \varepsilon^3}{1 \eta \bar{v}(1 - \varepsilon)^2} \tag{3.52}$$

where Σ is the specific surface area related to unit volume (m^{-1})
$\quad k_2$ factor (dimensionless) about 5, but has to be determined for each material
$\quad \Delta p$ pressure drop (Pa) across the length l (m) of the sample
$\quad \eta$ dynamic viscosity (Pa s)
$\quad \bar{v}$ mean flow velocity in the free channel before the sample $(m \; s^{-1})$
$\quad \varepsilon$ porosity (dimensionless)

The porosity is defined as the ratio of the void volume $V_{p,s}$ to the total volume of the sample V_t (compare Eqn. (2.7))

$$\varepsilon = V_{p,s} V_t^{-1} \tag{3.53}$$

and can be calculated using

$$\varepsilon = \frac{m}{\rho V_t} \tag{3.54}$$

with m the sample mass and ρ the true density of the compact sample material (see Section 2.2). The volume-related surface can be transformed to the mass-related surface area using Eqn. (2.3).

An equation has been given[207] covering both types of flow:

$$\frac{QL}{A \; \Delta P} = \frac{k_1 \varepsilon^3 \bar{P}}{(1 - \varepsilon)^2 S_e^2 \mu RT} + \frac{k_2 \varepsilon^2}{(1 - \varepsilon) S_0 (MRT)^{1/2}} \tag{3.55}$$

where Q is the flow rate (moles/second)
$\quad L$ the length of bed (cm)
$\quad \Delta P$ the pressure drop across bed (dynes/cm^2)
$\quad \varepsilon$ the fractional void volume
$\quad k_1$ a constant dependent on geometry (dimensionless, about 0.20)
$\quad k_2$ a dimensionless constant dependent on geometry (about 0.47)
$\quad S_e$ the external area of particles (cm^2/cm^3)
$\quad S_0$ the total area of particles excluding closed or blind pores (cm^2/cm^3)
$\quad \mu$ the viscosity in poises
$\quad \bar{P}$ the average absolute pressure in packed bed (dynes/cm^2)
$\quad A$ the cross section of bed (cm^2)
$\quad R$ the gas constant in ergs per degree per mole.

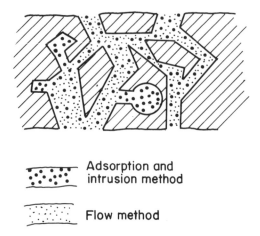

Adsorption and
intrusion method

Flow method

Fig. 3.30 Difference of surface area
measurements by adsorption, intrusion, and
flow method

From measurements at varying $\bar{P}$ and knowing ε independently, it is possible to evaluate both the external and internal area. If $QL/A\Delta P$ is plotted against $\bar{P}$, areas can be computed from the slope and intercept of the resultant straight line. Materials of relatively low porosity appear to be more convenient for such kinds of measurements, and if adsorption is not negligible, a term for surface diffusion should be added[210].

Carman[211] developed a technique based on liquid flow to determine the surface area of coarsely divided materials like sands and fine gravels[212]. A serious error of this method is caused by the immobile boundary layer reducing the effective pore diameter and causing simulation of a larger surface area because of a smaller permeability[213].

Another situation occurs using gases: obviously the surface of blind pores cannot be determined, as indicated in Fig. 3.30. A smoothing of the surface area is caused by the immobile boundary layer resulting in a apparently smaller surface area compared with that determined by adsorption measurements (Fig. 3.31).

In the practical design of gas permeability apparatus, two types can be distinguished: either the flow is generated by a constant pressure gradient and the flow velocity is measured (Carman, Malherbe, Lea and Nurse); or the time is measured within which the initial pressure gradient is reduced to a present value (Blaine, Friedrich).

The Lea and Nurse[214,215] apparatus (Fig. 3.32) comprises a pump which presses air through the powder bed. Prior to the measurement the weighed sample is compacted by a plunger up to a fixed height. The flow rate of the gas and the pressure drop along the sample are measured by means of oil mano-

Fig. 3.31 Difference of surface area determination according to the flow and the adsorption method

meters. The evaluation of the results is made using the equation[215]:

$$\Sigma^2 = k_3 \frac{\varepsilon^3}{(1 - \varepsilon)^2} \Delta p \qquad (3.56)$$

The factor k_3 is determined by the measurement of a capillary or a sample with known surface area. The different instruments in use vary in the method of measuring the porosity and the pressure drop.

As an example for a variable pressure apparatus, the widespread Blaine-test

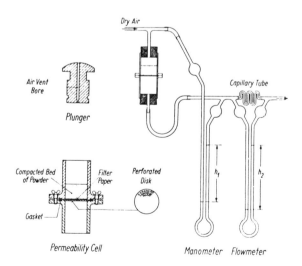

Fig. 3.32 Lea and Nurse air permeability apparatus

134

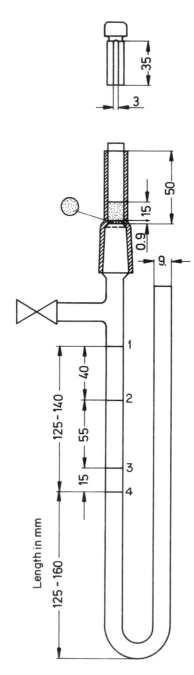

Fig. 3.33   Blaine air permeability apparatus

apparatus is shown in Fig. 3.33. It consists of an oil-filled U-tube monometer which has a slide outlet that can be closed. A perforated disk covered with a filter paper is placed at the bottom of the sample cell. The weighed sample is compacted with a plunger to about 2 cm^3. After the sample cell is placed on the monometer, the liquid is lifted above the uppermost line mark 1 by means of a squeeze bulb and the valve is immediately closed. Consequently liquid air will be sucked through the sample bed by the manometer until the menisci in both arms of the monometer approach each other. The time to cover the distance between mark 2 and 3 is measured. The surface area results from the equation

$$\Sigma^2 = k_5 \frac{\varepsilon^3}{(1-\varepsilon)^2} \frac{t_2 - t_1}{\eta} \tag{3.57}$$

k_5 is a factor depending on the instrument and the sample material. It is determined by blind experiments[209].

Instruments of these types are mostly used to characterize nonporous powders like cement or fibres (fasonaire apparatus)[210] and methods and instruments for this purpose have been standardized in many countries. Modifications both of instruments and of evaluation methods have been made for different materials, and automatic apparatus is on the market. The advantages of flow measurements for surface area determination consists in the experimental simplicity and the measuring speed. The method is fairly crude and suitable only for reference measurements on similar materials. Efforts to make the method more subtle by using correction terms for the calculation, therefore, are not of great value.

Barrer[216] proposed several methods in which the total surface area including that of blind pores and the roughness of particles from the change in flow rate upon sudden changes in the pressure gradient are obtained. Under certain conditions the data thus obtained can be compared with the results of the gas adsorption techniques.

For diffusive flow through solids, the diffusion constant D_k depends on pore dimension when mean free path (usually a few tens of nanometers) is greater than pore size. Therefore, it should be possible to determine the surface area by diffusion measurements under Knudsen flow conditions[210]. A relation was derived by Weiss[217], which is based on a random point nuclei uniform structure model, takes the form

$$S_0 = (1.75 \cdot 10^4)\, \varepsilon^3 (T/M)^{1/2}/D_k \tag{3.58}$$

Calculated surface areas are high for very fine-pore materials in which possible constrictions can markedly decrease D_k, and are low for a wide pore size distribution, in line with theory. If adsorption occurs, surface diffusion must also be considered beside gas-phase diffusion[210,218]. Barrer[216,219] has summarized the various experimental procedures which may be applied to gas flow to the evaluation of surface area.

3.8 Sedimentation Analysis

Particle size determination by the investigation of the sedimentation[220-224] of a powder in a liquid by gravitation or acceleration in a centrifuge may be regarded as the conversion of the observation of flow of a liquid through a porous system (Section 3.7). At low Reynolds numbers the settling rate is measured and related to particle size as an equivalent settling rate diameter. For an irregular particle, the equivalent settling rate diameter is usually slightly smaller than the volume diameter. As a consequence of an adhering, immobile liquid layer, surface roughness and pores do not contribute. Highly porous particles, however, exhibit a differing apparent density, and this should be taken into account. The sedimentation analysis results in a particle diameter distribution. The conversion of diameter to surface area is described in the following section.

For sedimentation analysis the particles are dispersed in a liquid with a lower density than that of the particles. The viscosity is chosen so that, on the one hand, coarse particles do not drop too fast, and on the other hand, the time for the complete analysis is not too long. The formation of agglomerates is impeded by means of a dispersion agent. A table of liquids and dispersion agents is included in DIN 66 111[225].

By gravity or in a centrifugal field the particles achieve a stationary velocity in the stagnant liquid dependent on diameter, shape, and density of the individual particles. The equivalent diameter d_s is calculated by means of a resistance law, in general Stokes's law:

$$d_s^2 = \frac{18\eta}{\rho_s - \rho_l} \frac{v}{g} \tag{3.59}$$

where η is viscosity, ρ_s density of the particles, ρ_l density of the liquid, v velocity of sinking, and g gravitational acceleration.

Analogously, by measurement using a centrifuge, we find

$$d_s^2 = \frac{18\eta}{\rho_s - \rho_l} \frac{\ln r/r_i}{\omega^2 t} \tag{3.60}$$

where r = radius of the centrifuge, r_i = radius of the surface of the liquid, ωt = angular velocity, and t = time.

The concentration of the particles over the length of the sedimentation chamber can be determined in various ways, and the many laboratory-made or commercial apparatus differ in this regard. For example, tube samples can be racked off with a pipette at different heights of sedimentation and the density of the liquid determined. The pipette method is not automated nor as convenient as some more modern methods but it is accurate and reliable and the mass distribution is directly obtained. Another method is the determination of the mass deposited at the bottom of the tube by means of a sedimentation balance as a function of time. Furthermore, by means of buoyancy bodies, the density distribution over the length of the tube can be determined. The pressure gradient as a result of the density gradient can be measured by simple differential manometers or sensitive pressure transducers. Commercial photosedimentometers use the extinction of light, X-ray absorbance, wide- and small-angle scattering of light to determine the density gradient, scanning over the length of the tube. In centrifuges the sedimentation of particles of size down to 10 nm have been investigated[226].

Sedimentation can be carried out of particles distributed in a gas and streaming through an electrical field[227]. The particles must exhibit sufficient conductivity.

3.9 Stereological Analysis

With stereological methods the three-dimensional object particle or pore is reconstructed from the measured screen points, lines, or two-dimensional plane pictures of the surface. According to Haynes[228] we can differentiate between areal analysis, in which plane sections or pictures are planimetered (Fig. 3.34); lineal analysis, in which lines are drawn from the sample projection or picture either parallel at regular intervals (Fig. 3.35) or randomly (Fig. 3.36); and point analysis, where screen points are counted (Fig. 3.37). Using computerized image analysers, stereological methods are gaining increasing importance. In the case of porous systems, however, only a cut-image can be investigated, and distinction between open and closed porosity is not possible. Connections cannot be detected and even cross-sectional size and shape can hardly be determined.

Applying the method shown in Fig. 3.37 on a pore system by measuring random intersections of a test line of length λ, it is possible to calculate the specific surface area Σ related to unit volume by means of Chalkley's equation[221]:

$$\Sigma = 4\varepsilon X_{\text{pm}}^{\lambda-1} T_{\text{p}}^{-1} \tag{3.61}$$

where ε = the porosity (see Section 2.2), T_{p} = the number of occasions on which an end of the line lies within a pore, and X_{pm} is the number of intersections with the pore/matrix boundaries. (For conversion to the mass-related specific surface area, see the introduction to Chapter 2.)

Some approaches have been made for the evaluation of the surface of nonporous grains from grain size. For some regular geometric bodies the surface area can be calculated from a typical diameter. Because in reality powders mostly exhibit an irregular shape and are often porous, it is not possible to obtain reliable results. Nevertheless, such calculations allow a rough estimate of the surface area from a microscopic inspection, for example to fix the sample mass for an adsorption measurement. Figure 3.38 gives the

Fig. 3.34 A real analysis of a plane section of a porous medium, The total shaded portion representing the matrix, the unshaded portions representing pores. (Courtesy J. M. Haynes)

Fig. 3.35 Lineal analysis. The total length of full line (matrix) and broken line (pore) are measured. (Courtesy J. M. Haynes)

Fig. 3.36 Point counting. The numbers of heavy and light dots (lying in matrix and pore, respectively) are counted separately. (Courtesy J. M. Haynes)

Fig. 3.37 Random intersections of a test line of length λ. Intersections of the line with the pore/matrix boundaries are indicated by open circles, and terminations of the line within a pore by closed circles. The number of times each occurs in a random placing of the line is denoted by X_{pm} and T_p, respectively. (Courtesy J. M. Haynes)

relation between surface area S and diameter d of a sphere according to the equation

$$S = \pi d^2 \tag{3.62}$$

Figure 3.39 shows the dependence of specific surface area S_m from diameter

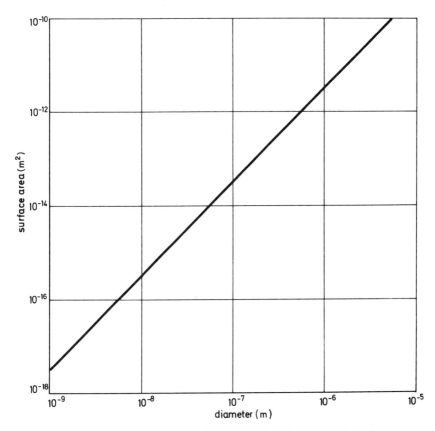

Fig. 3.38   Relation between diameter and surface area of a sphere

according to

$$S_m = \frac{6}{\rho d} \tag{3.63}$$

with ρ = density.

Figure 3.40 shows the same relation for fibres or cylindrical pores according to

$$S_m = \frac{4}{\rho d} \tag{3.64}$$

For an estimate of the surface area of a heterogeneous nonporous powder exhibiting a broad particle size spectrum it has to be noted that the smaller particles make a much larger contribution to the specific surface area than that made by the larger particles. This is demonstrated by the surface distribution shown in Fig. 3.41.

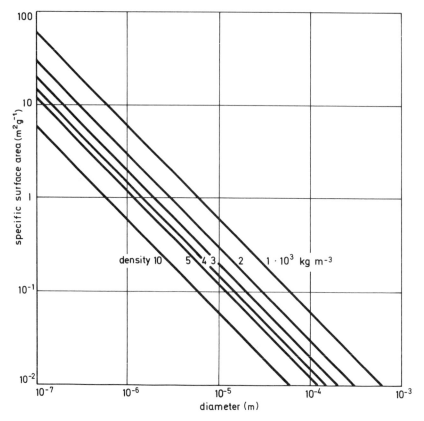

Fig. 3.39 Relation between diameter and specific surface area of a sphere

Stereological methods, in the strict sense, are light[229] and electron micros-copy[230,231]. The basic operations, limitations, and potential of the various electron optical instruments have been summarized by Sargent and Embury[232].

By 1954, particles as small as 5 nm could be resolved by electron micros-copy, although the limit with ultraviolet light was 0.01 μm. Improved electron microscope design since then has decreased the routine resolution limit to 1 nm, and using the scanning transmission mode with phase contrast imaging, resolutions of the order of 0.3 to 0.4 were produced[233,234]. The information available from the various techniques, particularly transmission and scanning electron microscopy, is that they are still capable of further refinement. Instruments are currently under development that combine existing electron optical techniques with analytical techniques such as Auger spectroscopy and secondary-ion analysis[235]. Also the field of combined scanning–transmission microscopy holds great potential for surface research. Finally, it must be emphasized that much progress has been made in the field of image process-

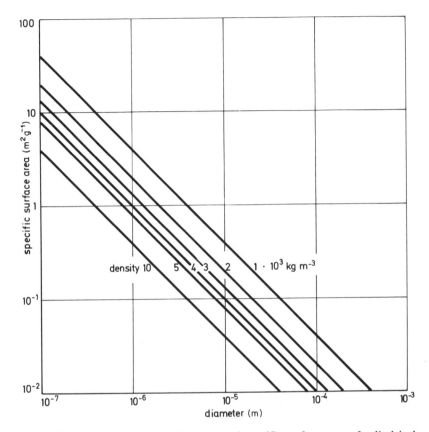

Fig. 3.40   Relation between diameter and specific surface area of cylindrical
fibres or pores

ing by optical and computer methods. The available techniques enable both
enhancement of image detail to be obtained and quantitative analysis of
images to be performed. An extensive literature now exists on these subjects[236].

The calculation of surface area in square centimetre per cubic centimetre
from microscopic examination commonly involves a summing of that area of
about 1000 randomly selected particles. The relation commonly used is:

$$S = 6 \, \Sigma(N_i d_i^2)/\Sigma(N_i d_i^3) \qquad (3.65)$$

where N_i refers to the number of particles with an effective diameter of d_i in
centimetres.

Evidently, translation of visual images to surface areas is approximate. The
main cause is that only the edge and contour structure or the surface structure
of particles (by replicas) is normally revealed, while the pore structure or even

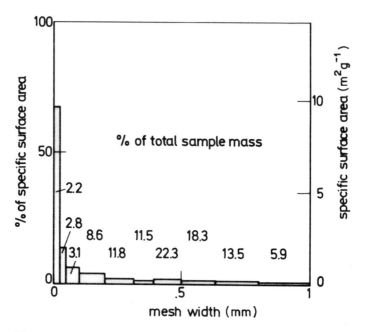

Fig. 3.41 Surface area distribution of a sieved quartz powder sample. Total specific surface area 14.3 m^2g^{-1}

the roughness factors are hard to evaluate[237]. However, electron micrographs have great value in giving general structural information and serve to complement data obtained by pore-size distribution studies[238]. The method has proved useful also in determining platinum and palladium areas on high area silica and alumina supports[239]. This is based on the differences in electron absorption between the high atomic weight component (Pt or Pd) and the base material (silica or alumina).

In particle size analysis, many laboratory and commercial instruments are based on stereological methods. Counting and size determination have been automatized on various principles. Either the sample consisting of a plane distribution of the particles in one layer is scanned, or the particles are diluted in air or a liquid and are fed separately through a slit. The widely used Coulter counter measures the change of the resistance of the liquid due to a particle passing the slit. The residual resistance is a measure of the particle size. A survey of instruments and evaluation methods is given by Alex[240]. By means of holography[241,242] it becomes possible to generate three-dimensional pictures of the particles and to measure the particle distribution in situ[240,242-246]. Small, single particles can be suspended in an electrical ac field according to Straubel[247]. In this way the surface area of airborne dust particles may be inspected.

3.10 X-Ray Methods

X-ray methods include:

1. Small-angle scattering which gives information on overall crystal size or pore size distribution.
2. Line broadening which gives information only on component crystal size.
3. X-ray, K-edge spectroscopy which gives information on elements of the first transition series (e.g. Mn and Co) in concentrations as low as $\frac{1}{2}$% even when present in amorphous form.

Since in this section we are primarily interested in surfaced area determination, discussion will be concentrated on the first two methods.

3.10.1 Small-angle scattering of X-rays

The method applies to finely divided porous or non porous solids, and provides a practical way to obtain the specific surface and the pore or particle size distribution curves.

The first step is to obtain the complete scattered intensity curve, $I(\theta)$, from 0 up to the angle at which the intensity is two or three times the background.

When the specific area is small ($10 \, m^2 \, g^{-1}$) it is unnecessary to go farther than $2\theta = 2°$ (Cu K_α), while with dense samples and high values of surface area one must go up to $2\theta \sim 6-8°$.

One can calculate the specific area by the Porod method[248,249]. For large values of the scattering angle, the product Is^3 remains constant over a reasonable range and the expression for the surface area S in $m^2 \, g^{-1}$ is:

$$S = \frac{16\pi^2 \cdot 10^4}{mva_T\mu^2} \lim_{s\to\infty} Is^3 \tag{3.66}$$

where

I = scattered intensity;

s = $\dfrac{2\theta}{10\lambda}$; θ = scattering angle in radians;

λ = is the wavelength in nm;

m = the sample weight in g;

a_T = the total energy of the transmitted beam; and

v = adsorption coefficient = $0.716 \, \lambda^2$

μ = the density of the material in $g \, cm^{-3}$.

By plotting Is^3 versus s^3, a practically straight line is obtained, and the correct value of the Is^3 limit is given by the intercept on the Is^3 axis.

The measured value of S includes pores, both open and closed, from about

0.2 to 50 nm diameter, and it also includes the external surface of particles of a similar size. For compounds of low density, it is necessary to desorb the water contained in the sample[250].

Small-angle scattering has at least one important advantage over other methods, in that surface areas may be obtained directly from the experimental data without resort to what may be arbitrary assumptions about the underlying texture of the material. The other methods yield some intermediate parameter, such as the volume of the monolayer covering the surface (in adsorption), or the linear dimension of the particles composing the material (in electron microscopy or in X-ray wide-angle line-broadening). From such parameters the surface area must then be deduced through subsequent calculations, which may involve supplementary hypotheses or additional data[251].

Most of the few surface area investigations carried out with small-angle X-ray scattering techniques have been done in conjunction with a gas adsorption technique. The frequent differences found in the two results has led to a greater understanding of the microstructure of the material under investigation.

Baro[252] made some comparisons between the surface areas obtained by the small-angle X-ray scattering and the BET measurements. For carbon blacks discrepancies existed, and he attributed the disparity to closed internal surfaces. In every instance the X-ray method gave higher values than the adsorption method. On the other hand, good agreement between the results obtained by the two methods has been found for silica gel, and this agreement was attributed to the fact that the inner surfaces of silica gel are sufficiently open and available to the adsorbing gases.

From the work of Baro and several other workers, it may be concluded that, when departures occur in the comparison of specific surface values determined by small-angle and BET methods, the small-angle values will be the larger. Discrepancies will be the most prevalent in porous materials in which voids are encapsulated by the solid matrix and thus rendered inaccessible to adsorption gases. It appears therefore that the small-angle X-ray scattering gives a more complete picture of the extent of the surface. However, since for practical uses one is primarily concerned with only these surfaces available for reaction, adsorption methods may yield more practical values. Nevertheless, combination of the two methods has proved successful in certain instances, and it has been possible to evaluate some structure parameters, such as the number of pores and the length of pores in the solid[253], which at present cannot be evaluated by any one of the two methods separately, nor by other methods. It should be borne in mind that the small-angle X-ray method is by no means a better substitute for other, more commonly employed surface area methods, but it is a valuable complement and supplement to these methods.

3.10.2 Line broadening

This method is useful in getting a measure of the surface area provided the solid is nonporous, otherwise it should be considered as a rough method. Strictly, it is applied only to crystalline solids, and is not applicable in studying amorphous materials.

This approach to studying the crystallite dimension of powders L_c is based on the simplified Scherrer relation:

$$L_c = 0.94\lambda/(W_x^2 - \omega^2)^{1/2}(\cos \phi)$$
$$= 0.9/(W_x - \omega^1)\cos \phi \tag{3.67}$$

where λ is the wavelength of the X-rays, ω the instrument width correction in radians, W_x the observed width of an X-ray pattern line in radians at half-peak height, ϕ the angle between incident and diffracted beams, and ω^1 the observed width for highly crystalline material.

In general, line broadening may indicate finer particle size than gas adsorption, particularly when the crystals are semiamorphous, simply because the gas molecules are accessible only to the micelle external surface, but X-rays 'see' all crystal interfaces.

3.11 Separation Methods

The separation methods[225] comprise mainly two procedures: sieving and air separation. Both methods only give information of the particle size and no hints as to the porosity of individual samples.

3.11.1 Sieve analysis[244,245]

Sieving is the most widely employed technique for determining particle size distribution. When powder passes through a sieve, its particles are finer than the holes in the sieve. Long-shaped particles nevertheless may have a relatively large mean diameter. Smaller particles may agglomerate and then be retained despite their smaller individual diameter. This drawback can be minimized for dry sieving by motion and dilution; for wet sieving detergents may also be used. In dry sieving, adhesion at the sieve surface by electrostatic forces is encountered. Traditional sieving methods are comparatively slow and require considerable effort. Therefore, automatic sieving apparatus have been constructed[244].

3.11.2 Air separation

There are separators of very different design on the market. Their common principle is the sedimentation of the particles in a gas, mostly in air. The sedimentation can be due to the gravitational field or in the acceleration field of a centrifuge and can be performed in a counterflow or by a flow normal to

146

the field. The place of deposition of the particles depends on the particle size. Particles in the size range of about 2 to 40 μm can be separated.

3.12 Roughness Measurement

A number of special methods are in use to examine the surface of a bulk material like steel or ceramics for use as tools or engine parts[254,255]. The remaining roughness after shaping can be inspected by optical means in comparison with comparison surfaces or by tracing with a sensing pin.

The design of a surface tracer is depicted schematically in Fig. 3.42. The sensing pin is drawn along a line by a motor and the motion of the arm is recorded. The method has a lower limit given by the radius of the pin of about 2 μm as shown in Fig. 3.43. The measuring range is divided according to Fig. 3.44 into shape deviation, undulation or waviness, and roughness. The range of each is not sharply defined. When measuring uneven surfaces or in order to suppress a signal coming from shape deviations, a guide shoe in connection with a flexible joint can be used as shown in Fig. 3.42. Because the roughness results from machining the surface, the result of tracing the surface depends mostly on the direction of the test line as shown in Fig. 3.45.

Many parameters to characterize the rough surface have been standardized with respect to the practical use of these measurements for testing piece parts. In connection with the scope of this book we define the roughness as the ratio of the true surface area S (measured e.g. by adsorption experiments) to the geometric projection area S_{geom}:

$$R = \frac{S}{S_{geom}} \qquad (3.68)$$

Using a surface tracer the roughness can be determined as a mean value of several tracings to

$$R = \frac{l}{l_t} \qquad (3.69)$$

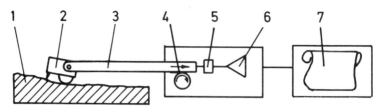

Fig. 3.42   Principle of a surface tracer; 1 sample, 2 sensing pin, 3 guide shoe, 4 motor, 5 motion sensor, 6 amplifier, 7 recorder

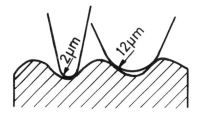

Fig. 3.43 Influence of the radius of the sensing pin on the resolution

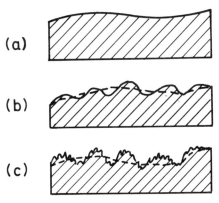

(a)

(b)

(c)

Fig. 3.44 Roughness definitions; (a) shape deviation, (b) waviness, undulation, (c) roughness

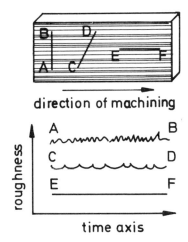

direction of machining

roughness

A   B

C   D

E   F

time axis

≙ length of trace

Fig. 3.45 Importance of the choice of trace direction

where l is the distance between start and end of the trace and l_t is the total length of the surface profile measured. With respect to the limited resolution, the value obtained in this way is always smaller than that obtained by the adsorption method.

3.13 Miscellaneous Methods

Other methods are also known for surface area determination, but they are less common and mostly restricted to certain types of solids. These include the following.

3.13.1 Multiple beam interference

Surface area determination by light interference from protective films on metals normally involves measuring the thickness of a representative oxidation film on a metal by light interference colours together with the oxygen content of the film. The ratio of volume of oxide to film thickness gives the area. Tolansky[256] has made notable advances in this field.

3.13.2 Capacitive measurements

Film thickness furthermore may be determined by capacitive measurements. This method serves as well for the detection of defects (pores) in the film.

3.13.3 Paramagnetism

Paramagnetism gives information on the degree of dispersion of compounds of the transition group elements[257].

3.13.4 Rate of solution in a solvent

Rate of solution, which is usually proportional to surface area, has promise, provided that transport processes do not limit the rate. It has been applied for surface area determination of catalytic components for which a suitable solvent is available (e.g. glass and metals). No recent developments are recorded in this field[258-260].

References

1. A. Adamson, *Physical Chemistry of Surfaces*, 2nd edn, Wiley (Interscience), New York, London, Sydney, 1967
2. C. Clement, *Rev. Inst. France Petrole Ann. Combust. Liquides*, **18**, 420, 1963
3. G. Jura, in: W. G. Berl (ed.), *Physical Methods in Chemical Analysis*, 2nd edn, Vol. 1, Academic Press, New York, 1960.
4. S. J. Gregg and K. S. W. Sing, *Adsorption, Surface Area and Porosity*, Academic Press, London, New York, 1967

5. P. H. Emmett, *Catalysis*, **1**, 31 (1954)
6. W. B. Innes, in: R. B. Anderson (ed.), *Experimental Methods in Catalytic Research*, Academic Press, New York, London, 1968
7. E. Robens and G. Walter, in: F. Korte (ed.), *Methodicum Chimicum*, Vol. 1, Part B; Academic Press, New York, 1974, p. 678
8. E. Robens, *J. Vacuum Sci. Techn.*, **17**, 92 (1980)
9. S. Ross and J. P. Olivier, *On Physical Adsorption*, Wiley Interscience, New York, 1964
10. H. W. Hapgood and J. F. Hanlon, *Can. J. Chem.*, **37**, 843 (1959)
11. Y. Kugl and Y. Yoshikawa, *Bull. Chem. Soc. Japan*, **38**, 948 (1965)
12. M. P. Freeman and K. Kolb, *J. Phys. Chem.*, **67**, 217 (1963)
13. M. P. Freeman, *J. Phys. Chem.*, **62**, 723 (1958)
14. W. A. Steele and G. D. Halsey, Jr., *J. Chem. Phys.*, **22**, 979 (1954)
15. J. Tuul and R. M. DeBaun, *Anal. Chem.*, **34**, 814 (1962)
16. J. Barker and D. H. Everett, *Trans. Faraday Soc.*, **58**, 168 (1962)
17. W. A. Steele, *Advance Chem. Ser.*, **33**, 269 (1961)
18. J. F. Harlon and M. Freeman, *Can. J. Chem.*, **37**, 1575 (1959)
19. G. D. Halsey, Jr., *J. Chem. Phys.*, **16**, 931 (1948)
20. G. D. Halsey, Jr., *J. Phys. Chem.*, **62**, 723 (1958)
21. R. Wolf and J. R. Sams, *J. Phys. Chem.*, **69**, 1129 (1965)
22. A. J. Andreatch and W. B. Innes, *Inst. Soc. Am.*, Preprint 46, 1960.
23. W. B. Innes and W. E. Bambrick, *J. Gas Chromatog.*, **2**, 309 (1964)
24. J. Tuul, *J. Phys. Chem.*, **66**, 1736 (1962)
25. S. Brunauer, P. H. Emmett and E. Teller, *J. Amer. Chem. Soc.*, **60**, 309 (1938)
26. G. S. Rushbrooke and H. I. Scoins, *Proc. Roy. Soc. London*, **230**(A), 74 (1955)
27. C. Domb, *Advan. Phys.*, **9**, 245 (1960)
28. A. Clarke, *The Theory of Adsorption and Catalysis*, Academic Press, New York, 1970, p. 418
29. B. J. Alder and T. E. Wainwright, *Phys. Rev.*, **127**, 359 (1962)
30. J. A. Barker and D. Henderson, *J. Chem. Phys.*, **47**, 2856, 4714, 1967; **52**, 2315, 1970
31. J. C. P. Broekhoff and R. H. Van Dongen, in: B. G. Linsen (ed.), *Physical and Chemical Aspects of Adsorbents and Catalysts*, Academic Press, London, New York, 1970, p. 63
32. W. A. Steele, *J. Phys. Chem.*, **69**, 3446 (1965)
33. W. A. Steele, *The Interaction of Gases with Solid Surfaces*, Pergamon Press, Oxford, 1974
34. D. Dollimore, P. Spooner, and A. Turner, *Surface Technology*, **4**, 121 (1976)
35. S. Brunauer, J. Skalny, and E. E. Boder, *J. Colloid Interface Sci.*, **30**, 546, (1969)
36. J. Frenkel, *Kinetic Theory of Liquids*, Clarendon Press, Oxford, 1946
37. G. D. Halsey, *J. Chem. Phys.*, **16**, 931 (1948)
38. T. L. Hill, *J. Chem. Phys.*, **17**, 590 (1949)
39. T. L. Hill, *Advan. Catalysis*, **4**, 211 (1952)
40. W. A. Steele and L. E. A. Flood (eds.), *The Solid–Gas Interface*, Vol. 1, Arnold, London, 1966, Chap. 10
41. L. G. Joyner and P. H. Emmett, *J. Amer. Chem. Soc.*, **70**, 2353 (1948)
42. W. B. Spencer, C. H. Amberg, and R. A. Beebe, *J. Phys. Chem.*, **62**, 719 (1958)
43. J. R. Sams, G. Constabaris, and G. D. Halsey, *J. Phys. Chem.*, **66**, 2154 (1962)
44. J. W. Ross and R. J. Good., *J. Phys. Chem.*, **60**, 1167 (1956)
45. J. Mooi, C. Pierce, and R. N. Smith, *J. Phys. Chem.*, **57**, 657 (1953)
46. A. A. Isirikyan and A. V. Kiselev, *J. Phys. Chem.*, **65**, 601 (1961); **66**, 210 (1962)
47. A. V. Kiselev, *Proceedings of the Second International Congress on Surface Activity*, Butterworth, London, 1957, p. 168.

48. T. N. Rhodin, *J. Am. Chem. Soc.*, **72**, 5691 (1950)
49. G. J. Young, J. J. Chessick, F. H. Healey, and A. C. Zettlemoyer, *J. Phys. Chem.*, **313** (1954)
50. E. V. Ballou and S. Ross, *J. Phys. Chem.* **57**, 653 (1953)
51. T. L. Hill, *Advances in Catalysis*, Vol. 4, Academic Press, 1952, p. 212
52. D. H. Everett, *Trans. Faraday Soc.* **46**, 453, 942, 957 (1950)
53. T. L. Hill, P. H. Emmett, and L. G. Joyner, *J. Amer. Chem. Soc.*, **73**, 5702 (1951)
54. C. Pierce and B. Ewing, *J. Phys. Chem.*, **68**, 2562 (1964)
55. H. P. Schreiber and R. L. McIntosh, *Canad. J. Chem.*, **32**, 842 (1955)
56. J. de D. Lopez-Gonzalez, F. G. Carpenter, and V. R. Dietz, *J. Phys. Chem.*, **65**, 112 (1961)
57. P. H. Emmett and S. Brunauer, *J. Amer. Chem. Soc.*, **59**, 1553 (1957).
58. H. K. Livingston, *J. Colloid Sci.*, **4**, 447 (1949)
59. N. Hansen, *Vakuum–Tech.*, **11**, 70 (1962)
60. K. Kodera and Y. Onishi, *Bull. Chem. Soc. Japan*, **32**, 356 (1959)
61. D. Brennan, M. Graham, and F. H. Hayes, *Nature*, **199**, 1152 (1963)
62. C. Pierce, *J. Phys. Chem.*, **73**, 813 (1969)
63. A. C. Zettlemoyer, *J. Colloid Interface Sci.*, **28**, 343 (1968)
64. J. D. Carruthers, D. A. Payre, K. S. W. Sing, and L. J. Strykar, *J. Colloid Interface Sci.*, **36**, 205 (1971)
65. A. V. Kiselev, *Disc. Faraday Soc.*, **40** 205 (1965); *J. Colloid Interface Sci.*, **28**, 430 (1968)
66. D. R. Bassett, E. A. Boucher, and A. C. Zettlemoyer, *J. Colloid Interface Sci.*, **27**, 649 (1968)
67. D. A. Payne, K. S. W. Sing, and D. H. Turk, *J. Colloid Interface Sci.* **43**, 287 (1973)
68. R. Sh. Mikhail and S. Brunauer, *J. Colloid Interface Sci.*, **52**, 572 (1975)
69. A. L. McClellan and H. F. Harnsberger, *J. Colloid Interface Sci.*, **23**, 577 (1967)
70. E. Robens, G. Sandstede, and G. Walter, in: A. W. Czanderna (ed.), *Vacuum Microbalance Techniques*, Vol. 8; Plenum Press, 1971, p. 111.
71. B. Schubart, J. A. Poulis, C. M. Massen, E. Robens, J. M. Thomas, and H. G. Wiedemann, *Thermochimica Acta*, **9**, 1 (1974)
72. V. R. Deitz and N. H. Turner, in: D. H. Emmett and R. H. Ottewill (eds.), *Proceedings of the International Symposium on Surface Area Determination*, p. 43. Butterworths, London, 1970
73. M. Troy and J. P. Wightman, *J. Voc. Sci. Technol.*, **8**, 743 (1971)
74. A. J. Krowles and J. B. Moffat, *J. Colloid Interface Sci.*, **37**, 860 (1971)
75. W. D. Harkins and G. Jura, *J. Am. Chem. Soc.*, **66**, 1362 (1944); *J. Chem. Phys.*, **13**, 449 (1945)
76. J. H. Clint, J. S. Clunic, J. F. Goodman, and J. R. Tate, in: D. H. Everett and R. H. Ottewill (eds.), *Proceedings International Symposium Surface Area Determination*, Butterworths, London, 1970, p. 299.
77. W. D. Diano and S. J. Gregg, *Colloques Internationaux CNRS*, No. 201, 471 (1971)
78. M. Lafitte and J. Rouquerol, *Bull. Soc. Chem.*, 3335 (1970)
79. C. Letoquart, F. Rouquerol, and J. Rouquerol, *J. Chim. Phys.*, **70**, 559 (1973)
80. R. Sh. Mikhail, Sh. Nashed, and A. M. Khalil, *Disc. Faraday Soc.*, No. 52, Surface Chemistry of Oxides, p. 187 (1971); *Surface Tech.*, **7**, 45 (1978)
81. R. L. Bond and D. H. T. Spencer, *Proc. Third Bienn. Conf. Carb.*, p. 357, Pergamon, 1959.
82. G. Constabaris, J. H. Singleton, and G. D. Halsey, *J. Phys. Chem.*, **63**, 1350 (1959); W. A. Steele and G. D. Halsey, *J. Chem. Phys.*, **22**, 979 (1954); *J. Phys. Chem.*, **59**, 57 (1955)

83. P. Zwietering and D. W. van Krevelin, *Tuel*, **33**, 331 (1954)
84. J. H. de Boer, *The Dynamical Character of Adsorption*, Oxford University Press, 1953; *Advances in Catalysis*, **8**, 117 (1956), Academic Press.
85. M. M. Dubinin, *J. Colloid Interface Sci.*, **23**, 487 (1967)
86. C. Pierce, *J. Phys. Chem.*, **63**, 1076 (1959)
87. C. Pierce, J. W. Wiley, and R. N. Smith, *J. Phys. Chem.*, **53**, 669 (1949)
88. A. V. Kiselev, *Structure and Properties of Porous Materials* p. 200, Butterworths, London, 1958.
89. S. J. Gregg and R. Stock, *Trans. Faraday Soc.*, **53**, 1355 (1957)
90. M. M. Dubinin, *Quart Rev. (London)*, **9**, 101 (1955)
91. M. M. Dubinin, in: P. L. Walker (ed.), *Chemistry and Physics of Carbon*, Vol. 2, p. 51, Arnold, London, 1966.
92. B. P. Bering, M. M. Dubinin, and V. V. Serpinsky, *J. Colloid Interface Sci.*, **21**, 378 (1966)
93. M. G. Kaganer, *Zh. Fiz. Khim.*, **33**, 2202 (1959)
94. M. M. Dubinin, E. D. Zaverina, and L. V. Radushkevich, *Zh. Fiz. Khim.*, **21**, 1351 (1947)
95. J. P. Hobson, in E. A. Flood, (ed.), *The Solid–Gas Interface*, Vol. 1, Ch. 14, Arnold, London, 1967.
96. H. G. Kaganer, *Russ. J. Phys. Chem.* (English Trans.), **33**, 352 (1959)
97. J. P. Hobson and P. A. Armstrong, *J. Phys. Chem.*, **67**, 2000 (1967)
98. H. Marsh and B. Rand, *J. Colloid Interface Sci.*, **33**, 101 (1970)
99. J. W. Sutherland, in: R. L. Bond (ed.), *Porous Carbon Solids*, Ch. 1, Academic Press, London, 1967
100. M. G. Kaganer, *Dokl. Akad. Nauk*, **138**, 405 (1961)
101. K. S. W. Sing, *Berichte d. Bunsen-Ges. f. Phys. Chem.*, **79**, 724 (1975)
102. K. K. Unger, *Porous Silica (J. Chromatography Library*, Vl. 16) Elsevier, Amsterdam, 1979, p. 80
103. S. D. Christian and E. E. Tucker, *Intern. Laboratory* **48**, (1981) Nov./Dec. + 40 (1982) Jan./Feb.
104. K. Unger, *Angew. Chemie*, **84**, 331 (1972).
105. British Standard 4359, British Standards Institution, 1969
106. DIN Taschenbuch 133: Normen über Siebböden und Kornmessung, Beuth Bauverlag, Berlin, 1980
107. E. L. Fuller, J. A. Poulis, A. W. Czanderna, and E. Robens, *Thermochimica Acta*, **29**, 315 (1979)
108. E. Robens, A. W. Czanderna, E. L. Fuller, and J. A. Poulis, *Keram. Z.*, **33**, 627 (1981)
109. S. Brunauer, R. Sh. Mikhail, and E. E. Bodor, *J. Colloid Interface Sci.*, **24**, 451 (1967)
110. K. S. W. Sing, *Berichte der Bunsengesellschaft*, **79**, 724 (1975)
111. P. H. Doe and J. M. Haynes, in S. J. Gregg, K. S. W. Sing, and H. F. Stoeckli (eds.), *Characterisation of Porous Solids*, Soc. of Chemical Industry, London, 1979, p. 253
112. G. L. Kington and P. S. Smith, *Trans. Faraday Soc.*, **60**, Pt. 4, 705 (1964)
113. D. O. Hayward and B. M. W. Trapnell, *Chemisorption*, Butterworths, London, 1964
114. O. Kuhaschevski and B. E. Hopkins, *Oxidation of Metals and Alloys*. Butterworth, London, 1964
115. O. Beeck, *Advances in Catalysis*, **2**, 151 (1950), Academic Press.
116. L. Spenadel and M. Boudart, *J. Phys. Chem.*, **64**, 204 (1960)
117. C. R. Adams, H. A. Benesi, R. M. Curtis, and R. G. Meisenheimer, *J. Catalysis*, **1**, 336 (1962)
118. S. A. Hassan, F. H. Khalil, and F. G. El-Gamal, *J. Catalysis*, **44**, 5 (1976)

152

119. W. A. Pliskin and R. P. Eischers, *Z. Phys. Chem.* (Frankfurt), **24**, 11 (1960)
120. D. Brennan, D. G. Hayward, and B. M. W. Trapnell, *Proc. Ray. Soc.*, **256**(A), 81 (1960)
121. D. Brennan and M. J. Graham, *Disc. Faraday Soc.*, **41**, 95 (1966).
122. W. E. Garner, F. S. Stone, and P. F. Tiley, *Proc. Roy. Soc.* **211**(A), 472 (1952)
123. J. M. Bridges, D. S. MacIver, and H. H. Tobin, *Proc. Sec. Int. Congr. Catal.*, Paper No. 110, 1960.
124. J. M. Bridges, G. T. Rymer, and D. S. MacIver, *J. Phys. Chem.*, **66**, 871 (1962)
125. O. Beeck, A. E. Smith, and A. Wheeler, *Proc. Roy Soc.*, **177**(A), 62 (1940)
126. M. A. H. Lanyon and B. M. W. Trapnell, *Proc. Roy. Soc.* **227**(A), 287 (1955)
127. J. Bragg and F. C. Tompkins, *Trans. Faraday Soc.*, **51**, 1071 (1955)
128. R. P. Eischens, S. A. Francis, and W. A. Pliskin, *J. Phys. Chem.*, **60**, 194 (1956)
129. R. P. Eischens and W. A. Pliskin, *Advances in Catalysis*, **10**, 1 (1918), Academic Press.
130. R. L. Moss, in: R. B. Anderson and P. T. Dawson (eds.), *Experimental Method in Catalytic Research*, Vol. II, Academic Press, New York, London, 1976, p. 72.
131. J. J. Kipling, *Adsorption from Solutions of Non-Electrolytes*, Academic Press, London, 1965
132. P. A. Elkington and G. Curthoys, *J. Phys. Chem.*, **72**, 3425 (1968)
133. A. C. Zettlemoyer and K. S. Narayan, in: E. A. Flood (ed.), *The Solid–Gas Interface*, Vol. I, Ch. 6, Marcel-Dekker, Inc., NY, 1966.
134. J. J. Chessick and A. C. Zettlemoyer, *Advan. Catalysis*, **11**, 263 (1959)
135. A. C. Zettlemoyer and J. J. Chessick, *Advan. Chem. Ser.*, **43**, 88 (1964)
136. A. C. Zettlemoyer, G. J. Young, J. J. Chessick, and F. H. Healey, *J. Phys. Chem.*, **57**, 649 (1953)
137. J. H. Whalen, *J. Phys. Chem.*, **66**, 511 (1962)
138. P. E. Berghausen, in: O. H. Clark, J. E. Rutzler, and R. L. Savage (eds.), *Adhesion and Adhesives*, Wiley, NY, 1954, p. 225.
139. G. E. Boyd and W. D. Harkins, *J. Am. Chem. Soc.*, **64**, 1190, 1195 (1942)
140. F. E. Bartell and R. M. Suggit, *J. Phys. Chem.*, **58**, 36 (1954)
141. R. Sh. Mikhail, Sh. Nashed, and A. M. Khalil, *Disc. Faraday Soc.*, No. 52, p. 187 (1971).
142. R. Sh. Mikhail, A. M. Khalil, and Sh. Nashed, *J. Appl. Chem. Biotechnol.*, **27**, 17 (1977).
143. R. Sh. Mikhail, Sh. Nashed, and A. M. Khalil, *Surface Techn.*, **7**, 45 (1978)
144. W. H. Wade and N. Hackerman, *J. Phys. Chem.*, **66**, 1823 (1962)
145. R. C. Asher, Ph. D. Thesis, London University, 1955
146. W. H. Wade and N. Hackerman, *J. Phys. Chem.*, **65**, 1682 (1961)
147. F. H. Healey, J. J. Chessick, A. C. Zettlemoyer, and G. J. Young, *J. Phys. Chem.*, **58**, 887 (1954)
148. H. Cochrane and R. Rudham, *Trans. Faraday Soc.*, **61**, 2245 (1965)
149. K. S. W. Sing, Ph. D. Thesis, London University, 1949
150. W. H. Wade and N. Hackermann, *Advan. Chem. Ser.*, **43**, 222 (1964)
151. A. C. Zettlemoyer, J. J. Chessick, and C. M. Hollabaugh, *J. Phys. Chem.*, **62**, 489 (1958)
152. F. L. Howard and J. L. Culbertson, *J. Amer. Chem. Soc.*, **72**, 1185 (1950)
153. G. I. Alexandrova, V. F. Kiselev, K. G. Krasil'nikov, V. V. Murina, and E. A. Sysoev, *Dokl. Akad. Nauk SSSR*, **108**, 283 (1956)
154. F. E. Bartell and R. M. Suggitt, *J. Phys. Chem.*, **58**, 36 (1954)
155. W. M. Block, M.S. Thesis, Lehigh University, Bethlehem, Pa., 1964
156. A. C. Zettlemoyer, G. J. Young, and J. J. Chessick, *J. Phys. Chem.*, **59**, 962 (1955)
157. R. Greene-Kelley, *Clay Minerals Bull.*, **5**, 1 (1952)

158. G. J. Young, J. J. Chessick, F. H. Healey, and A. C. Zettlemoyer *J. Phys. Chem.*, **58**, 313 (1954)
159. J. J. Chessick, F. H. Healey, and A. C. Zettlemoyer, *J. Phys. Chem.*, **60**, 1345 (1956)
160. G. Schay, in: D. H. Everett and R. H. Ottewill (eds.): *Surface Area Determination*, Butterworths, London, 1970 p. 273
161. W. B. Innes and H. H. Rowley, *J. Phys. Chem.*, **51**, 1176 (1951)
162. J. J. Kipling and D. B. Peakall, *J. Chem. Soc.*, 4828 (1956)
163. J. J. Kipling and E. H. M. Wright, *J. Chem. Soc.*, 855 (1962)
164. C. H. Giles, T. H. MacEwan, S. N. Nakhwa, and D. Smith, *J. Chem. Soc.*, 3973 (1960)
165. C. H. Giles and S. N. Nakhwa, *J. Appl. Chem.*, **12**, 266 (1962)
166. I. F. Padday, in: D. H. Everett and R. H. Ottewill (eds.), *Surface Area Determination*, p. 331, Butterworths, London, 1970
167. J. W. Hassler, *Activated Carbon*, Chemical Publishing, New York, 1963
168. Lurgi-Schnellinformation T 1091/8.75; Lurgi, Frankfurt am Main, 1975
169. Norit Testing Methods; Norit NV, Nijverheidsweg-Noord 72, Amersfoort, NL
170. DIN 19603, Beuth-Verlag, Berlin
171. ASTM Standard—C204–68
172. ASTM Standard D1783B
173. AWWA, Standard for Powdered Activated Carbon B600–66, American Water Works Association
174. Norit Bulletin No. 63; Norit NV, Nijverheidsweg-Noord 72, Amertsfoort, NL
175. Deutsches Arzneibuch, 8. ed. (DAB8), Deutscher Apotheker Vlg. Stuttgart 1978
176. AWWA B607–74, Am. Water Wks. Assn.
177. H. D. Bartholomä and H. E. Schwiete, *Ziegelind.*, **13**, 97, 421 (1960)
178. W. Patterson and D. Boenisch, *Techn. wiss. Beihilfe zur Giesserei*
179. P. T. Hang and G. W. Brindley, *Clays and Clay Min.*, **18**, 203 (1970)
180. G. M. Därr and U. Ludwig, *Matériaux et constructions*; **6**, 233 (1973)
181. A. Clauss, H. P. Boehm, and U. Hofmann, *Z. anorg. allg. Chem.*, **290**, 35 (1957)
182. J. M. Los and C. K. Tompkins, *J. Chem. Phys.*, **24**, 630 (1956)
183. C. Orr and P. T. Bankston, *J. Amer. Ceram. Soc.*, **35**, 58 (1952)
184. A. S. Russel and C. N. Cochran, *Ind. Eng. Chem.*, **42**, 1332 (1950)
185. H. E. Ries, M. F. L. Johnson, and J. S. Melik, *J. Phys. Coll. Chem.*, **53**, 638 (1949)
186. H. A. Smith and J. F. Fuzek, *J. Amer. Chem. Soc.*, **68**, 229 (1946)
187. W. D. Harkins and D. M. Gans, *J. Amer. Chem. Soc.*, **53**, 2804 (1931)
188. F. D. Bowden and E. K. Rideal, *Proc. Roy. Soc. (London)*, **A120**, 80 (1928)
189. D. Berndt, *Electrochimica Acta*, **10**, 1067 (1967)
190. C. Wagner, *J. Electrochem. Soc.*, **97**, 72 (1950)
191. H. Binder, A. Köhling, K. Metzelthin, G. Sandstede, and M.-L. Schrecker, *Chemie-Ing.-Techn.*, **40**, 586 (1968)
192. O. Hahn, *Applied Radiochemistry*, Cornell University Press, NY, 1936.
193. G. Glawitsch, *Atompraxis*, **2**, 395 (1956)
194. K. E. Zimens, *Z. phys. Chem. (A)*, **186**, 256 (1940)
195. A. C. Wahl, and N. A. Bonner, *Radioactivity Applied to Chemistry*; New York/London, 1951
196. G. B. Cook and E. W. Pront. *J. Inorg. Nucl. Chem.*, **3**, 225 (1956)
197. S. Brunauer, *Adsorption of Gases and Vapors*, Princeton University Press, Princeton, New Jersey, 1943.
198. L. Imre and J. Nazy, *Kolloid-Z.* **183**, 134 (1962)
199. K. A. Kini, R. M. Manser, and A. S. Joy, *J. Phys. Chem.* **72**, 2127 (1968)
200. P. Chènebault and A. Schürenkämper, *J. Phys. Chem.*, **69**, 2300 (1965)

201. K. Watanabe and T. Yamashina, *J. Catalysis*, **17**, 272 (1970)
202. J. T. Clarke, *J. Phys. Chem.*, **68**, 884 (1964)
203. D. C. Walker and H. E. Ries, *J. Colloid Sci.*, **17**, 789 (1962)
204. D. W. Aylmore and W. B. Jepson, *J. Sci. Instrum.*, **42**, 821 (1965)
205. J. P. W. Houtman and J. Medema, *Ber. Bunsenges. Phys. Chem.*, **70**, 489 (1966)
206. J. Medema and J. P. W. Houtman, *Analytical Chemistry*, **41**, 209 (1969)
207. G. Kravs and J. V. Ross, *J. Phys. Chem.*, **57**, 334 (1953)
208. H. P. G. D'Arcy, *Les Fontaines publiques de la Ville de Dijon*, Dalmont, Paris, 1856
209. P. C. Carman; *J. Soc. Chem. Eng. (London)*, **57**, 225 (1938); **58**, 1 (1939)
210. J. R. Dacey, *Advan. Chem. Ser.*, **33**, 172 (1961).
211. P. C. Carman, *J. Soc. Chem. Ind. Trans.*, **57**, 225 (1938)
212. H. Walther, *Silikattechn.*, **4**, 25 (1953)
213. K. Niesel, *Matériaux et constructions*, **6**, 227 (1973)
214. F. M. Lea and R. W. Nurse, *J. Soc. Chem. Ind. (London)*, **58**, 277 (1939)
215. DIN 66 126; Beuth, Vertrieb, Berlin, 1976
216. R. M. Barrer, in: D. H. Everett and R. H. Ottewill (eds.), *Surface Area Determination*, Butterworths, London, 1970, p. 155
217. P. B. Weiss and A. B. Swartz, *J. Catalysis*, **1**, 399 (1962)
218. R. Ash, R. M. Barrer, J. H. Clent, R. J. Dolphin, and C. L. Murray, *Phil Trans.* **275**(A), 255 (1973)
219. R. M. Barrer and E. V. T. Murphy, *J. Chem. Soc. (A)*, 2506 (1970).
220. R. Davies, *Ind. Engng. Chem.*, **62**, 87, no. 12 (1970).
221. K. Leschonski in *Ullmanns Encylopädie der Technischen Chemie*, Vol. 2, 24 (1972)
222. B. Koglin, K. Leschonski, and W. Alex, *Chemie-Ing.-Techn.*, **46**, 563, 729 (1974)
223. A. Bürkholz, *Staub–Reinh. Luft*, **32**, 442 (1972)
224. O. Lauer, *Aufbereitungs-Technik*, **20**, 677 (1979)
225. DIN 66 111, Beuth Verlag, Berlin
226. *An. Chem. Ztg.*, **93**, 638 (1969)
227. J. C. Giddings, K. A. Graff, M. N. Myers, and K. D. Caldwell, *Sep. Sci. Technol.*, **15**, 615 (1980)
228. J. M. Haynes, *Matériaux et Constructions*, **6**, 175 (1973)
229. M. Evans and H. Marsh, in S. J. Gregg, K. S. W. Sing, and H. F. Stoeckli (eds.), *Characterisation of Porous Solids*, Soc. of Chemical Industry, London, 1979, p. 53
230. G. Schimmel and W. Vogell (eds.), *Methodensammlung der Elektronenmikroskopie*, Wissenschaftliche Verlagsanstalt Stuttgart 1970
231. H. Rochow and G. Schimmel, in H. Freund and J. Grehn (eds.), *Handbuch der Mikroskopie in der Technik*, Vol. VII, Umschau, Frankfurt am Main, 1975, p. 1
232. C. M. Sargent and J. D. Embury, in R. B. Anderson and P. T. Dawson (eds.), *Experimental Methods in Catalytic Research*, Vol. II p. 139, Academic Press, NY, London, 1976.
233. J. R. Fryer, in S. J. Gregg, K. S. W. Sing, and H. F. Stoeckli (eds.), *Characterisation of porous solids*, Society of Chemical Industry, London, 1979
234. A. V. Crewe and J. J. Wall, *Mol. Biol.*, **48**, 375 (1970)
235. W. C. Lane, D. E. Pease, and N. C. Yew, *Proc. 6th Ann. Meeting Int. Microstructural Anal. Soc.*, California, Sept. 1973.
236. B. E. P. Beeston, R. N. Horne, and R. Markham, *Electron Diffraction and Optical Diffraction Techniques*, North-Holland Publ., Amsterdam, 1973.
237. J. R. Anderson, B. G. Baker, and J. Sanders, *J. Catalysis*, **1**, 443 (1962)
238. R. Sh. Mikhail, S. Hanafi, S. A. Abo-El-Enein, R. J. Good, and J. Irani, *J. Colloid Interface Sci.*, **75**, 74 (1980)

239. J. Scholten and A. Van Montfoord, *J. Catalysis*, **1**, 85 (1963)
240. W. Alex, *Aufbereitungs-Technik*, **13**, (1972) No. 2, 3, 10, 11
241. J. Gebhart, J. Bol., W. Heinze, and W. Letschert, *Staub*. **30**, 238 (1970).
242. K. Gürs. *Laser*, Umschau-Verlag, Frankfurt am Main, 1970
243. G. Seger and F. Sinsel, *Staub*, **30**, 471 (1970)
244. C. Orr, R. W. Camp, and D. K. Davies, in *Proc. International Powder and Bulk Solids Handling and Processing Conf.*, Rosemont, Illinois, 1977
245. K. Leschonski, in *Particle Size Analysis*, 1970; Soc. for Analytical Chemistry, London 1972, p. 409
246. G. H. Seger, *Meßtechnik*. **5**, 142 (193)
247. H. Straubel, *Phys. Blätter*, **28**, 65 (1972)
248. P. Krautwasser, KFA-Report Jül-1202, KFA Jülich 1975
249. G. Porod, *Kolloid Zeitschrift*, **124**, 83 (1951); **125**, 51+108 (1952)
250. A. Renouprez, in: D. H. Everett and R. H. Ottewill (eds.), *Surface Area Determination*, Butterworths, London, 1970, p. 361.
251. E. D. Eares and A. S. Posner, in: E. A. Flood (ed.), *The Solid–Gas Interface*, Dekker, Inc. New York, 1967, p. 976.
252. R. Baro, *J. Chim. Phys.*, **57**, 1029 (1960)
253. R. Sh. Mikhail, D. H. Turk, and S. Brunauer, *Cement and Concrete Research*, **5**, 433 (1975)
254. W. Hillmann, *Techn. Messen*, **47**, 169 (1980)
255. H. Dagnall, *Exploring Surface Texture*, Rank Taylor Hobson, Leicester, 1980
256. S. Tolansky, *Multiple Beam Interferometry of Surfaces and Films*, Oxford University Press, New York, 1948.
257. P. W. Selwood, *Adsorption and Collective Paramagnetism*, Academic Press, New York, 1962
258. E. V. Ballou and R. T. Barth, *Advan. Chem. Ser.*, **33**, 133 (1961)
259. C. V. King, *Surface Chemistry of Metals and Semiconductors*, Wiley, New York
260. B. C. Lippens and J. H. de Boer, *J. Catalysis*, **3**, 44 (1964)

Chapter 4

Methods of Pore Structure Analysis

Even though the role of surface in adsorption and catalysis was recognized long ago, until recently little attention was paid to the importance of the location of the surface. If the adsorbing surface of an active carbon or a catalyst is located in very narrow pores, the diffusion into or out of these pores may become the rate-determining step in adsorption or catalysis. In physical adsorption, the amounts adsorbed at equilibrium depend on the pore sizes[1]. The sizes of the pores can influence the order and the energy of activation of a catalytic reaction, the poisoning characteristics of the surface for one reaction compared with another, and the extent to which a porous solid can build up temperature and pressure gradients in the course of catalytic reactions[2]. The suitability of an adsorbent for certain specific applications, such as for example the chromatographic separation of adsorbates, may be determined by the sizes of the pores[3].

Pores may play vital roles in solids which are not catalysts and are not regarded ordinarily as adsorbents. An example of this is hardened portland cement paste, the reaction product of portland cement and water, the matrix in which the fine and coarse aggregate are embedded in concrete. Hardened paste is a porous solid with distribution of pore sizes. In very narrow pores, the hydration reaction stops because there is not enough room for the nuclei of the hydration products to grow into crystals. For the same reason, nuclei of ice cannot grow into crystals in the small pores, so water freezes only in the larger pores. The permeability of concrete in water depends primarily on the sizes of the pores in the hardened paste. Thus, small and large pores have different effects on important engineering properties of concrete[4].

Industries which produce catalysts and adsorbents have been using BET surface area determinations for a long time for research and control; lately they are adding pore structure analysis as an important tool both in research and in operation. In 1945, two methods for pores size distribution studies were introduced independently, which with various modifications are still in use: the nitrogen adsorption isotherm method of Wheeler[5] and the mercury porosimeter method of Ritter and Drake[6]. The former is applicable primarily to the analysis of pores ranging in radii or widths from about 1.5 nm to about 50 nm (mesopores); the latter is more suited for larger pores (macropores). There is a region of overlap, and in this region the two methods show good agreement when one of the parameters, the contact angle between mercury and the adsorbent, is adjusted to give agreement at one point. Both methods assume that all pores in the absorbent have cylindrical shapes.

Other methods covering the same range but more rarely used are the displacement of water out of the pore system by air, the adsorption of molecules of different size, decrease of freezing point in pores, and pre-adsorption of an adhering agent. All these methods will be discussed in this chapter. Analysis of micropores is still in its infancy and the only method available in the literature, namely the MP-method[7,8], will also be described.

4.1 The mercury porosimeter method

Over sixty years have passed since Washburn[9] first suggested the use of pressurized mercury to determine the pore-size distribution of porous solids. The relation proposed is as follows:

$$p = \frac{-2\gamma \cos \theta}{r} \qquad (4.1)$$

where r is the radius of the pore being intruded by mercury of surface tension γ, under pressure P, and at the contact angle θ between mercury and the material under test. This is the common capillary depression phenomenon.

.The capillary law governing liquid mercury penetration into a small pore may be derived easily. If the liquid wets the wall of the capillary (Fig. 4.1), the liquid surface must be parallel with the wall, and the complete surface (meniscus), will be concave in shape. The Young and Laplace equation

$$p = \gamma \left(\frac{1}{R_1} + \frac{1}{R_2} \right) \qquad (4.2)$$

can be used to express the pressure difference across the interface. Its sign is either positive or negative so that the pressure is less in the liquid than in the gas phase. The radii of curvature, where both are of the same sign, always lie on the side of the interface having the greater pressure.

If we have a small cylindrical capillary, the meniscus will be approximately hemispherical, and $R_1 = R_2$ and is equal to the radius of the capillary, r. Thus Eqn. (4.2) reduces to

$$\Delta p = 2\gamma/r \qquad (4.3)$$

The height of the meniscus above a flat liquid surface is h, for which $p = 0$; thus the hydrostatic pressure drop in the column of liquid in the capillary is also equal to Δp.

$$\Delta p = \Delta \rho g h \qquad (4.4)$$

$\Delta \rho$ is the difference in density between the liquid and gas phase, and g is the acceleration due to gravity. Combining Eqns (4.3) and (4.4)

$$\Delta \rho g h = 2\gamma/r \qquad (4.5)$$

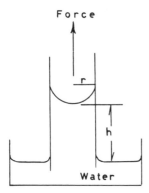

Fig. 4.1 Capillary rise, when liquid wets the wall of the capillary ($\theta = 0°$), concave meniscus

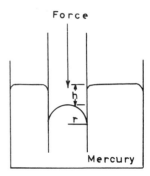

Fig. 4.2 Capillary depression, when liquid does not wet the wall of the capillary ($\theta = 180°$), convex meniscus

This equation also holds for capillary depression in a case of a liquid that completely fails to wet the walls of the capillary, and the contact angle with the wall is $180°$. The meniscus will now be convex (Fig. 4.2), and h is now the depth of the depression.

A more general case is one somewhere in between the range of the above two extremes of complete wetting and complete non-wetting of the solid by the liquid. Ordinarily, the liquid will meet the capillary wall at some angle θ, and the relationship between the radius of curvature R and the capillary radius r is $R = r/\cos \theta$. Therefore Eqn. (4.5) becomes

$$\Delta\rho g h = \frac{\pm 2\gamma \cos \theta}{r} \qquad (4.6)$$

The product $\Delta\rho g h$ has the dimensions of force per square centimetre, and can therefore also be designated as pressure p. Application of the plus or minus sign ($\pm$) to the equation depends on whether the resultant capillary force is up ($+$) or down ($-$), (cf. Figs. 4.1 and 4.2). Therefore, for the case of mercury we may write the Washburn equation as

$$p = \frac{-2\gamma \cos \theta}{r} \qquad (4.7)$$

Ritter and Drake[6] were the first to develop a method for determining the macropore size distribution in a porous solid. They applied external pressure to force the mercury (a non-wetting liquid) into some porous materials and measured the volume of mercury intruded as the function of pressure. They measured pressure–volume curves for a number of materials, for which the pore-size distributions were calculated. They developed apparatus and methods for measuring the penetration of mercury into pores down to 10 nm

Table 4.1 Pressure–pore radius relationship (using a mercury surface tension of 0.474 Nm^{-1})

Pressure (psia)	(bar)	Minimum pore radius (μm) penetrated at a contact angle of:				
		110°	120°	130°	140°	150°
1	0.068	47.0	68.8	88.4	105.4	119.1
3	0.204	15.7	22.9	29.5	35.2	39.7
10	0.68	4.70	6.88	8.84	10.54	11.91
30	2.04	1.57	2.29	2.95	3.52	3.97
100	6.80	0.471	0.688	0.885	1.055	1.192
300	20.42	0.157	0.229	0.295	0.352	0.397
1 000	58.05	0.047 0	0.068 8	0.088 4	0.105 4	0.119 1
3 000	204.2	0.001 6	0.022 9	0.029 5	0.035 2	0.039 7
10 000	680.5	0.004 70	0.006 88	0.008 84	0.010 54	0.011 91
30 000	2042	0.001 57	0.002 29	0.002 95	0.003 52	0.003 97
50 000	3403	0.000 94	0.001 37	0.001 76	0.002 10	0.002 37

in radius at 700 bar pressure. By 1949, Drake[10] had increased the capacity of his equipment to reach 4000 bar, and thus was able to penetrate mercury into the pores down to 1.8 nm in radius. He found that the surface tension concept still appeared to hold, and the maximum limit of the technique has not been reached with mercury, with an atom of about 0.314 nm in diameter.

Equation (4.7) shows that no pores or void spaces are penetrated by a non-wetting liquid under zero pressure. On the other hand, spaces having a radius of about 2.9 μm will be penetrated and an applied pressure of 2 bar if the contact angle is 130°. At other pressures, pores will be penetrated in accordance with the values of Table 4.1 or Fig. 4.3. For routine measurements, commonly contact angle of 130° or 140° are used.

As the pressure increases, the quantity of liquid forced into pores increases in proportion to the differential pore volume, the size of the pores corresponding to the instantaneous pressure. Thus increasing the pressure on a material having a given pore-size and/or void-space distribution results in an unique pressure–volume curve, typical examples of which are shown later. As used here the term 'void' means spaces among particles or the several pieces constituting the specimen. A single rigid object as the specimen would, by definition, reveal no voids. The cracks, crevices, holes, and fissures within the structure of the specimen, whether a single piece or a powder, are collectively termed 'pores'. Some independent evidence is sometimes needed to resolve the question of whether or not the revealed volume is void or pore spaces. The penetration technique requires, first of all, a means for generating a pressure and a means for determining how much mercury the application of a given pressure has forced into the pore or void spaces of the material being tested.

In Fig. 4.4 an apparatus is shown schematically. It is provided with a sample vessel, e.g. of glass within a steel container. Prior to the measurement, the

160

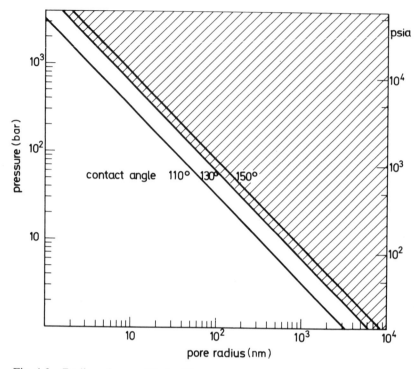

Fig. 4.3   Radius of pores filled with mercury at a preset pressure according to the Washburn equation for different contact angles. The hatched radius region is filled assuming a contact angle of 130°

sample has to be degassed with a two-stage rotary vane pump, preferably at elevated temperature (450 K for 24 hours is sufficient). After that, three-times distilled mercury is added and the sample vessel is provided with a capillary. By stepwise admission of air, the range up to 1 bar is measured. Subsequently the steel vessel is filled with a hydraulic liquid (alcohol, iso-propyl alcohol, or mineral oil) and the pressure is increased stepwise with a high-pressure pump. The pressure and height in the dropping mercury column in the capillary are recorded. The height of the meniscus can be measured by touching with an electrical contact, capacitively or inductively. The pressure transducer should be capable of measuring the pressures with a relative accuracy of at least ±2 per cent and the mercury volume should be measured to an accuracy of at least ±1 mm³ when using a sample vessel of about 10 cm³.

The pressure data are readily related to pore size by means of Eqn. (4.7). A plot of penetrated volume versus size, as calculated from the corresponding pressure information, results in a pore volume or size distribution, typical examples of which were presented by Orr[11], and which are shown in Fig. 4.5.

Curve 1 on the plot of typical data was obtained for a powder with relatively coarse grains. Accordingly, the curve consists of two distinct parts. The

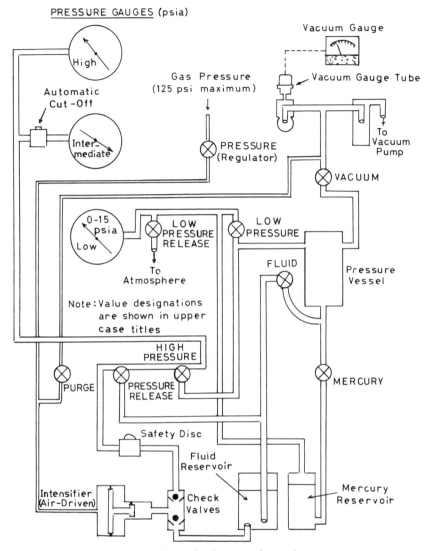

Fig. 4.4 Schematic diagram of porosimeter

volume of mercury penetrating the sample at pressures less than about 3 bar went into void spaces among the individual particles, while the volume above 3 bar penetrated pores within the powder grains. The steepness of rise of the first step shows that the particles were also rather uniform in size.

Curve 2 also represents a powder. Here, however, the particles were finer than for curve 1 and have very few pores. The void spaces predominate. Curve 3 represents a catalyst where the volume of pores exceeds the volume of void spaces. The pores tend to be predominantly about 0.005 μm in radius, while the volume average void space is of the order of 1 μm in radius. The

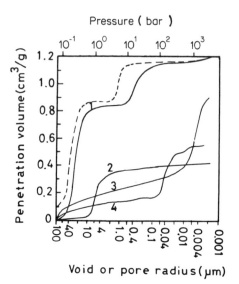

Fig. 4.5 Typical results obtained from porosimetry: Cumulative pore radius distribution

pores and voids thus differ greatly in size. Curve 4 is for a mineral having unique structural characteristics. It has pores, for example, predominantly of about 0.04 μm radius. It appears, further, to have a few pores of about 0.01 μm radius.

The plots shown in Fig. 4.5 are distribution curves. Pore size distribution can be obtained by another treatment of data when desired. Designating the volume of pores having radii between r and $r + dr$ by dV, it may be written that

$$dV = D(r)\,dr \qquad (4.8)$$

where $D(r)$ is the pore-size distribution function. Differentiating Eqn. (4.7) with γ and θ assumed constant, gives

$$p\,dr + r\,dp = 0 \qquad (4.9)$$

and then combining Eqns. (4.8) and (4.9) leads to

$$dV = -D(r)\frac{r}{p}\,dp \qquad (4.10)$$

In the actual determination, the volume measured is that of all pores having radii greater than r. The total pore volume V_t is thus diminished by the volume V of pores greater than r. Pressure–volume data are actually, therefore, values of $(V_t - V)$ and P; plotted, they would form a curve having the slope $d(V_t - V)/dP$ or $-dV/dP$. Equation (4.10) may then be rewritten in the form

$$D(r) = \frac{p}{r} \frac{d(V_t - V)}{dp}$$

(4.11)

the right-hand terms of which are determinable.

Experimental pressure–volume data may thus be employed to obtain a series of values of $d(V_t - V)dp$ as a function of p. Values of r corresponding to the chosen value of p are calculated from Eqn. (4.7) or read from the experimental plot of data. Values of $D(r)$ are then found from Eqn. (4.11). Plotting $D(r)$ against r gives, finally, the pore-size distribution. The distribution curve shown in Fig. 4.6 was obtained in this manner from curve no. 3 of Fig. 4.5.

Several factors, however, contribute to errors in mercury porosimetry, the most direct of which are the following:

1. Compressibilities of the solid, mercury, and residual air remaining in the sample space[12]. Remaining air in general affects the region of low pressures and thus of pores larger than 50 μm which are due to voids between grains, and therefore may be neglected. Roughness of the sample surface additionally can impede complete filling of the interspaces. At high pressure, several phenomena can produce errors: compressibility of the sample, the sample vessel, and mercury as well as temperature changes by pressurization. These errors can be taken into account by correction curves obtained by a blank test using a dummy.
2. Kinetic hysteresis effect, where a time factor enters into reading of the mercury penetration before equilibrium has been approached.
3. Volume hysteresis, which, in contrast to the kinetic hysteresis, is the retention of mercury by the pores of the sample after penetration and reduction of pressure to 1 atmosphere. This may be caused by the classic 'ink-bottle' type pores, or by some other shape pores with constricted 'neck' and large

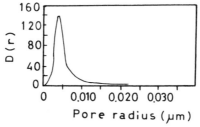

Fig. 4.6 Pore radius frequency obtained from porosimetry

void volumes. In such cases the pore diameter calculated by the Washburn equation is the diameter of the opening of the pore, and the analysis will consequently be biased toward the small pore size[12]

4. Assumption of a cylindrical pore shape model for the analysis of mercury porosimetry data may not best represent the actual situation under study. Most solids will give anything but cylindrically shaped pores. For cylindrical pores the shape factor is 0.500 according to the relation

$$\frac{\text{Total pore volume}}{\text{area} \times \text{average radius}} = \frac{V_p}{A_p \times r} = 0.500 \qquad (4.12)$$

Shape factors for a few pore models are listed in Table 4.2, and these examples illustrate the problem involved in interpretation of the pore-size distribution curves obtained by mercury porosimetry.

Table 4.2   Shape factor for various pore models

Pore model	Shape factor
cylindrical	0.500
cubic	0.304
tetragonal	0.144
hexagonal	0.117

5. The largest source of error in calculation of the equivalent cylindrical pore diameter from the mercury penetration data comes from the assumption of some constant average value for the contact angle θ for the mercury and the solid surface. Since this information is not readily available, most workers usually assume any angle between 130° and 140°, depending on their preference. Rootare[12] has shown that one can miss the actual pore diameter by 50% or 100% in an extreme case, by choosing an average value of either 130° or 140° for the contact angle, if, for example, the real value is either 160° or 110°. De Wit and Scholten[13] pointed out that the real value of θ depends on the pore size, and Good and Mikhail[14] suggested that for macropores and mesopores the contact angle that should be used is 180°, while for narrower pores the contact angle diminishes. Some examples of contact angle measurements are presented in Table 4.3[15].

6. The outgassing conditions seem also to be an important parameter, as has been suggested recently by Winslow[16], especially in the analysis of exceedingly fine pores where the existence of adsorbed layers would reduce both the effective pore diameter and pore volume and cause the mercury to measure an erroneous distribution.

7. Breakdown of the porous solid during the pressurization of the sample to force the mercury into the pores can be a source of error in porosity study. For equal wall thickness, the smaller pores are much stronger than the larger pores, whereas foam-type materials are especially subject to this

Table 4.3 Examples of measured contact angles of
mercury on various solids

Material	Contact angle
coconut shell	140°
nickel metal	130°
alumina pellets	127°
	130°
polymer spheres	123°
refractory (MgO, Al_2O_3) brick	128°
paraffin	112°
glass plate	137°
montmorillonite	139°
kaolinite	146°
clay minerals, asst.	147°

kind of 'squeeze' effect because their walls are thin and of low mechanical strength[12].

The mercury porosimetry method can also be used to calculate, beside the pore size and volume distribution, other parameters such as porosity, density, specific surface area, and particle size distribution in a similar way as adsorption isotherms, discussed later and in Chapter 2. Details of such calculations, with an extended list of references were cited by Orr[11]. Several papers give further details[17-24].

A report on mercury porosimeter measurements must include the following specific information: type of apparatus used; sample description; sample weight; out-gassing procedure; contact angle used in calculations; a table showing the corrected intrusion volumes per gram and the corresponding absolute intruding pressures; a graphical, cumulative pore volume distribution having the intruded volumes per gram on the ordinate with an arithmetric scale and the apparent pore diameters on the abscissa with a logarithmic scale; and precision and accuracy.

The estimated standard deviation of duplicate measurements of total pore volume on the same sample shall not exceed 2 per cent of the mean value for a given range of radii.

4.2 Water displacement porosimeter

If a porous system is completely filled with a wetting liquid, the pores can be depleted with a gas by applying pressure to overcome the surface energy of the water σ (Fig. 4.7). The pressure required depends on the pore radius r, assuming a cylindrical geometry, according to Cantor's equation

$$p = 2\sigma r^{-1} \cos \phi \qquad (4.13)$$

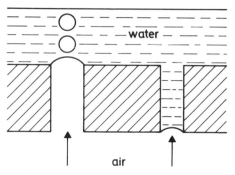

Fig. 4.7 Depletion of water of a soaked
pore system by air pressure

where $\cos \phi = 1$ in case of a total wetting liquid. According to d'Arcy's law, the specific conductance D for the gas can be calculated when measuring the gas flow Q as a function of the pressure p:

$$D = kQp^{-1} \qquad (4.14)$$

According to Žagar[25–28], the pore-size distribution can be calculated from conductance and radius using the equation

$$D = \Sigma r^2/8 \qquad (4.15)$$

Žagar's apparatus (Fig. 4.8) works as follows. The porous sample shaped as a flat cylindrical body is immersed in water and is fixed tightly in the measuring box. Then air pressure is applied from one side and increased uniformly up to 0.4 bar with an increasing rate of 0.2 bar h^{-1}. The biggest and subsequently smaller pores are depleted with increasing pressure first. The quantity of air streaming through the sample is measured as a function of pressure exerted. With the dry specimen the air quantity is proportional to the pressure. A completely soaked specimen, however, results in a bent curve, and this function is proportional to the pore size distribution. Pores open only on one side and through-holes can be differentiated to some extent. The method covers the pore range between 1 and 300 μm.

A modification of this method is described by Fischer and Jahn[29] measuring directly the displacement of water, acetone, or methanol out of the pore system in a capillary above the sample (Fig. 4.9). The method has been extended for the measurement of porous samples covering the sample with a fine-porous diaphragm. By this measure, however, the smallest radius detectable is limited by the pore width of the diaphragm (radius range 0.07 to 200 μm). Fischer and Jahn applied pressure not only to deplete the pore system of the fluid, but also refilled the pores using a vacuum. In this way they observed a hysteresis, which they attributed to ink bottle pore shapes.

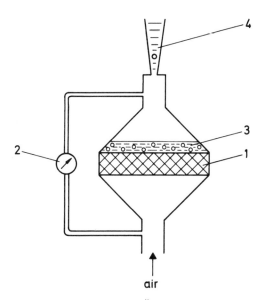

Fig. 4.8 Scheme of the Žagar porosimeter; 1 sample, 2 manometer, 3 water, 4 flowmeter

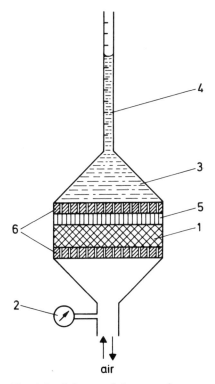

Fig. 4.9 Scheme of the porosimeter, after Fischer and Jahn; 1 sample, 2 manometer, 3 fluid, 4 calibrated capillary, 5 diaphragm, 6 filter plates

Astbury[30,31] describes the measurement of the pore size distribution, the specific area, the tortuosity and variations of the diameter of cylindrical shaped pore system by observing the filling process of the pore system. The sample is filled under pressure with an electrolyte (0.1 N potassium sulphate) and the increase of conductivity is measured. The lower limit of the method is 0.05 μm radius.

4.3 Isotherm method for pore structure analysis

4.3.1 Analysis of mesopores

In the isotherm method for mesopore analysis the basic assumption is that capillary condensation occurs in the pores at higher relative pressures according to the Kelvin equation. The adsorption–desorption isotherms of nitrogen, the adsorbate used by most investigators, show a hysteresis loop for porous solids, and the hysteresis region is considered to be the region in which multilayer adsorption is augmented by capillary condensation. This begins for nitrogen at p/p_0 of about 0.4. Because of the adsorbed layers on the walls of the cylindrical capillaries, the Kelvin radius of capillary condensation was assumed to be the pore radius minus the thickness of the adsorbed film. The thickness of the adsorbed film was evaluated from adsorption isotherms of nitrogen on nonporous adsorbents. On the basis of the assumptions, the volumes of the pores and the surface areas of the pore walls were evaluated for pore groups with radii between r and $r + \Delta r$.

Mesopore size calculations are usually made with the aid of the Kelvin equation in the form

$$\ln\left(\frac{p}{p_0}\right) = -\frac{2\gamma V_L}{r_K RT} \tag{4.16}$$

which relates p/p_0, the relative pressure at which condensation takes place, with r_K, the radius of the hemispherical meniscus. Here γ and V_L are the surface tensions and molar volume, respectively, of the condensed liquid.

Equation (4.16) may be derived from the Young–Laplace equation

$$\Delta p = \gamma\left(\frac{1}{r_1} + \frac{1}{r_2}\right) \tag{4.17}$$

which expresses the difference in pressure on the two sides of a meniscus as a function of its principal radii of curvature, r_1 and r_2. To obtain Eqn (4.16), r_1 and r_2 are either equated or r_K is taken as the mean radius of curvature.

In the application of the Kelvin equation to capillary condensation, it is necessarily assumed that r_K is directly related to the pore dimensions. In the

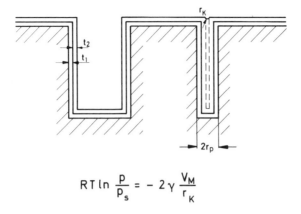

$$RT \ln \frac{p}{p_s} = -2\gamma \frac{V_M}{r_K}$$

Fig. 4.10   Illustration for the Kelvin equation with correction for multilayer thickness

simplest case (Fig. 4.10), the pore shape is regarded as cylindrical. If the pore radius is r_p and a correction is made for the multilayer thickness t, then

$$r_p = r_K + t \tag{4.18}$$

This approach implies that the meniscus shape is hemispherical and the pore radius is therefore given by the equation

$$r_p = \frac{2\gamma V_L}{RT \ln(p_0/p)} + t \tag{4.19}$$

If the meniscus is of spherical form and not hemispherical, the finite contact angle with the adsorbed multilayer must be introduced.

The relationship between the adsorbent pore geometry and the meniscus shape has been discussed in some detail by Karnaukhov[17,32]. In a number of cases (e.g. in slit-shaped and open-ended pores) the meniscus takes a cylindrical rather than a spherical shape. To deal with this situation we may put $r_2 = \infty$ in Eqn. (4.17) and the radius of an open-ended cylindrical pore is then given by

$$r_p = \frac{\gamma V_L}{RT \ln(p_0/p)} + t \tag{4.20}$$

If capillary condensation takes place in a parallel-sided slit, the slit width d_p is given by

$$d_p = \frac{2\gamma V_L}{RT \ln(p_0/p)} + t \tag{4.21}$$

Another possibility is capillary condensation around the point of contact of two spherical particles. In this case a saddle-shaped meniscus is formed and the more general equation containing both r_1 and r_2 (of different signs) must be employed to describe the process (see Chapter 2). It is clear, therefore, that the appropriate form of the Kelvin equation is dependent on the pore shape and the mode of capillary condensation.

The fact that capillary condensation takes place over a range of relative pressure demonstrates that the meso pore volume is distributed over a range of effective pore radius. Many attempts have been made to calculate the pore size distribution from the course of an adsorption isotherm. The various computational procedures have been described in some detail by Gregg and Sing[33], Broekhoff and Linsen[34] and Dollimore and Heal[35].

The calculation of the pore size distribution is complicated by the fact that capillary condensation and multilayer thickening are taking place over the same range of p/p_0. Similarly, on the desorption path capillary evaporation from pore is accompanied by a reduction in the multilayer thickness in the wider pores. This leads to a progressive change in the dimensions of internal regions in which condensation takes place. Also, the area of the walls covered by the adsorbed layer increases as the description progresses.

For the case of a set of cylindrical pores, Wheeler[36] introduced the basic relation

$$V_p - V_a = \int_{r_p}^{\infty} (r_p - t)^2 L(r)\, dr \qquad (4.22)$$

where V_p is the total pore volume, V_a is the volume of all those pores having radii less than r_p, and $L(r)$ is a pore size distribution function. The quantity $(V_p - V_a)$ is expressed as a liquid volume and is given as the difference between the amount adsorbed at $p/p_0 = 1$ and the amount adsorbed at the point on the isotherm corresponding to capillary condensation in pores of radius r_p.

Equation (4.22) states simply that the empty pore volume available for adsorption above a certain p/p_0 is the total remaining volume of cylindrical pores corrected for the space taken up by the adsorbed multilayer. Various methods have been introduced to obtain the distribution function. It is now customary to use numerical integration rather than assume a mathematical form for the distribution, but any attempt to achieve high accuracy is hardly justified in view of the uncertainties involved in the basic assumptions, e.g. the use of the bulk values of γ and V_L.

Not all investigators used the cylindrical idealization of pores, and some have employed a parallel-plate pore model instead of the cylindrical model. The Kelvin equation is formally the same for both models, except that for parallel plates r is the distance between the plates. The calculated pores sizes, however, differ because the correction for the adsorbed film is twice as large for parallel-plate pores. Roberts[37] developed a simplified method for calculating pore structures by both models.

Obviously, the pore shapes of very few adsorbents are known, but it seems quite unlikely that there is any solid which contains only pores of a given shape. Most of the pores of most solids have irregular shapes. This view led Brunauer, Mikhail, and Bodor[38] to develop a method of mesopore analysis which starts without assuming a pore shape model, and which is known as the 'modelless' method. This method makes use of the concept of hydraulic radius, which for a group of pores is defined as

$$r_{h,i} = \frac{V_i}{S_i} \qquad (4.23)$$

where V_i is the volume of the group of pores, and S_i is the surface area of the pore walls. In the case of cylindrical tubes this definition agrees with the conventional definition given in Fig. 2.1.

The modelless method is based on the equation originally derived by Kiselev[39];

$$\gamma \, dS = -\Delta\mu \, dn \qquad (4.24)$$

where dS is the multilayer area which disappears when the pore is filled with dn moles of condensed liquid at the p/p_0 corresponding to the change in chemical potential $\Delta\mu$ (i.e. $RT \ln p/p_0$). This process involves the filling of the 'core', i.e. the inner region remaining when the pore walls are covered by multilayer.

Integration of Eqn. (4.24) over the limits of capillary condensation gives the total mesopore surface area

$$S = \frac{RT}{\gamma} \int \ln(p_0/p) \, dn \qquad (4.25)$$

If the integration is carried out for a succession of small desorption steps (starting at saturation pressure), the area S_i of each group of cores is obtained. In the first stage, the hydraulic radius of the largest group of cores is given directly by

$$r_{h,1} = \Delta n_1 \cdot V_L/\Delta S_1 \qquad (4.26)$$

where Δn_1 is the number of moles removed, V_L is the molar volume of the liquid adsorptive, and ΔS_1 the core area. In the succeeding steps, the computation is a little more complicated because allowance must be made for the thinning of the multilayer on pores already emptied. The correction of the equation terms as one progresses from group to group till the correction becomes equal to the amount desorbed and at this stage the mesopores are assumed to be empty.

It is clear that this procedure gives the core size distribution, $\Delta V/\Delta r_h$ versus r_h, which is adequate for many purposes. The core size can of course be converted into a pore size by the application of an appropriate t-curve and pore model.

The relation between the volume, surface, and hydraulic radius of pore and core for spherical, cylindrical, and parallel plate pores is given respectively by

$$\frac{V_p}{V_c} = \left(\frac{3r_c + t}{3r_c}\right)^3; \quad \left(\frac{2r_c + t}{2r_c}\right)^2; \quad \left(\frac{r_c + t}{r_c}\right)^1 \tag{4.27}$$

$$\frac{S_p}{S_c} = \left(\frac{3r_c + t}{3r_c}\right)^2; \quad \left(\frac{2r_c + t}{2r_c}\right)^1; \quad \left(\frac{r_c + t}{r_c}\right)^0 \tag{4.28}$$

$$\frac{r_p}{r_c} = \frac{3r_c + t}{3r_c}; \quad \frac{2r_c + t}{2r_c}; \quad \frac{r_c + t}{r_c} \tag{4.29}$$

(see Fig. 4.11).

The cylindrical pore is intermediate between a completely curved pore (spherical) and a completely flat pore (parallel plate). For most adsorbents, the shapes of the pores are unknown. It is clear from the above equations that the best procedure in such cases is to convert core data into cylindrical pore data. If the shape of the pore approximates a sphere, less error is committed if it is considered a cylinder than if it is considered a parallel plate pore. Likewise, if the walls of the pore approximate parallel plates, less error is

pore model		V_p/V_c	S_p/S_c	r_p/r_c
hollow sphere	 ○	$\left(\dfrac{3r_c + t}{3r_c}\right)^3$	$\left(\dfrac{3r_c + t}{3r_c}\right)^2$	$\dfrac{3r_c + t}{3r_c}$
cylindrical tube	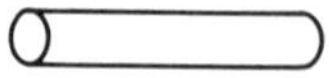	$\left(\dfrac{2r_c + t}{2r_c}\right)^2$	$\dfrac{2r_c + t}{2r_c}$	$\dfrac{2r_c + t}{2r_c}$
slit	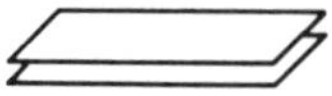	$\dfrac{r_c + t}{r_c}$	1	$\dfrac{r_c + t}{r_c}$

Fig. 4.11   Relation between volume, surface, and hydraulic radius of pore and core for different pore models

committed if the pore is considered cylindrical than if it is considered spherical.

Pores of irregular shapes may have flat, partly curved, or completely curved surfaces in random distribution. In such cases, good results may be obtained by assuming cylindrical pores.

The great superiority of the new method over the older cylindrical or parallel plate idealizations is that the older models are based on one value obtained from the isotherm, the volume of the core (the volume desorbed), but the hydraulic radius and the surface of the core are hypothetical. The new method is based on two values obtained from the isotherm, the volume and the surface of the core, which automatically gives the hydraulic radius of the core.

The question which dictates itself is whether the adsorption or the desorption branch should be employed for pore structure analysis. Several investigators have advanced convincing arguments showing that there is a delay in meniscus formation in the course of the adsorption process; consequently, the desorption branch represents true capillary condensation equilibrium[38]. It seems logical to believe that the desorption values represent equilibrium at a given relative pressure (p/p_0) if for no other reason than because they are larger than the adsorption values. It is easy to accept that for some reason meniscus formation is delayed on the adsorption side, but at saturation pressure all pores are filled with liquid; consequently, there cannot be a delay in meniscus formation on the desorption side.

The trouble is, however, that there may be a delay in the breaking of the meniscus on the desorption side. Hysteresis may be caused by inkbottle-shaped pores. On the adsorption side the narrow neck will fill at a relatively low pressure, and the wider body at a higher pressure. On the desorption side, however, the pore will empty only when the pressure is reduced so far that the liquid in the neck of the pore becomes unstable. For such pores, the adsorption branch represents true capillary condensation equilibrium, and if there is a delay in meniscus formation on the adsorption side, then neither branch corresponds to equilibrium.

Measuring the differential heat of sorption of argon in porous Vycor glass and chromia gel, which both dispose on pores of varying diameters, Kington and Smith[40,41] demonstrated that the adsorption branch of the hysteresis loop is associated with a reversible process, whereas the desorption of material from the capillaries is a spontaneous process. Since the Clapeyron heat calculated is greater than the calorimetric heat measured, and in agreement with the work performed in the hysteresis loop, it can be concluded that in desorption an irreversible process is involved. The conclusion supports any mechanistic theory of capillary condensation based on a neck-controlled desorption process.

Doe and Haynes[42] showed by probabilistic and Monte Carlo calculations that a pore network containing randomly distributed diameters results in a hysteresis resembling an inkbottle pore system. This pore blocking effect may seriously falsify the desorption branch in capillary condensation and mercury intrusion measurements. In general, therefore, for the calculation of the pore size distributions the adsorption isotherm is preferred. Further discussions are given by Brunauer, Mikhail, and Boder[38], Everett[43], and Ponec, Knor, and Černý[44].

Of course, other adsorbates condensing in the liquid state can be used for pore size determination. They should, however, not react with most materials or be dissolved in the bulk, and the van der Waals' forces should not depend largely on the kind of the surface as in the case of nitrogen. The molecule should be spherical or at least not chainlike. Thus other adsorbates are only used in special cases.

Only water has found wider application for determining the pore size distribution of carbons[45]. Water has high surface tension, small molecule diameter, and is not strongly adsorbed on activated carbons. It produces a sorption isotherm (Fig. 4.12) that is greatly different from those for gases as shown in Fig. 4.13. The isotherms invariably have large hysteresis loops which open at low water content and do not close at the upper end. Adsorption is usually nil at p/p_0 less than 0.3, while adsorption starts invariably at p/p_0 less than 0.6. Various studies indicate that the adsorption branch is associated with the pore cavity diameters whereas the desorption branch is due to the pore constriction diameters.

The Kelvin equation (4.16) with correction for the contact angle θ is

$$\ln p/p_0 = -\frac{2\gamma V_L}{r_K RT}\cos\theta \tag{4.30}$$

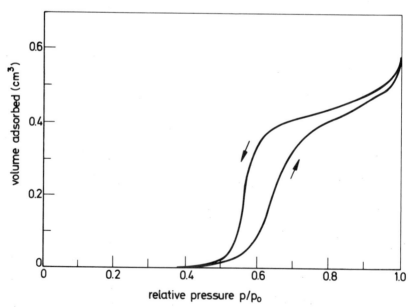

Fig. 4.12   Water adsorption isotherm at 298 K on activated carbon

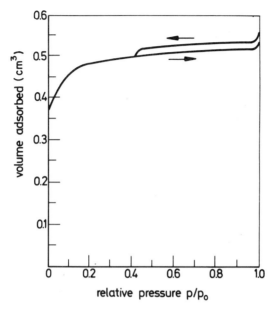

Fig. 4.13 Nitrogen adsorption isotherm at 77 K on activated carbon (same sample as for Fig. 4.12). (Courtesy A. J. Juhola)

where r_K is the core diameter, γ the surface tension, V_L the liquid molar volume at temperature T, and R the gas constant in joules. The surface tension γ amounts to 0.0728 Jm^{-2}. The liquid molar volume V_L at 298 K varies with p/p_0 from 18 to 22 $cm^3\ mol^{-1}$, but a mean constant value of 20 $cm^3\ mol^{-1}$ may be used. A practical value for the liquid phase contact angle is 62°. Polar compounds can reduce the contact angle, however, and thus carbons should be leached with acid and water to remove hydrophilic ash. For low-ash carbons, the removal of ash does not alter the pore structure significantly. Results of such pore size determinations are in good agreement with mercury intrusion measurements. The method is applicable in a radius range of about 1 to 200 nm.

4.3.2 Analysis of micropores

The only method available for the complete analysis of the pore size distribution of micropores was introduced in 1968 by Mikhail, Brunauer, and Bodor[46]. The authors named their method the micropore analysis or MP method.

The method is based on the use of an appropriate t-curve. Several investigations proposed t-curves for nitrogen adsorption on nonporous substances, and these have been discussed in Chapter 2.

The selection of the appropriate t-curve is far more important in the MP method than in the modelless method for two reasons. The heats of adsorption affect the film thickness strongly in the first adsorbed layer, weakly in the second, and hardly at all in the higher layers. The t-values used in the MP method are those obtained for p/p_0 less than about 0.4, whereas in the model-less method the t-values used are those obtained for higher relative pressure. Far more important than this is the fact that in the modelless method the t-values appear only as correction terms, whereas in the MP method they constitute the total pore volume, as will be seen later.

It was pointed out by Lippens and de Boer[47] that any adsorption isotherm for a nonporous solid can be converted into a straight-line plot according to the equation

$$t = 10^4 V_1/S_{BET} \tag{4.31}$$

For a given point of the isotherm, the volume or weight of adsorbed nitrogen is converted into V_1: the t-value for the corresponding p/p_0 is read from the t-curve, and V_1 is plotted against t. Furthermore, even in pores the amounts adsorbed at low pressures should be in agreement with the amounts adsorbed on a free surface, except when the width of the pore approaches the diameter of a nitrogen molecule, 0.35 nm. The V_1–t plot for a nonporous solid should, therefore, be a straight line from the origin, through the entire adsorption range, up to the V_1 and t-values corresponding to p_0. For porous solids, a straight line is usually obtained at least in the low-pressure region.

The slope of the straight line in the V_1–t plot gives the surface area of the adsorbent. This surface was designated S_t, and, barring disturbing factors, it should be identical with S_{BET}, as Eqn. (4.31) shows. Nevertheless, it has been found for numerous adsorbents that the two were not equal, though no difference greater than 17% has been reported so far.

The most obvious reason for the discrepancy is that the t-curve employed was not the right one for the particular adsorbent. If the adsorbent has higher heats of adsorption than the adsorbents on which the t-curve is based, S_t will give an erroneously high result for the surface. For a given value of V_1, the value of t will be read for the corresponding p/p_0 from the t-curve. However, for that value of p/p_0 the correct value of t is greater than that obtained from the t-curve, because of the higher heats of adsorption of absorbent. Thus, the slope of the straight line of the V_p–t plot will be steeper than it should be, leading to a too high value of S_t. Obviously, the reverse is true if adsorbent has lower heats of adsorption than the adsorbents of the t-curve; S_t will then give too low result for the surface.

There are two criteria for testing the correctness of the t-curve to be used for the analysis of the micropores of a given adsorbent. The first follows from the above considerations; S_t must be close to S_{BET}. The second criterion is connected with the first. The C constant of the BET equation is a good measure of the adsorptive power on a unit surface of a given adsorbent at a given p/p_0 in the relative pressure range employed in the MP method. The C constant of the t-curve must therefore be close to the C constant of the absorbent analysed. The two criteria are interconnected because at any given value of V_1 and p/p_0, the surface parameter V_m and the C constant are connected by the BET equation.

The method will be illustrated by analysing the pore structure of a silica gel, which contains only micropores[46]. It was kindly donated by the Davidson Division of W. R. Grace and Company, and it is designated Davidson O3. In the analysis, de Boer's t-curve was used. The C constant for this curve as well as for the silica gel is 130. The value of S_{BET} for Davidson O3 is 793 m^2/g, and S_t is 792 m^2/g, an agreement far better than is warranted by the errors in both values. The Cranston–Inkley t-curve in the range employed in the analysis indicates 10 to 14% higher t-values than does the de Boer curve.

The adsorption–desorption isotherm of nitrogen on Davidson O3 is shown in Fig. 4.14. It appears to be a type I (or Langmuir-type) isotherm, but it is not; the four points at the lowest pressures give an excellent straight-line BET plot, giving $S_{BET} = 793$ m^2/g. The complete reversibility plus the fact that the pores are almost full at low relative pressures indicate that the silica gel contains only micropores.

The isotherm was converted into a V_t–t plot, as described above, and the

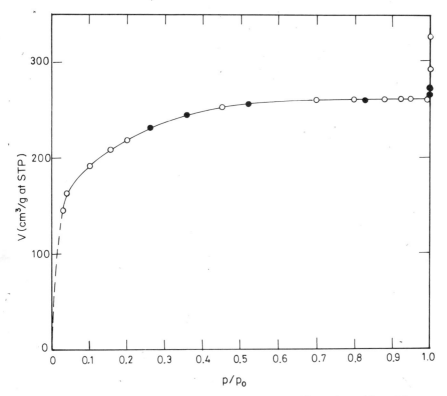

Fig. 4.14   Nitrogen isotherm at 77 K obtained for silica gel Davidson 03

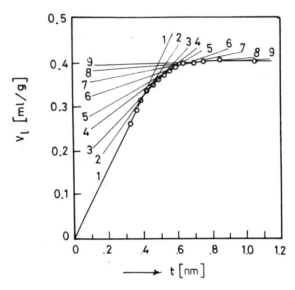

Fig. 4.15 Nitrogen isotherm at 77 K obtained for silica gel Davidson 03 converted into a v–t plot

plot is shown in Fig. 4.15. The slope of straight line 1 gives S_t, which is 792 m²/g.

As mentioned in Chapter 2, Lippens and de Boer[47] have advanced three possibilities with regard to the shape of the V_l–t plot: (1) As long as multilayer adsorption occurs unhindered, the plot remains a straight line. (2) If multilayer adsorption at some pressure begins to be augmented by capillary condensation in a porous solid, the points begin to deviate upward from the straight line. (3) If some narrow pores are filled up by multilayer adsorption, further adsorption does not occur on the entire surface because a part of the surface has become unavailable. The points on the V_l–t plot then begin to deviate downward from the straight line. This fact was used by de Boer and his coworkers to separate the pore system into two parts, narrow and wide pores, and it enabled them to calculate the surface areas and volumes of the totality of narrow pores and the totality of wide pores. They called their method the t-method, and the presently described MP method is an extension of the t-method. The downward deviations in the V_l–t plot can be used for the determination of the pore volume and pore surface distribution of micropores.

In Fig. 4.15, downward deviations begin as one proceeds from $t = 0.40$ to $t = 0.45$ nm. Straight line 2 has a smaller slope than straight line 1, and the surface indicated by the slope is 520 m²/g. Thus, a group of narrow pores has become filled with adsorbed nitrogen, and the surface of these pores is $792 - 520 = 272$ m²/g. If the pore walls are visualized as parallel plates, the average statistical thickness of the adsorbed film in the filled-up pores is

0.425 nm, and this is also half the distance between the plates (the hydraulic radius). The volume of the first group of pores is therefore given by

$$V_1 = 10^4 (S_1 - S_2) \frac{t_1 + t_2}{2} \qquad (4.32)$$

where S_1 and S_2 are the surface areas obtained from the slopes of straight lines 1 and 2, and t_1 and t_2 are the statistical thicknesses of the films in the narrowest and widest pores of the group. The units are the same as in Eqn. (4.31).

One then proceeds in a similar manner to the second pore group, with hydraulic radii between 0.45 and 0.50 nm, and so on. The analysis is continued until there is no further decrease in the slope of the V_r–t plot, which means that no further blocking of pores by multilayer adsorption occurs. The pore volume distribution curve is shown in Fig. 4.16. The maximum is at 0.46 nm. If the pores are considered parallel plates, then the most frequent pore width is about 0.9 nm. The largest pores have a width of about 1.6 nm, showing that the gel contains only micropores. The cumulative pore surface and pore volume were in excellent agreement with the BET surface and the total pore volume: the discrepancy was less than 1.4% for each.

It is shown by the authors that with values of S and t taken from the V_r–t plot, the volume of the pore is the product of the two whether the pore walls are parallel plates or cylinders. It was pointed out in the original paper[46] that because the micropore adsorption isotherm ends in a horizontal plateau, the

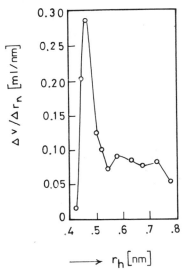

Fig. 4.16 Pore volume distribution curve (pore radius frequency) of silica gel Davidson 03

cumulative pore surface must be the same as S_t, and because the t-curve was so selected that S_t should agree with S_{BET}, the cumulative pore surface must agree with S_{BET}. This agreement does not prove the validity of the micropore analysis, but it was thought at the time that the volume agreement was significant. However, Dubinin[48] later proved mathematically that when an adsorbent contains only micropores and the adsorption ends in a horizontal plateau, the cumulative pore volume must agree with the volume adsorbed at p_0; thus, both proofs are invalid.

Fortunately, however, the situation is different if an adsorbent contains both micropores and wider pores. In this case, the isotherm usually is type II or type IV. The cumulative micropore surface cannot agree with S_t or S_{BET}, because the total cumulative surface, i.e., the cumulative surface of micropores plus wider pores, must agree with S_{BET}, and the cumulative volume of micropores plus wider pores must agree with the volume adsorbed at p_0. Thus, for such adsorbents, the two criteria of the correctness of the analysis are valid.

Since the t-plot is not independent of the BET surface area, and since the MP method uses the t-plot as a starting point in the analysis, adverse criticism was advanced against the correctness of the surface area in micropores[49], based on the idea that the mechanism of micropore filling is volume filling[50] and not layer by layer filling as described by the BET treatment. The cumulative surface area values obtained by the MP method were found to agree well with surface areas obtained by independent techniques such as by small-angle X-ray scattering, X-ray diffraction, and by the Kaganer method, which are totally independent of the BET method[51]. This agreement between the areas obtained by the MP method and the other methods just mentioned led Brunauer[51] to assume that the entropy of an adsorbate molecule in a narrow pore should be lower than on a free surface, and that the entropy decrease in going from the gas phase to the adsorbed phase should be greater for adsorption in a narrow pore. The amount adsorbed is a function of the free energy of adsorption, and the higher heat of adsorption in narrow pores may be at least partly compensated by the larger decrease in entropy. Possibly it may even be overcompensated.

In their original paper, Mikhail et al.[46] pointed out that the analysis did not apply to very small micropores, which they called *ultramicropores*. The authors did not define the boundary line of ultramicropores except by implication. Dubinin[48] pointed out the lack of definition of ultramicropores, and Brunauer et al.[52] later defined ultramicropores as pores which have hydraulic radii smaller than one molecular diameter. This means that for water vapour and nitrogen the MP method is not applicable for pores of radii less than about 0.6 and 0.7 nm, respectively. Dubinin's volume-filling theory was applied to such adsorbents as active carbons and synthetic zeolites, having radii not exceeding 0.6 or 0.7 nm. Consequently, in his later papers, Dubinin admits, at least by implication, the feasibility of the MP method for those micropores for which the method was not claimed to be applicable[53,54]. With this confusion in nomenclature (micropores in Dubinin's sense are ultra-micropores in the MP sense), one should stick to the IUPAC nomenclature, which makes the MP method applicable to micropores of radii ranging from 0.6 to 2.0 nm.

In adsorbents which contain both micropores and mesopores, the sum of the analyses by both the MP method and the modelless method should give the complete pore structure analysis of the solid. The application of both methods to wide varieties of solids, both in industry and in research, has undoubtedly paved the road to a better understanding of the role played by the various types of pores in adsorption, catalysis, and in various other fields such as in building materials, and in particular hardened cement pastes. The

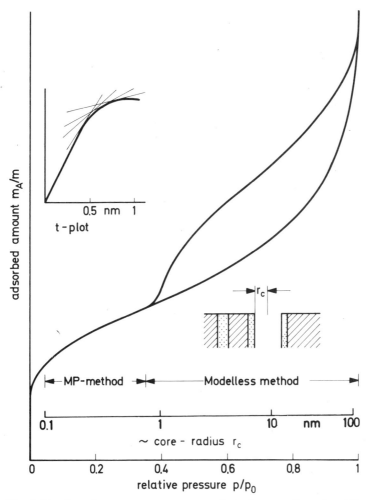

Fig. 4.17 Complete pore structure analysis by coupling the MP method and the modelless method

effects of pore narrowing were studied for the adsorption of several organic molecules on silica gels, not only as a function of pore size, but also as a function of the type of interaction between the solid and the gas[55]. Also the effects of pore narrowing were studied on other phenomena, such as: orientation and packing in micropores[56], hydrophilicity versus hydrophobicity as a function of pore size[57], variation of heats of immersion in nonpolar liquids[58], and in polar liquids such as water[59,60]. In catalysis, the effects of pore narrowing were studied on some solids known by their cracking activity and the results were also correlated with the chemistry of the surface[61]. In hardened cement pastes it could be shown that the physical state of the hydration products varies according to the space available for their formation, and that pore narrowing could affect the microstructure, and consequently the main physical and engineering properties of the hardened paste[62]. Needless to say, in such applications one needs to have information on the *complete* pore structure of the sample, and this can be achieved only by coupling the MP method for micropores with the modelless method or any other method suitable for analysing the mesopores (Fig. 4.17).

4.3.3 Ultramicropores

Obviously the above presentation dealt mainly with the three pore categories recognized by the IUPAC, namely macropores, mesopores, and micropores. Mention was also made of pores of sizes below the lower limit of applicability of the MP method, and these were termed ultramicropores[52], with an upper size limit of 0.6 to 0.7 nm. Since some important solids, such as carbons and zeolites, contain only pores of such size, one can easily develop the idea that ultramicropores constitute a fourth category beside the other three recognized already by the IUPAC.

In solids containing ultramicropores, if the adsorbate can enter the pores or pore entrances then the amount adsorbed simply rises to a limiting value, usually at a low value of p/p_0 and then stays almost constant for the remainder of the adsorption isotherm. In the limits such an isotherm is associated with an adsorbed layer one molecule thick but, in most cases of physical adsorption which conform to this pattern, it is probably associated with a pore structure where the size of the pores is of the same magnitude as the adsorbate molecule[63].

There are two limiting cases. In the first, the molecule of the adsorbate just fits into the cylindrical pore, and it was demonstrated[64] that the BET transformation of the so-called statistical monolayer into a surface area is too small, provided the system is composed of channels. The second case concerns molecular sieves and many carbons, in which the ultramicroporous character arises because of restrictions on exits or entrances, behind which are cavities of high adsorptive capacity. This gives BET surface areas that are too high[65,66]. Application of the formula

$$V_s/S = \bar{r}/2 \qquad (4.33)$$

to the complete adsorption data (where V_s is the volume uptake near saturation, taken as a liquid, S the surface area, and $\bar{r}$ the mean pore radius) is suspect if the pores are in the ultramicroporous range[67]. On the basis of the conventional model of cylindrical nonintersecting pores we have

$$S = kV_m \tag{4.34}$$

where k is a constant.

This then gives

$$V_s/kV_m = \bar{r}/2 \tag{4.35}$$

As the knee of the isotherm becomes acute, $V_m \rightarrow V_s$, and

$$V_m/V_s \rightarrow 1$$

and

$$\bar{r} \rightarrow \text{a constant minimum value.}$$

In the case of nitrogen adsorption this value is 0.7 nm[68]. This is the same as the value arbitrarily set by Brunauer et al.[52]

The use of the above formulae therefore fails to give a real value to $\bar{r}$ below a certain minimum value. This type of adsorption isotherm is often found with carbons[65], and the general term used to describe these adsorbents as being 'microporous' is not strictly valid since they are obviously 'ultramicroporous', and Dollimore and Heal[68] have shown that the general pore radius never appears less than twice the adsorbate diameter from use of the calculation using the equation $\bar{r} = 2V_p/S$. An alternative procedure in investigating structures of this type is to measure the adsorption capacity at a p/p_0 value near to saturation in terms of a volume of condensed liquid (condensed adsorbate) for a series of different sized adsorbate molecules, and then to interpret this in terms of the pore volume available to differently sized molecules by plotting the available pore volume against the size of the adsorbate molecules. This is shown in Fig. 4.18 for a silica sample[63,64]. The main difficulty is to obtain a set of molecular diameters for the adsorbate that are consistent. This is not always possible, but perhaps the best values are those calculated from bond angles and atomic radii (Table 4.4). The table also lists bond diameters calculated from other data such as liquid densities or the van der Waals' constants.

A curve such as that in Fig. 4.18 can be transformed by differentiation into structure curve.

Juhola[69] and Jäntti[70] included in such pore size determinations adsorption data from solutes like iodine, potassium permanganate, methylene blue, and molasses. They attributed the surface areas determined to such regions of pores which are available for the respective molecules with respect to their diameter.

184

Table 4.4   Values of adsorbate molecular diameters and liquid densities

Adsorbate	Temperature (K)	Density (g cm^{-3})	Molecular diameters[*]				
			1	2	3	4	5
nitrogen	77	0.808	0.315	0.370	0.300	0.353	0.433
methane	90	0.457	0.324	0.414		0.430	0.457
ethane	195	0.533	0.376		0.420		
propane	195	0.624	0.406		0.489		
butane	273	0.601	0.460		0.489		0.620
benzene	298	0.874	0.451		0.680		0.592
cyclopropane	195	0.720			0.475		0.515
argon	77	1.427	0.295	0.358	0.384	0.286	0.409
nitrous oxide	195	1.201	0.327				
carbon dioxide	195	1.14	0.324	0.454	0.280	0.340	

[*]Molecular diameters: Column 2, calculated from van der Waals' co-volume; 2, calculated from viscosity data; 3, calculated from bond lengths, etc.; 4, calculated from heat conductivity; 5, calculated from liquid density.

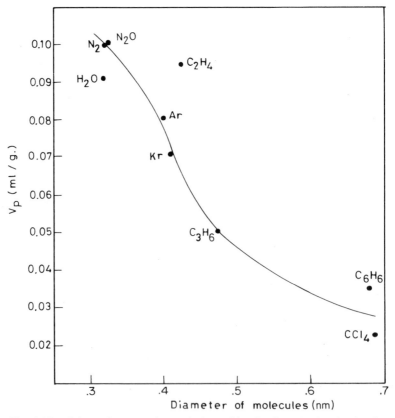

Fig. 4.18   Adsorption capacity variation with adsorbate molecule size for ultramicroporous silica[68]

Gregg and Langford[71] advanced a new method of assessing microporosity by pre-adsorption of nonane. In this method the sample after outgassing was exposed at 77 K to n-nonane vapour, which was then outgassed at room temperature, a process which removed the n-nonane from the external surface but not from the micropores. A residual part of a monolayer, as shown in Fig. 4.19[72], does not seriously disturb the results in the case of highly microporous samples. A nitrogen isotherm was measured before and after the treatment with n-nonane. The difference between the two nitrogen adsorption isotherms is then a measure of the microporosity. Such a method obviously cannot differentiate between micropores and ultramicropores, and does not give any indication on the sizes of pores involved. At best, the method can be used to detect collectively for micro- and ultramicropores, and possibly can be used to assess their total volumes.

The general understanding now is that the Polanyi potential theory of adsorption[73], as used by Dubinin[74], proved to be quite successful in the analysis of ultramicropores, although as mentioned earlier, the name of 'micropores' has always been attached to it. The method proved most successful in the analysis of carbons and zeolites and other materials which are mostly ultramicropores. The equation is used by Dubinin in the form

$$W = W_0 \exp(-k\varepsilon^2) \tag{4.36}$$

where W is the volume of 'micropores' filled by converting the gas volume aV to liquid volume using the density of the adsorbate in liquid form. If a is in mol g^{-1} then $W = aV$, where V is the molar volume in cm^3. W_0 is the total volume of all the 'micropores' and ε is the adsorption potential defined as the difference in chemical potential between liquid adsorbate in bulk and in the 'micropores', at the same temperature. The factor k is a constant for any one solid, but depends on the form of the adsorption space and the distribution of micropore sizes. More details were given in Chapter 3.

It has been suggested in this chapter that pores in solids should be classified according to size into four groups, and not three groups as currently adopted

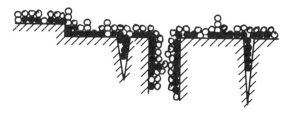

Fig. 4.19 Principle of the method of Gregg and Langford for micropore evaluation by pre-adsorption of n-nonane and nitrogen adsorption before and after the nonane treatment. (Courtesy of Stoeckli and Pressl-Wenger[72]

by the IUPAC. These four groups, in decreasing order, are macropores, mesopores, micropores, and ultramicropores. Recommended methods of analysis are given for each group of pores separately, but most of the problems arise because of 'borderline' cases, when the size of pores predominating in a given solid lies intermediate between two groups. The theory of adsorption is far from being perfect to help in setting sharp size limits between the various pore groups. The field is still challenging and more work is needed before one method of analysis can be introduced to analyse the four groups collectively and to yield 'total' pore structure analysis.

4.3.4 Experimental procedure

Measurement

In most cases investigations of the surface structure are made using a very small sample from a large quantity of material. Thus it is very important to take a representative sample. The respective rules issued by various administrations should be carefully followed because of the time-consuming measuring procedure. Control measurements are in general avoided.

First the samples are micronized. (The microstructure—pore size distribution and specific surface area—in general is not seriously distributed by the crushing.) Then the sample is subdivided systematically, using for example a rotating rifling process. Sample dividers are commercially available, and some companies perform sample division by contract.

Prior to adsorption measurements, the sample surface has to be baked in a vacuum to remove adsorbed species from the surface. In order to speed up the degassing process the baking temperature is chosen as high as possible but not so high as to damage the surface structure. The appropriate temperature and the minimum time for complete degassing in the case of gravimetric measurements can be found by observing the weight decrease with time (cf. Fig. 2.15). For physically adsorbed layers the curvature is exponential towards a final mass value. At higher temperature this value may be somewhat lower due to decomposition of more stable surface compounds and desorption of chemisorbed species. A linear mass decrease reveals a bulk decomposition and must be avoided (see Part 3). For volumetric experiments the maximum degassing temperature and the minimum degassing time must be found by trial-and-error experiments; that means surface area and pore size measurement of several samples pretreated at increasing temperatures.

For measurements with water or hydrocarbon vapour, salts or fats have to be removed to avoid the generation of solutions. Likewise, the sample vessel in the case of volumetric experiments, and the balance in case of gravimetric experiments, must be cleaned by washing with solvents (acetone) and hot water[75].

After degassing of the sample, the measurement should be started immediately to avoid contamination by redeposition of molecules coming from the vacuum line (pump oil) or from gaskets. At 10^{-4} Pa, some 10^{15} molecules per second strike 1 cm^2 of the sample. If the sticking probability is unity, this area will be covered by a complete monolayer within one second (see Part III). Fortunately, the internal surface behind the projection area of this square centimetre is several times larger than the outer surface, and, furthermore, such readsorbed species have only a negligible influence on the geometric structure and thus do not noticeably falsify the values of the specific surface area and the pore size distribution in the mesopore and macropore range.

As mentioned above, nitrogen is the best suited adsorptive for the pore structure analysis. In general, nitrogen does not react with the sample material, but sometimes the quadrupole moment of the nitrogen molecule effects a faster or oriented binding on special adsorption sites. In a few cases this may lead to anomalies in the isotherm shape or the C-value of the BET equation. In general, however, the isotherm can be evaluated using the constant value of 0.162 nm^2 for the molecular cross-sectional area for the adsorbed nitrogen molecule at 77 K.

Using other adsorbates, the value of the cross-sectional area depends more on the sample material (see Appendix C). Possible chemical reactions, chemisorption, or solution in the bulk material have to be considered. using water or hydrocarbons the sample surface must be free from salts or fats, respectively, which may form a solution with the adsorbent. In some cases (e.g. activated carbon), such soluble constituents can be removed by washing or neutralizing.

The adsorptives used must be of high purity. Gases stored in metal flasks always contain water vapour, and this as well as oxygen and the small components of gases which solidify at the isotherm temperature have to be carefully trapped by catalysts and desiccant cartridges. it has to be taken into account that organic vapours may change their chemical nature by polymerization processes during a long period of storage. Liquid adsorptives can be degassed by alternate boiling and freezing periods under vacuum conditions. Drying agents like sodium metal or molecular sieves can be placed into the liquid.

Prior to the measurement[76] using a gravimetric assembly, buoyancy has to be compensated for using counterweights of the same density as the sample. Residual buoyancy has to be determined by blank experiments and corrected by calculation taking into account the temperature difference to the measuring temperature. The sample is placed in the balance tube at a depth of at least seven times the internal diameter of the tube and it is shielded against radiation of ambient temperature by metal screens. In this way the sample temperature will deviate from the thermostat temperature by less than 0.1 K. The initial vacuum must be better than 10^{-3} Pa to avoid disturbances of the zero point by thermal gas flow. The gravimetric technique is described in more detail in Part III.

In volumetric apparatus, the critical factor for the gas dosing system is tightness, and this has to be carefully checked. Pumping can be replaced by washing the apparatus several times with an appropriate gas at ambient or elevated temperature. For the adsorption bulb a capillary diameter of 2 to 3 mm is recommended as a good compromise between the needs of outgassing and those of volumetryic accuracy. The capillary length should be 150 mm. The dead space is carefully controlled at room temperature with nitrogen or helium as nonadsorbable gas. In the calculations, the components of dead space at room temperature and that of thermostat temperature have to be considered separately. To avoid changes of the respective components, the level of the cryogenic liquid (nitrogen) is controlled automatically.

Besides the normal laboratory safety measures for working with vacuum equipment, the use of liquid gases and high temperatures requires some caution. Glass or quartz parts which are exposed to temperature gradients may implode when evacuated, especially when the temperature is changed too quickly. This applies also to working with Dewar vessels. Wire nettings, which serve as splinter protection in the case of a visual observation of the glass parts, are required. The use of safety glasses is essential.

If a large leak occurs, air condenses in the sample space when cooled with liquid nitrogen. In this case the Dewar vessel should not be removed too quickly to avoid sudden boiling of the liquid air, and the apparatus should be evacuated cautiously. Because a sudden pressure rise of boiling condensate may occur when measuring near the condensation pressure, the apparatus should be provided with a pressure relief valve.

The mass of the degassed sample in the gravimetric experiment results from the initial mass diminished by the mass lost during baking, and can be observed directly. This value is exact, if the initial sample mass is determined directly by the vacuum balance during use. Very often the sample mass exceeds the indicating range of the vacuum balance, in which case it is determined using a separate analytical balance. After this procedure, a serious error may occur if the sample is allowed to adsorb water from the humid air during transportation from the analytical to the vacuum balance. Disturbances of the mass indication after baking by thermal gas flow must be avoided by working in a high vacuum of at least 10^{-3} Pa. In particular, the zero point can be affected by thermal gas flow. A buoyancy error has to be considered if the sample is not compensated adequately or if the counterweight is not held at the same temperature.

In volumetric experiments the dry sample mass is determined by weighing the sample with a sample bulb, in case an error may arise by adsorption of humidity when the bulb is disconnected from the apparatus and open to the air.

After these preparations, the measurement starts by thermostatting the sample; in the case of nitrogen isotherms, by cooling with liquid nitrogen in a Dewar vessel. During the measurement the temperature of the liquid nitrogen has to be observed because it varies with the ambient pressure and by dissolution of oxygen from the air.

The measurement is started with high vacuum and (in gravimetry) observation of the zero point. In general, if the micropore structure is not the subject

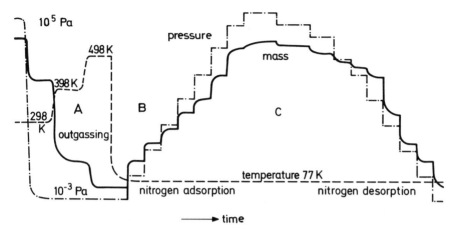

Fig. 4.20   Record of a nitrogen isotherm measured gravimetrically

of the investigation, nitrogen is introduced up to about 2.10^4 Pa. After equilibrium has been established, a second amount of nitrogen is introduced and subsequently the adsorption isotherm is measured stepwise up to the saturation point. After that the desorption isotherm is measured in the same way, decreasing the pressure stepwise down to vacuum. The BET range (2.10^4 to 4.10^4 Pa) should be covered with at least five measuring points and each branch of the isotherm with at least 30 measuring points. A typical run is shown in Fig. 4.20.

When observing an adsorption step of the adsorption branch, an unintentional pressure drop of more than 10 Pa should be avoided as well as similar pressure increases in the desorption branch, because in both cases a value within the isotherm hysteresis may be attained.

If it is intended to evaluate the desorption branch it is necessary to fill up all pores by remaining at saturation pressure for a considerable time period. To ensure complete filling it is advisable to increase the pressure several times above the saturation value.

The measurement of the saturation pressure is somewhat difficult because of small temperature variations of the thermostat and of the sample and because the adjustment of the equilibrium value is sluggish. Different methods are discussed in Part 3.

Evaluation

The most suitable tool for a calculation of the pore size distribution from the nitrogen isotherm at 77 K is the Kelvin equation, (4.16) and (4.30), respectively (compare Fig. 4.22), or the Cohan equation

$$\ln p/p_0 = - \frac{\gamma V_L}{r_c RT} \tag{4.37}$$

190

(r_C = Cohen pore radius) which differs from the Kelvin equation by the factor 2, and was originally derived for slit-shaped pores. The calculation is simply an abscissa transformation in the isotherm plot. In the case of stepwise measurements at given p/p_0 values, a table similar to Table 2.3 could be used, by which calculations could be avoided altogether. However, a precondition of this table is the control of the relative pressure steps during the measurements which depends on the varying saturation pressure p_0, and thus on the atmospheric pressure and the purity of the nitrogen bath.

In the resulting cumulative pore radius distribution the final value of the curve is the cumulative surface area. From the cumulative pore radius distribution the differential distribution is derived by differentiation of the curve, which may be carried out goemetrically by pointwise measuring of the slope. A survey is presented in Figs. 4.21–4.23.

Apart from the volume, the pore surface area or the pore length can be used as a measure of frequency[77]. The frequency curves $f_V(r)$, $f_S(r)$, and $f_L(r)$ can be converted one into the other. By integration one obtains from a specific frequency curve the corresponding summation curve:

$$\beta(r) = \int h(r) \, dr \qquad (4.38)$$

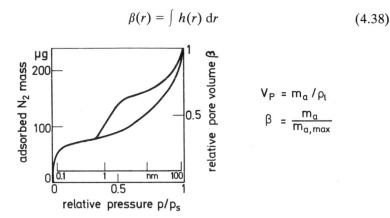

$$V_P = m_a / \rho_l$$

$$\beta = \frac{m_a}{m_{a,max}}$$

Fig. 4.21   Nitrogen isotherm at 77 K on Al_2O_3

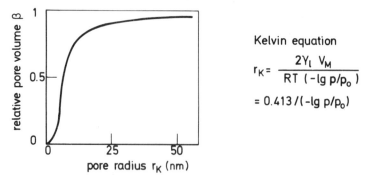

Kelvin equation

$$r_K = \frac{2\gamma_l \, V_M}{RT \, (-\lg p/p_0)}$$

$$= 0.413 / (-\lg p/p_0)$$

Fig. 4.22   Cumulative pore radius distribution

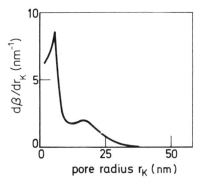

Fig. 4.23   Pore radius frequency

The value of the most frequent pore radius depends on which of the three frequency curves is considered. This quantity is defined by

$$\bar{r} = \frac{2V_s}{S} \tag{4.39}$$

where V_s = the specific pore volume related to unit sample mass, and S = the specific surface area. V_s can be derived from the maximum mass or volume adsorbed at saturation pressure. The calculation of the porosity is described in Chapter 2.

Computerized computation

Calculations of both the specific surface area and the pore size distribution can be carried out by means of a computer, a programmable pocket calculator being sufficient. As regards the calculation of the pore size distribution, methods based on Wheeler's[5] work are suitable for the numeric calculation. Cranston and Inkley[78], de Boer, Broekhoff, Linsen, and Lippens[34,47], Jäntti, Kankare, and Penttinen[70,79,80,81], Brunauer, Bodor, Mikhail, Odler, and Skalny[38,46,52,82] and others improved and modified this method with respect to the pore shapes and more sophisticated adsorption theories. To give an example of such a computer program, that of Philips and Skalny[83], which is based on the 'modelless method', is presented in Tables 4.5 and 4.6. Jäntti[80] presented a program which permits mixtures of cylindrical and slit-shaped pores to be calculated and which may be useful if the shape is ascertained in another way, e.g. by electron microscopy.

Büchner *et al.*[84–86] worked out extensive frame programs incorporating the Cranston/Inkley and the modelless method. The structural diagram, coding sheet, plotted isotherm, BET diagram, *t*-curve, the distribution curves, and the table of results are shown in Figs. 4.24 to 4.30 and Table 4.7.

Additional methods are discussed in Section 9.5.

192

Table 4.5 FORTRAN program for the computation of the pore size distribution on the basis of the 'modelless method' according to Philips and Skalny

THE PROGRAM

```
        DIMENSION TCUR(18),VVAL(18),X(18),SUR(18),VCOR(18),RADH(18)
        DIMENSION SCU(18),RPP(18),RCP(18),VCP(18),SCP(18)

        READ (0,1) MW,DADS,TEM,ST,(TCUR(I),I=2,18),(VVAL(I),I=1,17)
    1 FORMAT (F6.2,F7.4,F6.1,F6.2,17F6.2,17F7.4)

        K=1.92096E4*TEM*DADS/(ST*MW)
        CX=.02
        X(1)=1.00

        WRITE(1,2)
        WRITE(1,3)
    2 FORMAT (10/,48HCOMPLETE PORE VOLUME AND SURFACE ANALYSIS USING,
        /26H    ADSORPTION – WIDE PORES,3/,7HSAMPLE:,22X,7HBRANCH:,4/,
        16HCORE PROPERTIES:/)
    3 FORMAT (63H    GROUP    PRESSURE    CORE     CORE    CORE VOLUME
        CORE SURFACE/60H                       OF     RANGE    RADIUS      (ML/G)
        (SQ.M/G)/63H  PORES    (P/PS)   (ANG)    GROUP    CUMUL
        GROUP    CUMUL/)

    200    DO 240 I=1,16
        IF(I.EQ.6) CX=.05
        X(I+1)=X(I)–CX
        DV=VVAL(I)–VVAL(I+1)
        DT=(TCUR(I)–TCUR(I+1))*1E–4
        RADH(I)=2E4/(K*(–ALOG10(X(I)*X(I+1))))
        IF(I–1)210,210,220
    210 VCOR(I)=DV
        GOT0230
    220 VCOR(I)=DV–DT*SCU(I–1)
```

```
230 SUR(I)=VCOR(I)*1E4/RADH(I)
    VCUM=VCUM+VCOR(I)
    SCUM=SCUM+SUR(I)
    SCU(I)=SCUM
    IF(I.EQ.1) GOTO240
    IF(VCOR(I).LE.O) GOTO300
240 WRITE(1.4) I.X(I).X(I+1).RADH(I),VCOR(I),VCUM,SUR(I),SCUM
  4 FORMAT (4X.I2.3X.F4.2.1H-.F4.2,4X,F5.1,3X,2(F6.4,2X),1X,2(2X,F6.2)

    WRITE(1.5)
    WRITE(1.6)
  5 FORMAT (4/.16HPORE PROPERTIES:,2/60HGROUP   PARALLEL PLATE PORES
                    CYLINDRICAL PORES)
  6 FORMAT (71H NO.    RADIUS VOLUME CUMUL         RADIUS  VOLUME  CUMUL
SURFACE    CUMUL/72H              (ANG) (ML/G) VOLUME    (ANG)  (ML/G)
VOLUME  (SQ.M/G)  SURFACE/)

300 L=I-1
310 DO 320 I=1,L
    AVT=(TCUR(I+1)+TCUR(I+2))/2.
    RPP(I)=RADH(I)+AVT
    VPP=VCOR(I)*RPP(I)/RADH(I)
    VCUMPP=VCUMPP+VPP
    RCP(I)=RADH(I)+AVT*.5
    VCP(I)=VCOR(I)*(RCP(I)/RADH(I))**2
    VCUMCP=VCUMCP+VCP(I)
    SCP(I)=SUR(I)*RCP(I)/RADH(I)
    SCUMCP=SCUMCP+SCP(I)
320 WRITE(1.7) I.RPP(I).VPP.VCUMPP,RCP(I),VCP(I),VCUMCP,SCP(I),SCUMCP
  7 FORMAT (1X.I2.2(4X.F5.1.2(1X,F6.4),3X),2(1X,F6.2,2X))
```

```
      WRITE(1,8)
    8 FORMAT (4/,48HDISTRIBUTION RESULTS ASSUMING CYLINDRICAL PORES:,2/,
     10X,54HAVERAGE RADIUS        DELTA S/DELTA R      DELTA V/DELTA R/
     14X,5H(ANG),12X,12H(SQ.M/G/ANG),8X,10H(ML/G/ANG)/)

  400    DO 410 I=2,L
         RAV=(RCP(I-1)+RCP(I))/2.
         DR=RCP(I-1)-RCP(I)
         DSDR=SCP(I)/DR
         DVDR=VCP(I)/DR
  410 WRITE(1,9) RAV,DSDR,DVDR
    9 FORMAT (14X,F5.1,15X,F5.2,14X,F7.5)

      STOP
      END
```

Table 4.6   List of variables used in Table 4.5

AVT	Average t-curve value for a core group, in Å
DADS	Density of adsorbate at TEM, in g/cm^3
DR	Change in hydraulic radius, in Å
DSDR	Average surface area of a core group, in m^2/g
DVDR	Average volume of a core group, in ml/g
DV	Change in volume of a core group, in ml/g
DT	Change in t-curve values of a core group, in Å
K	Constant for adsorbate, $\dfrac{2.303 \, R*TEM*DADS}{ST*MW}$
MW	Molecular weight of adsorbate
R	Universal gas constant, in $(dyne/cm)/mole$ K
RADH	Hydraulic radius of the core group, in Å
RAV	Average hydraulic radius of a core group, in Å
RCP	Hydraulic radius of cylindrical pores, in Å
RPP	Hydraulic radius of parallel-plate pores, in Å
SCP	Surface area of cylindrical pores, in m^2/g
SCU, SCUM	Cumulative surface area of the core groups, in m^2/g
SCUMCP	Cumulative surface area of cylindrical pores, in m^2/g
ST	Surface tension of liquid adsorbate, in $dyne/cm$
SUR	Surface area of a core group, in m^2/g
TCUR	t-curve values at appropriate pressure leads, in Å
TEM	Temperature of adsorption, in K
VCOR	Corrected volume of a core group, in ml/g
VCP	Volume of cylindrical pores, in ml/g
VCUM	Cumulative volume of the core groups, in ml/g
VCUMCP	Cumulative volume of cylindrical pores, in ml/g
VCUMPP	Cumulative volume of parallel-plate pores, in ml/g
VPP	Volume of parallel-plate pores, in ml/g
VVAL	Volume input from the isotherm, in ml/g
X	Relative pressure, p/p_0, of a core group

Table 4.7   Results of a pore size and surface area analysis of Al_2O_3

initial mass of sample	25.27 mg
mass decrease within 30 min at 10^{-3} Pa, 298 K	1.50 mg
mass decrease within 30 min at 10^{-3} Pa, 425 K	8.76 mg
mass decrease within 30 min at 10^{-3} Pa, 475 K	5.18 mg
mass of degassed sample, m	9.83 mg
density of degassed sample, δ	3.68 g cm^{-3}
maximum amount of sorbate, m_a^{max}	5.26 mg
pore volume, V_1	6.5 mm^3
specific pore volume, V_s	0.66 cm^3 g^{-1}
porosity, P	0.71
mean pore radius, r_m	2.9 nm
most frequent pore radius, r_f	2.6 nm
amount of N_2 monolayer sorbate at 77.6 K, m_m	1.32 mg
surface area of sample, S_m	4.59 m^2
specific surface area, S_s	466 m^2 g^{-1}

196

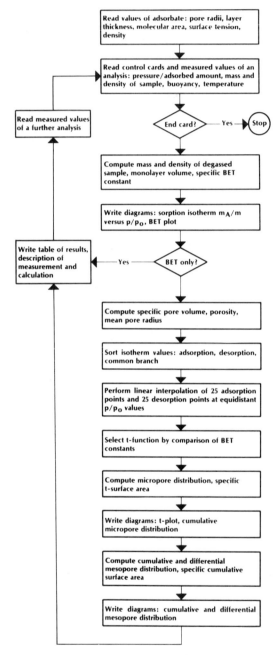

Fig. 4.24   Flow chart for the electronic evaluation
of adsorption isotherms

Specific Surface Area and Pore Size Distribution						
1	Name	Tel.	Date	year	month	day
2	Sample designation					
3	Measurement No.	Account				
4	Sorptiv: Nitrogen	0 Krypton	1 Other:			
5	Initial mass (g)					
6	Degassing time (h)	pressure (Pa)	mass loss (g)			
	" "	"	"			
	" "	"	"			
	" "	"	"			
7	Density (g cm^{-3}): sample	counterweight				
8	Buoyancy measured with nitrogen (μg $\cdot$ Pa^{-1})					
9	Temperature (K): ambient	thermostat				
10	BET only	0 model-less	1 Kelvin	2 Cohen	3	
	Cranston/Inkley: cylinder	4 deBoer: slit	5			
11	Begin of hysteresis loop (Pa)					
12	Remarks:					

Fig. 4.25   Coding sheet for data processing of the measured isotherm

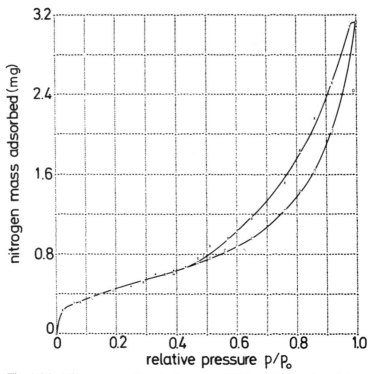

Fig. 4.26 Nitrogen sorption isotherm at 77 K on Al_2O_3 plotted by a computer

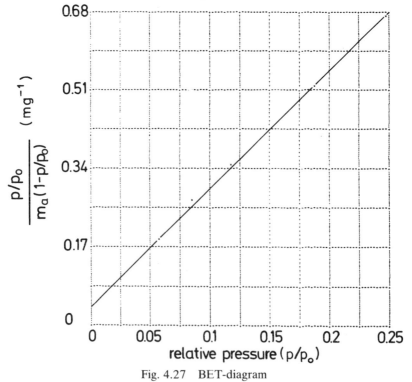

Fig. 4.27 BET-diagram

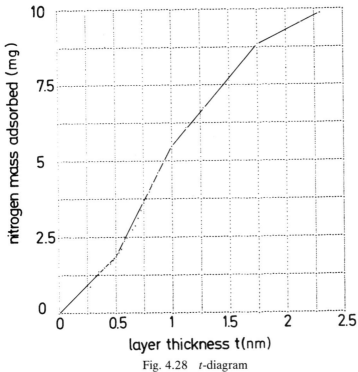

Fig. 4.28 t-diagram

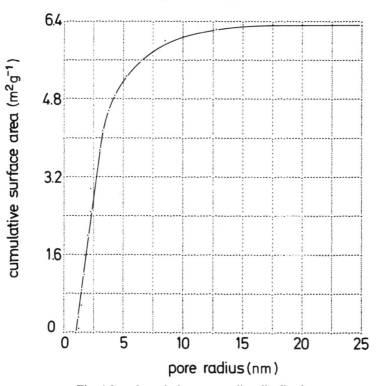

Fig. 4.29   Cumulative pore radius distribution

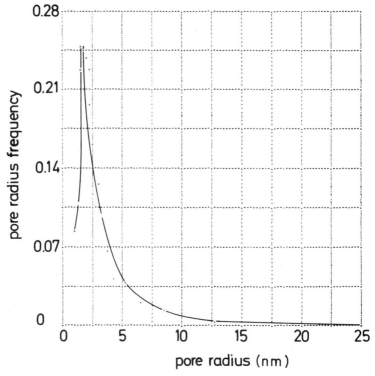

Fig. 4.30 Differential pore radius frequency

4.4 Pore structure analysis from caloric data

Besides the possibility of determining isotherms by calorimetric measurements and calculating the pore size distribution from the isotherm, there exist
certain direct relationships between caloric data of the saturation of a condensate with the pore size. The curvature of the surface in a pore is connected
with changes of the triple point temperature, the freezing point temperature,
and the heat of solidification. These relationships constitute the basis of a
calorimetric method for the pore size distribution in the mesopore region
proposed by Eyraud[87-89]. A typical thermogram obtained when cooling down
a porous sample immersed in liquid slightly above the triple point is shown in
Fig. 4.31. The peak 1 is due to the normal solidification of the excess liquid in
multiple layers at the outer surface of the solid sample. The second broader
peak 2 is produced by the phase transformation in pores of various diameters
and associated with the cavity radius and not with the neck radius. Starting
from the Gibbs–Duhem relation, Eyraud derived a relation between the
temperature decrease of the triple point and the pore radius:

$$\Delta T = -2 \int_0^{\gamma_{sl}/r_c} \frac{V_l}{\Delta s_f} d\left(\frac{\gamma_{sl}}{r_c}\right) \qquad (4.40)$$

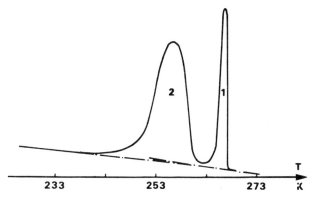

Fig. 4.31   Calorimeter thermogram obtained when cooling
down a porous sample immersed in a liquid slightly above
the triple point. Peak 1: solidification of the excess liquid.
Peak 2: solidification of the liquid. (Courtesy C. Eyraud)

where ΔT is the difference of the regular triple point temperature and that in
a pore with a core radius r_c, that is the pore radius minus the thickness of layer
not taking part in the solidification process; γ_{sl} is the free energy of the
extension of the solid/liquid interphase; $s_f = s_l - s_s$ is the change of the
entropy of fusion. Experimental results with water and benzene are shown in
Fig. 4.32. Another expression can be derived for the change of the entropy of
fusion; experimental and theoretical results are shown in Fig. 4.33.

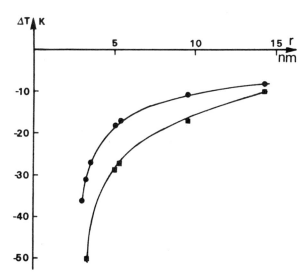

Fig. 4.32   Decrease of the triple point as a function of
the core radius of pores; ● water, ■ benzene. (Courtesy
C. Eyraud)

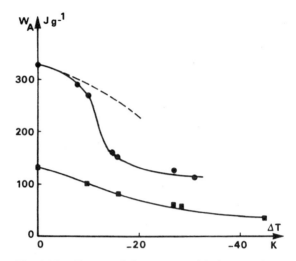

Fig. 4.33 Change of the entropy of fusion as a function of triple point decrease (compare Fig. 4.32); ● water, ■ benzene, – – – theoretical curve. (Courtesy C. Eyraud)

With regard to the more suitable relation between triple point and pore radius, benzene should be used for this method of pore size determination. The operation is as follows. The evaporated porous sample (about 2 g) is placed in a microcalorimeter and is saturated by condensation of the vapour or by immersion in the liquid. Subsequently a thermogram is measured decreasing the temperature linearly. The thermogram (1) drafted in Fig. 4.34 is evaluated to derive the pore radius range by means of the calibration curve

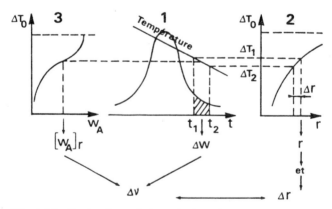

Fig. 4.34 Evaluation of the calorimetric measured thermogram (1) from Fig. 4.31 using the calibration curve (2) from Fig. 4.32 and determination of the respective pore volume as a function of the core radius. (Courtesy C. Eyraud)

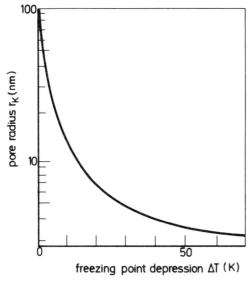

Fig. 4.35 Freezing point depression as a function of the Kelvin radius of pores. (Courtesy Fagerlund)

(2) taken from Fig. 4.32. The dashed region below the curve of the thermogram corresponds to the energy set free by the solidification. Using the calibration curve (3) depicted in Fig. 4.34, the apparent fusion energy per unit liquid volume is determined, and the respective volume of the pores and the cumulative volume calculated.

Fagerlund[90] used the freezing point depression of water for pore size determination. A semi-empirical equation

$$r_K = -\frac{2\sigma_{lg}}{\rho_l \Delta H} \cdot \frac{M}{\ln\left(\dfrac{T_0 - \Delta T}{T_0}\right)} \tag{4.41}$$

gives a relation between the Kelvin radius r_K and the freezing point depression ΔT from the regular freezing temperature T_0, with σ_{lg} the interfacial tension of the liquid/gas interface, ΔH the molar heat of fusion, ρ_l the density of the liquid, and M its molecular mass. This relation is drafted in Fig. 4.35. The measurement can be carried out using ordinary difference calorimeters ranging to 240 K in the usual DTA-techniques.

Powers and Brownyard[91] used the expansion of the frozen water of about 9% for the determination of the freezing point depression. They crushed the sample (Portland cement paste) into granules which were saturated with water. The granules were put in a glass bulb and frozen to 195 K by means of a

204

solids CO_2/alcohol cooling mixture and subsequently slowly heated. The expansion curve of the ice/water was measured by observing the level of a toluene columns in a calibrated capillary on the top of the sample bulb. The authors found a hysteresis between ice formation and melting.

References

1. S. Brunauer, *Adsorption of Gases and Vapors*, Ch. 11, Princeton University Press, Princeton, 1943.
2. P. H. Emmett, Chemisorption and Catalysis, in: *Symposium on Properties of Surfaces*, ASTM Special Technical Publication No. 340, 1963, p. 42.
3. A. V. Kiselev, *Gas Chromatography 1962*, Butterworths, London, 1962, p. 34.
4. R. Sh. Mikhail, L. E. Copeland and S. Brunauer, *Can. J. Chem.*, **42**, 426 (1964).
5. A. Wheeler, *Advan. Catalysis*, **3**, 250 (1951)
6. H. L. Ritter and L. C. Drake, *Ind. Eng. Chem. Anal. Ed.*, **17**, 782 (1945)
7. R. Sh. Mikhail, S. Brunauer and E. E. Bodor, *J. Colloid and Interface Sci.*, **26**, 45 (1968)
8. R. Sh. Mikhail, S. Brunauer and E. E. Bodor, *J. Colloid and Interface Sci.*, **26**, 54 (1968)
9. E. W. Washburn, *Proc. Nat. Acad. Sci.*, **7**, 115–116 (1921)
10. L. C. Drake, *Ind. Eng. Chem.*, **41**, 780 (1949)
11. C. Orr, Jr., *Powder Technology*, **3**, 117 (1969/70)
12. H. M. Rootare, *Aminco Isb. News* (24) 3:4A–4A, Fall, 1968
13. L. A. de Wit and J. J. F. Scholter, *J. Catalysis*, **36**, 36 (1975)
14. R. J. Good and R. Sh. Mikhail, *Powder Technology* (in press)
15. N. Pernicone: Recommendations for Mercury Porosimetry Measurements for the BCR Working Group, Particulate Materials. European Communities, Brussels 1980
16. D. N. Winslow, *J. Colloid Interface Sci.*, **67**, 42 (1978)
17. A. P. Karnaukhov, *Kinetika Kataliz*, **8**, 172 (1967)
18. E. W. Washburn and E. N. Bunting, *J. Am. Ceram. Soc.*, **5**, 48–51 (1922)
19. R. P. Mayer and R. A. Stowe, *J. Colloid Sci.*, **20**, 893 (1965)
20. D. H. Everett, G. D. Parfitt, K. S. H. Sing and R. Wilson; *J. appl. Chem. Biotechnol.* **24**, 199 (1974)
21. E. Robens, *Technisches Messen*, 369 (1980)
22. K. K. Unger, *Porous Silica* (*J. of Chromatography Library*, Bd. 16), Elsevier, Amsterdam, 1979, S. 23, 37–39
23. B. Rasneur, G. Schnedecker and J. Charpin, *Silicates Industriels*, 165 (1972)
24. W. Libal and R. Hausner, *Berichte der Deutschen Kermischen Gesellschaft*, **50**, 8, 35 (1973)
25. L. Žagar, *Archiv f. Eisenhüttenwesen*, **26**, 561 (1955)
26. L. Žagar, *Archiv f. Eisenhüttenwesen*, **27**, 657 (1956)
27. L. Žagar, *Berichte Deutsche Keram. ges.*, **35**, 294 (1958)
28. L. Žagar, *Silicates Industriels*, **24**, 306 (1959)
29. W. Fischer and D. Jahn; *Meßtechnik*, 309 (1968)
30. N. F. Astbury, *Trans. Brit. Ceram. Soc.*, **67**, 319 (1968) and *Ber. Dt. Keram. Ges.*, **49**, 52 (1972)
31. D. G. Beech, *Trans. Brit. Ceram. Soc.*, **70**, 87 (1971)
32. A. P. Karnaukhov, in: S. Modry (ed.) *Pore Structure and Properties of Materials*, Pt. 1, A. S., Academia, Prague, 1973
33. S. J. Gregg and K. S. W. Sing, *Adsorption, Surface Area and Porosity*, Academic Press, London and New York, 1967
34. J. C. P. Broekhoff and B. G. Linsen, in: B. G. Linsen, (ed.), *Physical and*

Chemical Aspects of Adsorbents and Catalysts, Academic Press, London and New York, 1970, p. 1
35. D. Dollimore and G. R. Heal, *J. Colloid Interface Sci.*, **42**, 233 (1973)
36. A. Wheeler, in: P. H. Emmett (ed.), Catalysis Vol. 2, Reinhold, New York, 1955, p. 18
37. B. F. Roberts, *J. Colloid Interface Sci.*, **23**, 266 (1967)
38. S. Brunauer, R. Sh. Mikhail and E. E. Bodor, *J. Colloid Interface Sci.*, **24**, 451 (1967); **25**, 353 (1967).
39. A. V. Kiselev, *Usp. Khim.* (in Russian), **14**, 367 (1945).
40. G. L. Kington and P. S. Smith, *Trans. Faraday Soc.*, **60**, 705 (1964)
41. H. L. Kington and P. S. Smith, *Trans. Faraday Soc.*, **60**, 721 (1964)
42. P. H. Doe and J. M. Haynes, in: S. J. Gregg, K. S. W. Sing and H. F. Stoeckli (eds.), *Characterisation of Porous Solids*, Soc. of Chemical Industry, London, 1979, p. 253
43. D. H. Everett, in: S. J. Gregg, K. S. W. Sing and H. F. Stoeckli (eds.), *Characterisation of Porous Solids*; Soc. of Chemical Industry, London, 1979,
44. V. Ponec, Z. Knor and S. Černý, *Adsorption on Solids*, Butterworths, London, 1974
45. H. J. Juhola, *Kemia-Kemi*, **4**, 543, 653 (1977)
46. R. Sh. Mikhail, S. Brunauer and E. E. Bodoer, *J. Colloid Interface Sci.*, **26**, 45 (1968)
47. B. C. Lippens and J. H. de Boer, *J. Catalysis*, **4**, 319 (1965).
48. M. M. Dubinin, *Surface Area Determination*, Butterworths, London, 1970, p. 77
49. H. Marsh and B. Rand, *J. Colloid Interface Sci.*, **33**, 478 (1920)
50. M. M. Dubinin, in P. L. Walker, Jr. (ed.), *Chemistry and Physics of Carbon* Vol. 2, Arnold, London, 1966, p. 51
51. S. Brunauer, *J. Colloid and Interface Sci.*, **39**, 435 (1972)
52. S. Brunauer, J. Skalny and I. Odler, in: S. Modry (ed.), *Pore Structure and Properties of Materials* Pt. 1, C–3, Academia, Prague, 1973
53. M. M. Dubinin, General report, in; *S. Modrý, M. Svaté (eds.) Pore Structure and Properties of Materials*, Academia, Prague, 1974, p. C-5
54. M. M. Dubinin, *J. Colloid Interface Sci.*, **46**, 351 (1974)
55. R. Sh. Mikhail and T. El-Akkad, *J. Colloid Interface Sci.*, **51**, 260 (1975)
56. R. Sh. Mikhail and F. A. Shebl, *J. Colloid Interface Sci.*, **32**, 505 (1970)
57. R. Sh. Mikhail and F. A. Shebl, *J. Colloid Interface Sci.*, **34**, 65 (1970)
58. R. Sh. Mikhail, S. Nashed and A. M. Khalil, *Disc. Faraday soc.*, No. 52, p. 187 (1971)
59. R. Sh. Mikhail, S. Nashed and A. M. Khalil, *Surface Techn.*, **7**, 45 (1978) (1977)
60. R. Sh. Mikhail, S. Nashed, and A. M. Khalil, *Surface Techn.*, **7**, 45 (1978)
61. R. Sh. Mikhail, A. M. Youssef and T. El-Nabarawy, *J. Colloid Interface Sci.*, **70**, 467 (1970)
62. R. Sh. Mikhail, S. A. Abo-El-Enein and S. Hanafi, Paper Presented Before the 7th International Congress on Chemistry of Cement, Paris, June 29–July 4, 1980.
63. D. Dollimore and G. R. Heal, *Trans. Faraday Soc.*, **59**, 189 (1963)
64. D. Dollimore and T. Shingles, *J. Colloid Interface Sci.*, **29**, 601 (1969)
65. A. N. Ainscough, D. Dollimore and G. R. Heal, *Carbon*, **11**, 189 (1973)
66. D. Dollimore and A. Turner, *Trans. Faraday Soc.*, **66**, 2655 (1970)
67. D. Dollimore and G. R. Heal, *Nature* (London), **208**, 1092 (1965)
68. D. Dollimore and G. R. Heal, *Surface Technol.*, **6**, 231 (1978)
69. A. J. Juhola, Structure and adsorption data on PCC and competitive activated carbons; Report No. 400 S9; Pittsburgh Coke and Chemical Company, 1951
70. O. Jäntti, *22nd National Symposium of the American Vacuum Society*, 1975; *J. Vacuum Sci. Techn.*, **13**, 475 (1976)

206

71. S. J. Gregg and J. Langford, *Trans. Faraday Soc.*, **65**, 601 (1969)
72. F. Stoeckli and R. Pressl-Wenger; *Bull. Soc. neuchâteloise des Sciences naturelles*, **101**, 139 (1978)
73. M. Polanyi, *Verh. Dtsch Phys. Ges.*, **16**, 1012 (1914) *Trans. Faraday Soc.*, **28**, 316 (1932).
74. M. M. Dubinin, *2nd Carbon and Graphite Conf.*, Soc. of Chemical Industry, London, 1958, p. 219.
75. E. Robens, G. Robens and G. Sandstede, *Vacuum*, **13**, 303 (1963)
76. J. Rouquerol, Recommendations for the Nitrogen adsorption measurements of the BCR, Brussels, 1980
77. E. Robens and G. Sandstede, *Z. Instrumentenkunde*, **75**, 167 (1967)
78. R. W. Cranston and F. A. Inkley, *Adv. in Catalysis*, **9**, 143 (1957)
79. J. Kankare, O. Jäntti, *Suomen Kemistilethi*, **B40**, 50 (1967)
80. O. Jäntti and M. Penttinen, *Suomen Kemistilethi*, **B43**, 239 (1970)
81. E. Eckman, O. Jäntti and J. Ranta; Report No. 17; Reports of Fuel and Lubricant Research Laboratory of Technical Research Center of Finland (1978)
82. R. Sh. Mikhail, S. A. Selim and A. Goned, *Egypt J. Chem.*, **118**, 5, 957 (1975)
83. J. C. Philips and J. P. Skalny, *Pacific Conference on Chemistry and Spectroscopy*, Anaheim, California, 1971
84. M. Büchner and E. Robens, in: T. Gast and E. Robens (eds.) *Progress in Vacuum Microbalance Techniques*, Vol. 1, Heyden, London, 1972, p. 333
85. M. Büchner, E. Robens and R. Sh. Mikhail in *Progress in Vacuum Microbalance Techniques*, Vol. 3 C. Eyraud and M. Escoubes (eds.), Heyden, London, 1975, p. 324
86. M. Büchner, R. Sh. Mikhail and E. Robens, *Vakuum-Technik.*, **8**, 227 (1975)
87. C. G. Litvan and C. Eyraud, in: S. Modrý and M. Swatá (eds.) *Pore Structure and Properties of Materials*, Vol. IV; Academie, Prague, 1974, p. C-215, 219
88. C. Eyraud, M. Brun, L. Eyraud, A. Lallemand and P. Eyraud, *C. R. Acad. Sc. Paris*, **273**(B), 645 (1971)
89. C. Eyraud, M. Brun, A. Lallemand, J. Quinson and L. Eyraud, in: S. Modrý and M. Swata (eds.), *Pore Structure and Properties of Materials*, Vol. I Academia, Prague, 1973, p. C-81
90. G. Fagerlund, *Matériaux et constructions*, **6**, 215 (1973)
91. T. C. Powers and T. L. Brownyard: Physical properties of cement-paste. Res. Labs. Portland Cement Ass. Bulletin No. 22, Chicago, 1948

Part 2

Chemistry of Solid Surfaces

Introduction to Part 2

The chemical nature of surface functional groups is largely responsible for determining the types of interaction which exist at the interface, and these in turn have an important influence on the practical use of the solid in specific applications. Thus, for example, the adsorption process depends on the interplay of molecular forces at the interface. The dispersion of powder in paint initially involves the breakdown of aggregates of particles which are held together by interparticulate bonds. The strength of bonds will depend to a great extent on the nature of surface groups. The bonding of surfactants with pigment and filler particles, and the bonding of water with cement particles also influences the rheological properties of paint dispersion and the rheological properties of cement slurries.

The term 'surface' can mean different things to different investigators. To the chemist interested in heterogeneous catalysis, the surface may well mean the outermost monolayer of atoms where the chemical reactions of interest occur. To the physicist interested in semiconductor surface electrical properties, the term can include the whole space-charge region to a depth hundreds of nanometers units into the bulk. In a general sense, however, the word 'surface' may be used to designate that region of a solid lattice near its termination, in which the chemical, structural, and electronic properties of the material differ from those in the bulk solid.

A schematic view is presented by Hagstrum et al.[1] of a planar cut parallel to the surface normal into a crystalline solid. This is shown in Fig. 1, and it

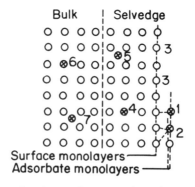

Fig. 1 Schematic diagram showing a planar cut into the near surface region of a crystalline solid. Deviation of atomic position from the bulk lattice position is used to differentiate selvedge from bulk. Two specific monolayers at the surface are designated. Foreign atoms in various positions are shown as cross-hatched circles. Atoms in positions 1 and 2 are adsorbed to the crystal surface, atoms in position 3 absorbed or incorporated into the surface monolayer, atoms in position 3 absorbed or incorporated into the surface monolayer, atoms in positions 4 and 6 substitutionally absorbed, atoms in positions 5 and 7 interstitially absorbed into selvedge and bulk, respectively (after Hagstrum, Rowe, and Tracy[1])

suggests a depth profile of the deviation of atomic position from the bulk lattice site positions extrapolated into the surface regions. The term 'selvedge' was suggested by Wood[2] for that near-surface region over which relative atomic positions deviate from those specified by the bulk lattice. In Fig. 1 specific planes at the surface of a solid are identified. The outermost layer of the lattice is termed the surface monolayer, while the layer of adsorbed foreign atoms is designated the adsorbate monolayer. The surface positions of atoms may differ appreciably from the positions of corresponding atoms in the bulk. Adsorption of foreign atoms at a surface opens up a whole new set of surface structural possibilities. Various positions that a foreign atom can occupy on a surface, in the selvedge, or in the bulk are also illustrated in Fig. 1. Several kinds of local structure that a foreign atom might assume relative to the host lattice are shown in Fig. 2. Each such local surface complex or surface molecule can be associated with specific repeat pattern on the surface. Sorbed atoms shown in Fig. 2 could also be constituents of a free-space molecule adsorbed in its entirety to the surface.

We are, however, interested in a more detailed identification of the surface properties of a solid that can be given by the depth profiles of planar averages we have been discussing. Thus the surface electronic structure is profoundly modified by the presence of foreign atoms adsorbed to or incorporated into the surface monolayer, or present in one position or another in the selvedge. The nature of the modification of electronic structure depends on the strength of interaction. The surface functional groups as well as the type of interaction between these functional groups and foreign molecules can be identified by both chemical and physical tools. Chapter 5 will deal with the first of these two topics, namely the determination of the surface functional groups by chemical means, as well as their reactions with specific reagents, while Chapter 6 will be more concerned with their identification by physical tools, mainly through spectroscopic studies.

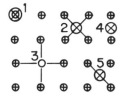

Fig. 2 Schematic illustration of various lateral positions that a foreign sorbed atom may occupy at a crystal surface. The substrate atoms are indicated by open circles, the sorbed atom by cross-hatched circles. The sorbed atom's position normal to the surface is indicated by the size of the circle: larger than that of the host lattice atom if it lies in an adsorbate monolayer above the surface monolayer as at positions 1, 2, 4, 5; same size as that of the host lattice atom if it is incorporated into the surface monolayer as at position 3. Bulk lattice positions are indicated by + to emphasize possible lateral displacements of surface atoms as at 5. Designating the atom of the host lattice as M and the foreign atom as X, the chemical composition of the surface complexes shown may with varying degrees of approximation be indicated as 1: MX; 2,3 M_4X; 4,5:M_2X (after Hagstrum, Rowe and Tracy[1])

References

1. H. D. Hagstrum, I. E. Rowe, and J. C. Tracy, in: R. B. Anderson and P. T. Dawson (eds.), *Experimental Methods in Catalytic Research*, Vol. 3, Ch. 2, Academic Press, New York, San Francisco, London, 1976.
2. E. A. Wood, *J. Appl. Phys.*, **15**, 1306 (1964)

Chapter 5

Solid Surfaces and their Characterization by Chemical Means

Many solids, especially oxides, mixed oxides, carbons, and clay minerals, are described as having functional groups on their surfaces that govern many of their behaviour during application. Many of these functional groups show acidic character and/or basic character, and this character is thought to be localized at specific sites. Therefore, in dealing with the surface chemistry of solid surfaces, qualitative as well as quantitative description of these sites (the two are not always independent), cannot be avoided. A sizable fraction of this chapter will be devoted therefore to measurement of surface acidity and/or basicity, and this treatment will be followed by description of the reactions of surface functional groups with specific reagents.

It is generally accepted that the strengths of these sites are heterogeneous, although their quality, for example for acid sites, whether they are Lewis or Bronsted acids is still a matter of debate. Other concepts for surface acidity, besides Lewis and Bronsted sites, have also been expressed. Some have questioned whether the active sites are simply acid sites or whether basic sites might not also be important. Actually the concept of localized sites is too specific and a simpler concept of patches of surface with characteristic force fields would be more realistic.

A range of expected values has developed for the density and strength of these sites on various solid surfaces. For example, with silica-alumina cracking catalysts values around 10^{12}–10^{14} sites/cm^2 of surface have been estimated for acid sites. The fraction of the total surface area covered by active sites can be estimated by assuming a cross-sectional area for a probe molecule and multiplying it by the chemisorption capacity of the surface for that molecule. Using 0.2 nm^2/site as an estimate for the area of an average acid site, for example, surfaces with 10^{12}–10^{14} sites/cm^2 have between 0.2 and 20% of their surfaces covered with acid sites. Obviously these are empirical estimates. There is, however, a theoretical upper limit for the density of acid sites, which is the reciprocal of the cross-sectional area of the probe molecule.

The different experimental methods used for measurement of both surface acidity and surface basicity of solids will be presented in this chapter, and are grouped in terms of techniques used rather than the more conventional grouping in terms of the probe molecules used[1]. This procedure provides more information on the experimental methods and techniques used, with a trial to provide means of interpretation of data as well.

There are many definitions of acids and bases in the literature, notably

Table 5.1   Solid acids

1. Natural clay minerals: kaolinite, bentonite, attapulgite, montmorillonite, clarit, fuller's earth, zeolites.

2. Crafted acids: H_2SO_4, H_3PO_4, H_3BO_3, $CH_2(COOH)_2$ Crafted on silica, quartz sand, alumina or diatomaceous earth

3. Cation exchange resins

4. Mixtures of oxides: $SiO_2 \cdot Al_2O_3$, $B_2O_3 \cdot Al_2O_3$, $Cr_2O_3 \cdot Al_2O_3$, $MoO_3 \cdot Al_2O_3$, $ZrO_2 \cdot SiO_2$, $Ga_2O_3 \cdot SiO_2$, $BeO_2 \cdot SiO_2$, $MgO \cdot SiO_2$, $CaO \cdot SiO_2$, $SrO \cdot SiO_2$, $Y_2O_3 \cdot SiO_2$, $La_2O_3 \cdot SiO_2$, $SnO \cdot SiO_2$, $PbO \cdot SiO_2$, $MoO_3 \cdot Fe_2(MoO_4)_3$, $MgO \cdot B_2O_3$, $TiO_2 \cdot ZnO$

5. Inorganic chemicals: ZnO, Al_2O_3, TiO_2, CeO_2, As_2O_3, V_2O_5, SiO_2, Cr_2O_3, MoO_3, ZnS, CaS, $CaSO_4$, $MnSO_4$, $NiSO_4$, $CuSO_4$, $CoSO_4$, $CdSO_4$, $SrSO_4$, $ZnSO_4$, $MgSO_4$. $FeSO_4$, $BaSO_4$, $KHSO_4$, K_2SO_4, $(NH_4)_2SO_4$, $Al_2(SO_4)_3$, $Fe_2(SO_4)_3$, $Cr_2(SO_4)_3$, $Ca(NO_3)_2$, $Bi(NO_3)_3$, $Zn(NO_3)_2$, $Fe(NO_3)_3$, $CaCO_3$, BPO_4, $FePO_4$, $CrPO_4$, $Ti_3(PO_4)_4$, $Zr_3(PO_4)_4$, $Cu_3(PO_4)_2$, $Ni_3(PO_4)_2$, $AlPO_4$, $Zn_3(PO_4)_2$, $Mg_3(PO_4)_2$, $AlCl_3$, $TiCl_3$, $CaCl_2$, $AgCl$, $CuCl$, $SnCl_2$, CaF_2, BaF_2, $AgClO_4$, $Mg_2(ClO_4)_2$.

6. Charcoal heat-treated at 300 °C.

those of Arrhenius[2], Franklin[3], Bronsted[4], Germann[5], Lewis[6], Ussanowitch[7], Bjerum[8], Johnson[9], Lux, Flood and Forland, and Tomlinson[10], Shatenshtein[11], and Pearson[12]. We may strictly follow both the Bronsted and Lewis definitions, in which a solid acid shows a tendency to donate a proton or to accept an electron pair, whereas a solid base tends to accept a proton or to donate an electron pair. These definitions are adequate for an understanding of the acid–base phenomena shown by various solids. Tables 5.1 and 5.2 summarize a list of solid acids and bases as given by Tanabe[13]. Later sections

Table 5.2   Solid bases

1. Crafted bases: $NaOH$, KOH crafted on silica or alumina; alkali metal and alkaline earth metal dispersed on silica, alumina, carbon, K_2CO_3 or in oil; NR_3, NH_3, KNH_2 on alumina; Li_2CO_3 on silica.

2. Anion exchange resins

3. Mixtures of oxides: $SiO_2 \cdot Al_2O_3$, $SiO_2 \cdot MgO$, $SiO_2 \cdot CaO$, $SiO_2 \cdot SrO$, $SiO_2 \cdot BaO$

4. Inorganic chemicals: BeO, MgO, CaO, SrO, BaO, SiO_2, Al_2O_3, ZnO, Na_2CO_3, K_2CO_3, $KHCO_3$, $(NH_4)_2CO_3$, $CaCO_3$, $SrCO_3$, $BaCO_3$, $KNaCO_3$, $Na_2WO_4 \cdot 2H_2O$, KCN.

5. Charcoal heat-treated at 900 °C or activated with N_2O, NH_3, or $ZnCl_2$–NH_4Cl–CO_2

will describe the amount, strength, and nature of acid and base centres on various solid surfaces.

Special mention should perhaps be made of the fact that alumina, zinc oxide, and silica-alumina show both acidic and basic properties, which make them widely used in acid–base bifunctional catalysis.

5.1 Surface acidity

Evaluation of surface acidity on solid surfaces necessitates the determination of the acid strength, and the amount and nature (Bronsted or Lewis acid type) of the acid centres.

5.1.1 Acid strength

The acid strength of a solid surface is its ability to convert a neutral base adsorbed on the surface into its conjugate acid[14], and when the reaction proceeds by means of proton transfer from the surface to the adsorbate, the acid strength is expressed by the Hammett acidity function H_0[15]:

$$H_0 = - \log a_{H^+} f_B/f_{BH^+} \tag{5.1}$$

or

$$H_0 = pK_a + \log [B]/[BH^+] \tag{5.2}$$

where a_{H^+} is the proton activity, $[B]$ and $[BH^+]$ are respectively the concentration of the neutral base and its conjugate acid, and f_B and f_{BN^+} the corresponding activity coefficient.

At the equivalence point in a titration $[B]/[BH^+] = 1$ and $pK_a = H_0$. Therefore by titrating a single solid with a series of indicators (different pK_a values), one obtains an acid strength distribution in terms of H_0's.

Titration with adsorbed indicators in liquid media

To determine the acid strength, the titration should be carried in nonaqueous media, and this has frequently been referred to as the Benesi or Tamele method. It is based on Walling's analysis[14] of an adsorbed acid–base indicator interacting with acid sites on the surface.

The procedures used in these experiments have not changed very much since they were first described by Benesi[16,17]. In practice, the determination is made by placing about 0.2 ml of the sample in powder form in a test tube, and adding 2 ml of nonpolar solvent containing predetermined amounts of base. After a period for equilibration, an indicator is added (about 0.2 mg) that adsorbs on the catalyst surface and colours it with either the acid or base colour of the indicator. The slow step involves equilibration of the base with the surface acid sites. Bertolacini[18] developed a modification of the procedure that reduces the equilibrium time from hours to minutes.

Probably the most frequent source of error in these experiments comes from contamination with water, which should compete with the indicator and the other bases for the acid sites. For silica-alumina catalysts, for example, about 0.5% of water remains after it has been dried in air at about 600 °C. If all this water were associated with surface sites, and if the surface area is 300 m^2/g, this could account for 5×10^{13} sites/cm^2, a number remarkably close to values reported for the density of surface acid sites.

The endpoints in these titrations are generally detected visually, and thus it is difficult to titrate coloured solids. However, Voltz et al.[19] reported that if the coloured solid (catalyst) is mixed with a colourless reference solid, it is possible to determine the acidity of the coloured solid by difference. Particle size is an extremely important parameter, since it not only affects the equilibrium time but also affects the ease of seeing the different colours.

The precision expected in experiments of this type is of the order of 0.02 milli-equivalents per gram, or for a surface of 200 m^2/g about 6×10^{12} sites/cm^2.

Benzene and n-butylamine are solvent and base combinations of frequent use. Also iso-octane as a solvent has also been used with various bases such as ethylenediamine, quinoline, and pyridine. It is essential that the solvent be inert and that consideration be given to both the strength and stereochemistry of the base. Table 5.3 is a list of H_0 indicators.

The colour of the indicator adsorbed on the surface will give a measure of its acid strength. Thus if the colour is that of the acid form of the indicator, then the value of the H_0 function of the surface is equal to or lower than the pK_a of the indicator. Lower values of H_0, of course, correspond to greater acid

Table 5.3 H_0 indicators

Indicator	pK_a	Acid colour	Base colour
p-ethoxychrysoidin	+5.0	red	yellow
4-phenylazo-1-naphthalamine	+4.0	red	yellow
aminoazoxylene	+3.5	red	yellow
N,N-dimethyl-p-phenylazoaniline (butter yellow)	+3.3	red	yellow
2-amino-5-azotoluene	+2.0	red	yellow
1,4-diisopropylaminoanthraquinone	+1.7	red	blue
4-phenylazodiphenylamine	+1.5	violet	yellow
4-dimethylzoamino-azo-1-naphthalene	+1.2	purple	yellow
p-nitrobenzeneazo-(p'-nitro)-diphenylamine	+0.43	violet	orange
o-chloraniline	−0.17	colourless	
p-chloro-o-nitroaniline	−0.91	colourless	
dicinnamalacetone	−3.0	red	orange
benzalacetophenone (chalcone)	−5.6	yellow	colourless
anthraquinone	−8.2	yellow	colourless

Table 5.4 H_R indicators

4,4′,4″-trimethoxytriphenylmethanol	+0.82
4,4′,4″-trimethyltriphenylmethanol	−4.02
triphenylmethanol	−6.63
3,3′,3″-trichlorotriphenylmethanol	−11.03
diphenylmethanol	−13.3
4,4′,4″-trinitrophenylmethanol	−16.27
2,4,6-trimethylbenzyl alcohol	−17.38

strength. Thus for indicators undergoing colour changes in this way, the lower the pK_a, the greater is the acid strength of the solid. For example, a solid which gives a red colour with dicinnamalacetone ($pK_a = -3.0$), but is colourless with benzalacetophenone ($pK_a = -5.6$), has an acid strength H_0 which lies between -3.0 and -5.6. Also a solid having $H_0 \leqslant -8.2$ will change all indicators listed in Table 5.3 from the basic to the acid colours, whereas one which changed none of them would have an acid strength of $H_0 = +5.0$ or even less.

H_R indicators, which are series of allylalcohols that react with acids to form carbonium ions, are also available for acid strength determinations in certain specialized cases[20]. Table 5.4 contains a list of them. They are supposed to be specific for protonic acids.

The acid strengths of some solids determined by titration method are given in Table 5.5.

In determining the acid strength of solid surface, it would be highly desirable to measure the number of acid sites immediately after, for example by amine titration, and this will be discussed later in this chapter.

Table 5.5 Acid strength of some solids

Solid acids	H_0		Reference
original kaolinite	−3.0	−5.6	16
hydrogen kaolinite	−5.6	−8.2	16
original montmorillonite	+1.5	−3.0	16
hydrogen montmorillonite	−5.6	−8.2	16
$SiO_2 \cdot Al_2O_3$		−8.2	16
$Al_2O_3 \cdot B_2O_3$		−8.2	16
$SiO_2 \cdot MgO$	+1.5	−3.0	16
1.0 mmol/g H_3BO_3/SiO_2	+1.5	−3.0	16
1.0 mmol/g H_3PO_4/SiO_2	−5.6	−8.2	16
1.0 mmol/g H_2SO_4/SiO_2		−8.2	16
$NiSO_4 \cdot x\,H_2O$ heat-treated at 350 °C	+6.8	−3.0	13
$NiSO_4 \cdot x\,H_2O$ heat-treated at 460 °C	+6.8	+1.5	17
ZnS heat-treated at 300 °C	+6.8	+4.0	13
ZnS heat-treated at 500 °C	+6.8	+3.3	13
ZnO heat-treated at 300 °C	+6.8	+3.3	13
TiO_2 heat-treated at 400 °C	+6.8	+1.5	13

The course of titration can also be followed potentiometrically, in which case the solid powder is slurried in acetonitrile and titrated with n-butylamine, with a glass and a calomel electrode immersed in the slurry. The entire operation has been automated[21], but the disadvantage to the method is that the origin of the potentiometric signal is not well understood. Nevertheless, results using this method compare well with those using the H_0 indicators. In this case the magnitude of the potentiometric signals correspond to acid strengths.

Heat of immersion method

Another method is the measurement of heats of immersion, which is a calorimetric method described for solids in which the base was n-butylamine[22,23]. For pre-evacuated samples, sudden immersion of the solid in liquid n-butylamine liberates heat, which in this case is an integral heat of reaction. However, Zettlemoyer and Chessick[22,23] were able to get differential heats by pre-equilibrating samples of their solids with different amounts of n-butylamine before immersing them. The curves in Fig. 5.1 are differential heats of adsorption as a function of surface coverage. These curves reflect acid strength distributions. The curve K-2 shows an inflection at a surface coverage near 0.25. It shows a maximum near 0.35 and then drops off with higher coverage. The appearance of the maximum was attributed to the development of adsorbate–adsorbate interactions, which exceeds the decreasing heat of reaction between adsorbate and progressively weaker surface sites. Eventually the decreasing energies with the surface sites gained control

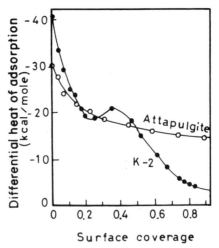

Fig. 5.1 Differential heat of adsorption at 25 °C for n-butylamine on a kaolin-pelletized catalyst K-2 and on attapulgite clay[23]

and the curve declined again. The entire energy distribution curve, from surface coverages around 0.2 and higher, was disturbed by adsorbate–adsorbate interactions.

Gas-phase adsorption methods

Adsorption of ammonia, as a base, has been used extensively to determine acid strengths. Although there are advantages to gas-phase methods for studying surface acidity, it seems that ammonia adsorption on acid sites is so strong that it is indiscriminate with regard to sites of different strengths. Since a base adsorbed on a strong acid site is more stable than one adsorbed on a weak acid site, it would be more difficult to desorb. Thus the proportion of adsorbed base evacuated at various temperatures can give a measure of acid strength.

Before any adsorption experiment, the solid should be pretreated to a 'clean' condition under vacuum. The surface can be cleaned to a reproducible condition of any volatile contamination either by evacuation or purging it with an inert gas. Also the surface area of the solid should be known corresponding to that pretreatment. The surface is then equilibrated with a predetermined amount of ammonia, and a desorption method is applied in which the proportion of adsorbed base evacuated at various temperatures is determined.

Numerous desorption methods have been used with ammonia, including:

1. Thermal desorption into a vacuum[24,25], in which the temperature of the sample was raised in increments, and the desorbed ammonia was collected at each temperature[25]. An alternative method was developed in which the rate of desorption was measured at two temperatures, and the rates at the two temperatures were extrapolated to a common surface coverage, and in this method an energy of activation for desorption can be calculated at that coverage[24].
2. Thermal desorption in a closed system[26], in which ammonia was desorbed in a closed system, and the pressure in the system increased.
3. Flash desorption into a carrier gas stream[27,28]. In this method ammonia is desorbed continuously into a helium stream which then passes into a thermal conductivity cell. The sample is heated according to a programmed rate, and an activation energy for desorption can be calculated from the shift in the characteristic desorption temperature as a function of heating rate.

The thermal desorption experiments into either a vacuum or a volume at ambient pressure were interpreted similarly. The adsorption capacities at low temperatures were taken as a measure of the total number of acid sites, while the adsorption capacities at high temperatures were taken as a measure of strong sites only. The general trend noticed in most of the data obtained is the wide range distribution in these sites[29].

218

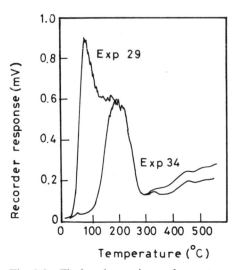

Fig. 5.2 Flash desorption chromatograms[28]. Experiment 29; evacuated before flashing 10 minutes at room temperature; $\beta = 16.03°/$minute. Experiment 34: evacuated before flashing 60 minutes at 100 °C; $\beta = 15.90°/$minute

Typical flash desorption chromatograms are shown in Figs. 5.2 and 5.3, for ethylene on alumina and for ammonia on alumina[28]. For ethylene on alumina there are two peaks corresponding to two sites with different adsorption energies, and when the sample was pre-evacuated at 100°C, the first peak disappeared. For ammonia, on the other hand, no peak resolution was obtained, and with successive evacuations at increasingly high temperatures, the result was simply to decrease the area under the peak and to shift its maximum to higher temperatures. The surface coverage for ammonia was about 10 times greater than for ethylene. Obviously for ethylene there were only two different energies, while for ammonia on the same surface, the heterogeneity in site energies was so great that the peaks all overlapped. It is the adsorbate–site interaction which determines the height of the peak, while the location of the peak was found to be affected by the rate of heating as well (cf. Eqn. (5.3)).

Equation (5.3) is suitable for the calculation of activation energies for adsorption (E_d) from the chromotogram. If the experiments are done at different heating rates β, and maximum peak temperature T_M, then

$$2 \log T_M - \log \beta = E_d/2.3 \, RT_M + \log E_d V_m/Rk_0 \qquad (5.3)$$

where R is the gas constant, V_m is the monolayer capacity for adsorbate, and k_0 is the temperature-independent part of the desorption rate constant. When the sites are heterogeneous, as in the case of ammonia, the T_M values must be for pretreated samples that have the same surface coverage.

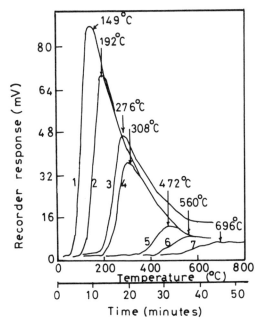

Fig. 5.3 Flash desorption chromatograms for different amounts of ammonia[28]. The rate of flashing was 15.2°/minute. Smoothed out chromatograms are reproduced for simplicity. Evacuation before flashing were made for 2.5 hours at the following temperatures: curve 1, 24 °C; curve 2, 75 °C; curve 3, 150 °C; curve 4, 175 °C; curve 5, 325 °C; curve 6, 400 °C; and curve 7, 500 °C

5.1.2 Amount of acid (acidity)

The amount of acid on a solid surface, commonly known as surface acidity, is expressed as the number of mmol of acid sites per unit weight or per unit surface area of the solid. Surface acidity can be measured by base titration either in liquid media or in the gaseous phase.

Titration methods in liquid media

Titration in aqueous solutions. When an acidic solid is slurried in water, the pH of the solution phase often decreases. The slurry, or a portion of the solution phase, may be titrated with a standard base solution. For non-coloured slurries an indicator technique can be used, while for coloured slurries a potentiometric method is used. An alternative method is to neutralize the acid sites by aqueous solution of potassium hydroxide as revealed by subsequent titration with hydrochloric acid. The disadvantages of this method are: (1) a strong alkali may attack other parts of the surface than the acid sites[13]; (2) a water molecule may react with a Lewis acid and so change the acidic properties of the surface; (3) a water molecule may react with an anhydrous substance causing error in the titration; (4) a solid with acid strength greater than that of an oxonium ion would be reduced by water molecules acting as strong base; and (5) the method fails completely if the solid is water-soluble.

Titration in nonaqueous solutions—Amine titration method. The method consists of titrating a solid suspended in benzene with *n*-butylamine, using p-dimethylamino-azobenzene as an indicator[30]. The indicator colour changes from yellow (basic) to red (acidic) when adsorbed on the solid acid. Thus the volume of *n*-butylamine required to restore the yellow colour gives a measure of the number of acid sites on the surface. The amount of acid traced by using this particular indicator ($pK_a = +3.3$) is actually the amount of those sites having acid strengths with $H_0 \leqslant +3.3$. Consequently the use of various indicators with different pK_a values provides a means of estimating the amounts of acid at various acid strength by amine titration. The method is suitable for the determination of the totality of both Bronsted and Lewis acid, since both electron pair acceptors and proton donors on the surface will react with either the electron pair ($-N=$) of the indicator or that of the amine ($\equiv N$:) to form a coordination bond.

The method has been extended by Johnson[31] to include the use of carbon tetrachloride and iso-octane as solvents, and benzylamine as the titrating base. A drop of 0.05N trichloroacetic acid in benzene was added to minimize the adsorption of amine on the nonacidic portions of the surface.

However, the titration by this method is slow and might take two or three days if the amine is added drop by drop. This led Benesi to modify the technique by adding portions of the solid in suspension after the solid sample has reached equilibrium with *n*-butylamine and the endpoint can be determined by a series of successive approximations[17]. The modified procedure appreciably reduces the time of equilibrium, and accordingly reduces the chances of any contamination with traces of moisture in the course of titration. Also endpoints for titration of a particular solid can be determined by means of as many as ten different indicators with little extra work than that for a single indicator.

In general, however, the amount of acid as measured by Johnson's method is almost independent of the amount of indicator added beyond 0.2 ml and changes very little for titration times more than 50 hours. The serious effects are those due to moisture contamination, where full poisoning of almost all acid sites can take place by exposure for 10 minutes in an atmosphere of 90% humidity[13].

Obviously the method described so far is limited to non-coloured solids. For coloured solids, Johnson[31] described a method by which titration can be carried out by adding a small known amount of a white solid acid. The endpoint is taken when the colour change takes place on the white solid and a correction is made for the amount of butylamine used for the added white material.

The acidity of coloured solids was also determined colorimetrically by Trambouze[32], using n-butylamine, ethylacetate, or dioxane as the base. The method was further developed by Topchieva et al.[33] and by Tanabe and Yamaguchi[34]. A detailed procedure was described by Tanabe[35], and the experimental results obtained seemed to indicate that the acid sites are energetically heterogeneous.

Adsorption from the gas phases

The amount of acid on the surface of a solid can be determined from the amount of base chemisorbed from the gas phase. Gravimetric techniques are usually employed, where the acid sample is first saturated with the base vapour, followed by prolonged evacuation, and the base which is retained upon the sample is acknowledged to be chemically adsorbed[36].

The bases used so far include quinoline[37,38], pyridine[36,39,40], piperidine[41], trimethylamine[36,41,42], n-butylamine[23,40], pyrrole[42], and ammonia[39,40,42,43]. It is generally noticed that various bases are adsorbed to different extents on one and the same catalyst. These differences are probably due to differences in the basicity of the adsorbates. Also the amounts of bases adsorbed depend on the thermal treatment of the solid[43], and a typical example is shown in Fig. 5.4 for the adsorption of various basic vapours on SiO_2/Al_2O_3 catalyst evacuated at different temperatures. The considerable differences which occur at low evacuation temperatures are probably due to differences in the extent to which various vapours diffuse into the interior of the solid through micropores.

Differential thermal analysis (DTA) and thermogravemetric analysis

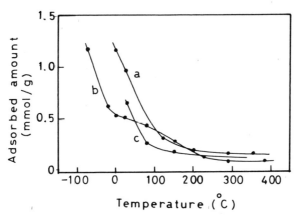

Fig. 5.4 Amounts of basic vapours chemisorbed on $SiO_2 \cdot Al_2O_3$ vs. evacuation temperature[13] a: n-butylamine, b: NH_3, c: pyridine

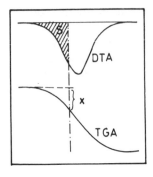

Fig. 5.5 Schematic DTA and TGA curves[13] (see text for significance of S and x.)

(TGA) of a solid on which various bases have been adsorbed can be utilized to estimate the amount of acid together with the acid strength of the solid[44]. Figure 5.5 illustrates this method, in which the amount x of the base retained on the solid (from the TGA curve), and the corresponding amount of heat absorbed (from the area S in the DTA curve) can be related by plotting x against dS/dx, which gives the heat required for the desorption of the base, which is a measure of the acid amounts at the various acid strengths.

Adsorption of the base from the gas phase carries the advantage that its measurement can be done at high temperatures to suit the working conditions of practical catalysts. Also, unlike the titration method, the colour of the solid is no obstacle to the measurement. The major disadvantages are the common lack of sharp demarcation between chemical and physical adsorption and differentiation between the amounts of acid at various acid strengths.

Figure 5.6 demonstrates the relationship between acid amount and acid strength for three solid acids, namely $SiO_2 \cdot MgO$, $SiO_2 \cdot Al_2O_3$, and filtrol. The amount of acid at various strengths was obtained by the amine titration

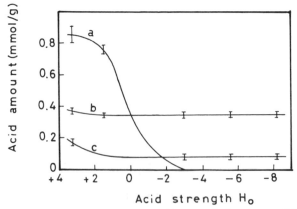

Fig. 5.6 Acid amount vs. acid strength for three solid acids[13]; a $SiO_2 \cdot MgO$, b $SiO_2 \cdot Al_2O_3$, c Filtrol

method using various basic indicators (cf. Table 5.3). The number of acid sites determined by using an indicator with $pK_a = +3.3$ is 0.85 mmol/g for $SiO_2 \cdot MgO$, which represents all acid sites with $H_0 \leq +3.3$. Also, the amount obtained by using an indicator of $pK_a = +1.5$ is 0.78 mmol/g which represents all the acid sites with $H_0 \leq +1.5$ for $SiO_2 \cdot MgO$, and the difference $0.85 - 0.78 = 0.07$ mmol/g, gives a measure of the acid sites in the range H_0 from $+3.3$ to $+1.5$.

The results of Fig. 5.6 indicate that $SiO_2 \cdot MgO$ is catalytically inactive in reactions where a strong acid strength ($H_0 \leq -3$) is required, but highly active for reactions requiring weak acid strengths ($H_0 > -1$).

Each of the methods for determining the strength and amount of acid described so far measures the sum of the amounts of Bronsted acid and Lewis acid at a certain acid strength. Experimental chemical means to date have not been able to distinguish between them clearly, and the reader may refer to more specialized books on the subject which treat the subject in more detail[1,13]. This distinction is easier when physical means are employed, and this will be treated in Chapter 6.

5.2 Surface basicity

Measurement of the basic properties of solid surfaces requires, as in the case of acid properties, determination of both the basic strength and the amount of base. In spite of the limited amount of work done in determining the surface basicity of solids, it is noticed that the methods used are similar to those described for measuring surface acidity.

5.2.1 Basic strength

The basic strength of a surface is its ability to convert an adsorbed electrically neutral acid to its conjugate base or its ability to donate an electron pair to an adsorbed acid. In the same way as for the acid strength, the basic strength can be estimated either by the indicator method in liquid media or from the vapour phase adsorption of an acid, namely phenol.

Titration with adsorbed indicators in liquid media

When an acid indicator, which is electrically neutral, is adsorbed on a solid base from a non-polar solution, the colour of the indicator changes when the solid imparts electron pairs to the acid. It is thus possible to observe the colour changes of acid indicators over a range of pK_a values.

The reaction between the solid base B and an indicator AH proceeds according to:

$$AH + B^- \rightleftharpoons A^- + B^-H^+ \tag{5.4}$$

and the basic strength H_0 of the solid base is given by the equation

$$H_0 = pK_a + \log [A^-]/[AH] \qquad (5.5)$$

where $[A^-]$ and $[AH]$ are the concentrations of the basic form and the acidic form of the indicator, respectively.

The approximate value of the basic strength of the surface is given by the pK_a value of the adsorbed indicator at which intermediate change of colour appears[45]. This is based on the observation that the first noticed colour change of the indicator occurs when about 10% of the adsorbed indicator is in the basic form, or when the ratio $[A^-]/[AH]$ is approximately $0.1/0.9 \cong 0.1$ ($pK_a = -1$). Also, further increase in the intensity of the colour is noticed when about 90% of the indicator is in the basic form, or when $[A^-]/[AH] = 0.9/1.0 \cong 1.0$ ($pK_a = +1$). The intermediate colour appears when $[A^-]/[AH] = 1$, and then $H_0 = pK_a$.

Table 5.6 gives a list of some indicators used for the measurement of the basic strength. These should dissolve in nonpolar solvents as benzene or iso-octane.

Solids investigated by this method includes CaO, MgO, Al_2O_3, Na_2CO_3, K_2CO_3, $KHCO_3$, $(NH_4)_2CO_3$, $BaCO_3$, $SrCO_3$, $5ZnO \cdot 2CO \cdot 4H_2O$, $KNaCO_3$, $Na_2WO_4 \cdot 2H_2O$, and KCN[49,50].

Table 5.6   Indicators used for the measurement of basic properties[46,47]

Indicators	Colour		pK_a
	Acid form	Base form	
bromothymol blue	yellow	green	7.2
2,4,6-trinitroaniline	yellow	reddish-orange	12.2
2,4-dinitroaniline	yellow	violet	15.0
4-chloro-2-nitroaniline	yellow	orange	17.2
4-nitroaniline	yellow	orange	18.4
4-chloroaniline	colourless	pink*	26.5†

*The colour disappears with the addition of benzoic acid.
†The value was estimated from the data of Stewart and Dolman[48].

Vapour adsorption method

Phenol vapour is the common adsorbate used in these measurements due to its stability at relatively high temperatures. Adsorption of phenol vapour takes place at a given pressure at a constant temperature, and this is followed by outgassing at high temperature in order to determine the amount of phenol retained by the basic sites on the surface. Results of measurement[51] have indicated that the basic strength of metal oxides decreases in the following order: CaO > BeO, MgO, ZnO > SiO_2gel, aluminosilicates.

5.2.2 Amount of base (basicity)

Similar to the amount of acid, basicity is commonly expressed as the number of mmol of basic sites per unit weight or per unit area of the solid. The amount of basic sites can be estimated by a titration method, by an adsorption method, or by a calorimetric method.

Titration method

In this method the amount of base can be determined by titrating a suspension in benzene containing the solid on which an indicator has been adsorbed in its basic form with benzoic acid dissolved in benzene. The benzoic acid titres are a measure of the amount of basic sites having a strength corresponding to the pK_a value of the indicator used[47].

The amounts and the strengths of the basic sites in magnesium oxide (prepared by heating its basic carbonate at 600 °C for 20 hours) on calcium oxide (prepared by heating its carbonate at 900 °C for 20 hours), and on strontium oxide (prepared by heating its hydroxide at 850 °C for 20 hours), were obtained by Yoneda et al.[46], by the titration method, and the results are shown in Fig. 5.7. It is worth noting that calcium oxide prepared from the hydroxide does not show any basicity even at the weakest basic strength of $H_0 = +7.1$, whereas a sample prepared from the carbonate shows strong basicity (cf. Fig. 5.7). The same observation also holds for magnesium oxide.

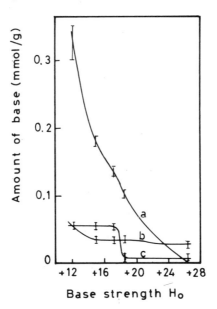

Fig. 5.7 Amount and strength of base for alkaline earth metal oxides[45]; a MgO, b CaO, c SrO

226

Malinowski and Szezepanska[45] devised several titration methods for use with aqueous solutions and with anhydrous acetic acid solution. The former consist of titration of a solid suspended in water with sulphuric acid solution, and the latter involve potentiometric titration with perchloric acid solution in anhydrous acetic acid. However, with titration methods involving aqueous solutions, one has to be careful in handling the results, especially with oxides.

Acid adsorption method

The amount of basic sites can also be determined by measuring the amounts adsorbed of acids such as benzoic, acetic, and hydrochloric acids in water. In the classical work of King[52], the basicity of charcoal attains a maximum value when it is heated to about 900 °C, while the acidity attains its maximum value when the charcoal is heated to 400 °C. The acidity was determined from the adsorption of NH_4OH and $NaOH$. The results are shown in Fig. 5.8.

In some studies, the number of carbon dioxide molecules adsorbed per unit area of the surface was considered to measure the amount of basic sites[53].

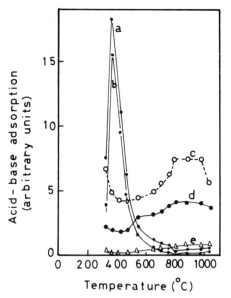

Fig. 5.8   Adsorption of acids and bases on pure charcoal vs. activation temperature[51]; a (———●———) NH_4OH, b (———▲———)NaOH, c(———○———) C_6H_5COOH, d(-- ● --)CH_3COOH, e(-- △ --)HCl

Calorimetric method

The amount of base can also be determined by observing the rise in temperature due to the heat of reaction between the basic sites and acid in benzene. A titration curve for the basicity of silica–alumina is shown in Fig. 5.9, which indicates that 3 ml of the acid is required to neutralize the basic sites, and the estimated basicity according to this figure was found to be about 0.6 mmol/g[34].

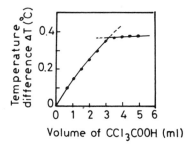

Fig. 5.9 Calorimetric titration curve: 4.15 g $SiO_2 \cdot Al_2O_3$ with trichloracetic acid in benzene[34]

5.3 Interaction of surface functional groups with specific reagents

In addition to acidic and/or basic sites on solid surfaces, many different types of functional groups may exist on certain solids. The presence of such functional groups has been demonstrated by a variety of experimental techniques, including the use of chemical reagents which form identifiable products which may either become desorbed from the surfaces or remain as adsorbed species. Studies of the nature and rates of some of these reactions have provided valuable methods which assist in the characterization of surface functional groups. The interaction of surface functional groups existing on carbon blacks and on oxides with various specific reagents will be discussed in this section, as two examples which contain together quite a number of groups characterizing the majority of solids used in practice as catalysts or as solid adsorbents.

5.3.1 Surface functional groups on carbon blacks

In general the effectiveness of the functional groups on solids are largely determined by the accessibility to the various parts of the surface, i.e. by the microstructure and the pore-size distribution of the solid. In carbon blacks, the surface properties are also affected by the size and perfection of graphitic basal layers and by the distribution of oxygen- and hydrogen-containing functional groups. It is now widely accepted that the term 'functional group' means a group which is chemically bonded to the carbon atoms of the basal planes, just as with derivatives of polyaromatic molecules. Essentially, all combined oxygen and much of the hydrogen are at or near the surface. Oxygen comes as a result of oxidation of the carbon previously formed, and can be determined by pyrolysis or more accurately by neutron activation analysis. Hydrogen can be determined by pyrolysis of the carbon to produce molecular hydrogen and methane or by combustion to water.

The presence of many different types of chemical groups on the surfaces of carbon has been demonstrated by a variety of experimental techniques, and there is sufficient evidence to indicate the presence of at least five major groups on commercial carbon blacks, namely, aromatic hydrogen, phenol, quinone, carboxylic acid, and lactone[54-56]. Other groupings may also exist on the surface, and these include free radicals and carbon–hydrogen, carbon–halogen, carbon–nitrogen, and carbon–sulphur species. Studies of the reactions of surface functional groups with chemical reagents have played an important role in the characterization. However, attempts to determine surface functional groups by conversion to stable derivatives have been hampered by the insolubility of carbon black, by autocatalysis of side reactions, or by adsorption of reagents or products on the surface. For these reasons, the products are usually not isolated, but the derivatives are identified on the surface. Some of the methods which are generally applicable to these surface reactions include: monitoring of stoichiometrically related soluble (or gas) products[57]; elemental analysis[58]; tracer analysis with a labelled reagent[58]; electrochemical measurement[60]; and identification of pyrolysis products after derivatization[61].

Also, chemical analysis has proved to be an important tool in characterizing solid surfaces, and analysis of gas composition always shows three major components, namely hydrogen, carbon monoxide, and carbon dioxide, together with small amounts of water, methane, hydrogen sulphide, carbonyl sulphide, sulphur dioxide, carbon disulphide and nitrogenous compounds[62]. Each of the gases evolved on pyrolysis is related to one or more functional groups. For example, carbon dioxide is related to the presence of carboxylic acid and lactone groups, whereas carbon monoxide is derived from phenols and quinones, and hydrogen results from the dissociation of C–H and O–H bonds.

From the analysis of the evolved gas in combination with measurements of the amounts of total acids and of strong acids, surface group distributions can be estimated. Total acids are measured by reaction with a very strong base such as the hydride ion of $LiAlH_4$ in diethyl carbitol. Strong acids are determined by neutralization with an excess of aqueous $NaHCO_3$. Rivin[63] has suggested the following scheme which has been successfully applied in many instances for the calculation of surface group concentrations:

— Carbon-bound hydrogen ($>$—H) = total hydrogen − total acids.
— Phenol or hydroquinone ($>$—OH) = weak acids = total acids − strong acids.

— Quinone and neutral groups with one oxygen ($>=O$) = carbon monoxide — weak acids.
— Carboxylic acids ($>-COOH$) = strong acids
— Lactones and neutral groups containing two oxygens ($>-CO_2-$) = carbon dioxide — strong acids.

A brief summary of the reactions which have enabled the characterization of specific surface functional groups is given below.

Surface phenolic hydroxyl groups

Surface phenolic hydroxyl groups on carbon react with diazomethane, Grignard reagents, thionyl chloride, acetyl chloride, dimethyl sulphate, and lithium aluminium hydride. These same reagents also react with carboxylic acid groups, and alternative reagents to acetyl chloride for the acetylation of phenolic groups are acetic acid and acetic anhydride. Boehm et al. have established the use of 2,4-dinitrofluorobenzene and 4-nitrobenzoylchloride for the specific detection and estimation of phenolic hydroxyl groups[64,65]. These reagents gave estimates of phenolic hydroxyl groups in good agreement with those obtained from determination of non-hydrolysable methoxyl groups formed by reaction with diazomethane. Methoxyl groups formed from surface carboxyl groups are readily hydrolysed by hot dilute hydrochloric acid, and therefore reaction of surface groups with a methylating agent followed by hydrolysis enabled Boehm et al.[64] to distinguish between carboxyl groups and phenolic hydroxyl groups on carbon.

Representative derivatives which have been identified are summarized in Table 5.7.

Surface carbonyl groups

The existence of carbonyl groups on carbon surfaces is attributed to the presence of surface lactone and quinone species. Quinones are reduced to the corresponding quinols, or their anions, by catalytic[66] or thermal hydrogenation[67]; or by reaction with lithium aluminium hydride[63], sodium borohydride[66], or Ti^{3+} ions[55]. Quinones also undergo characteristic condensation reactions with aniline or isobutyronitrile[68], or iso-octane[69]. Hydroxylamine was found to react with surface 1,4-quinone to give an oxime[54,55]. Boehm[54] observed that semicarbozide or 2,4-dinitrophenylhydrazine react with approximately half of the carbonyl groups present in carbon surfaces, and this might indicate that pairs of carbonyl groups exist as close neighbours on the surface.

Lactone groups on the surface react with hydrobromic acid, ammonia[55], and lithium aluminium hydride[63]. Boehm et al.[64] detected the presence of

Table 5.7 Analytical derivatives of carbon black surface groups (After Medalia and Rivin[74])

Derivative	Reagent	Reference
1. Phenolic hydroxyl ($>$—OH)		
$>$—OCH$_3$	diazomethane, dimethylsulphate	66, 70, 54
$>$—OCOCH$_3$	acetyl chloride, acetic acid, or acetic anhydride	55, 75, 76
$>$—OC$_6$H$_3$(NO$_2$)$_2$	2,4-dinitrofluorobenzene	75, 65
$>$—OCOC$_6$H$_4$NO$_2$	p-nitrobenzoylchloride	75, 65
2. Quinone		
—C(CH$_3$)$_2$CH$_2$C(CH$_3$)$_3$ (with OH, OH)	iso-octane	69
—NHC$_6$H$_5$ (with OH, OH)	aniline	68
(with NOH, NOH)	hydroxylamine	55
3. Lactone ($>$—C=O, $>$—O)		
$>$—CONH$_2$	ammonia	55
$>$—OH		

Table 5.7 (*continued*)

Derivative	Reagent	Reference
>—CO$_2$H >—Br	hydrogen bromide	55
4. Carboxyl (>—CO$_2$H)		
>—CO$_2$CH$_3$	diazomethane, dimethylsulphate	66, 70, 54
>—COCl	thionylchloride, phosphorus pentachloride	75, 65, 77
>—COC$_6$H$_4$N(CH$_3$)$_2$	thionylchloride/dimethylaniline	75, 65
>—NHCO$_2$C$_2$H$_5$	thionylchloride/sodium azide/ ethanol	54

lactones or carbon from studies of the acid–base character of surface functional groups before and after reduction of the groups, as for example with zinc and hydrochloric acid. It is suggested that suitable combination of acid–base titration, chemical modification, and hydrolysis reactions provide a useful method for characterizing functional groups on carbon[64].

Representative reactions with surface quinones and lactones are summarized in Table 5.7.

Surface carboxylic groups

Surface carboxylic groups undergo esterification reactions with diazomethane[64,66], alcohols[64], and dimethyl sulphate[64,70]. It is to be noticed, however, that the reactions of diazomethane and dimethyl sulphate are not specific to carboxyl groups. Thionyl chloride[63,64] and phosphorus pentachloride[71] react with surface carboxyl groups to give acid chlorides which can be characterized by reaction with an aromatic amine to give an anilide[64,65]. Boehm was able to show that thionyl chloride reacts with adjacent carboxylic groups on carbon to form a carboxylic anhydride[54,64]. Methyl magnisium iodide[57] and lithium aluminium hydride[72] react with carboxylic acid groups to give methane and hydrogen, respectively, but these reactions are not specific to carboxyl groups and react with other functional groups on the surface of carbon[71,73].

Some reactions with surface carboxyl groups, as well as their derivatives, are summarized in Table 5.7.

Surface free radicals

Carbon blacks were shown to have a well-defined electron spin resonance spectrum which was persumed to be due to the presence of unpaired electrons in the π-bond of the graphite layers[78]. Elucidation of free radical character by chemical means suggests that these unpaired spins are not reactive toward organic free radicals[71,79,80].

Donnet[71,73] prescribed the use of lauroyl peroxide 2,2′-azobisisobutyronitride, and 3,5-dichlorobenzoyl peroxide for the quantitative estimation of surface radicals on carbon. These reagents themselves produce free radicals which are taken by free radical sites on the surface and may be subsequently estimated by determination of the adsorbed hydrogen, nitrogen, or chlorine respectively. Garten and Sutherland[81] estimated the radical content by reaction with an oxidation product of benzidine. Donnet[71,73], and Deviney[82] have pointed out the correlation between the chemically determined radical-accepting character of surfaces and the estimated surface population of quinonoid groups.

5.3.2 Surface functional groups on oxides

Many chemical reagents react with surface hydroxyl groups on oxides to form identifiable products which help in characterizing the surface hydroxyl groups. When measurements are made on oxides of known surface area, the surface concentrations of hydroxyl groups can be evaluated.

Chlorination reactions

Thionyl chloride react with hydroxy groups on silica according to the reaction:

$$\rightarrow SiOH + SOCl_2 \longrightarrow SiCl + SO_2 + HCl \qquad (5.6)$$

The reaction can also be used for some clay minerals[83]. Boehm and Schneider[84,85] developed this reaction to be used for the quantitative estimation of surface hydroxyl groups. The method involves refluxing thionyl chloride with silica for more than 8 hours, followed by outgassing of the treated oxide at 200 °C for 48 hours. A certain weight of the sample is heated with a solution of sodium hydroxide and the chloride liberated is estimated by titration. The method is unsatisfactory for samples containing micropores, since neither the reagent nor the products of reaction can be removed from the pores by evacuation at 200 °C[84].

Alkylation reaction

The reaction between diazomethane and surface hydroxyl groups to form methoxy groups has been used to estimate the hydroxy group content on silica[84], anatase[86,87], rutile, η-alumina, α-iron(III)oxide, cerium (IV) oxide, tin(IV) oxide, and zinc oxide[87]. Boehm[54,86] also used phenyldiazomethane, which benzylates surface hydroxyl groups, for the estimation of hydroxyl groups on anatese.

Surface hydroxyl groups are esterified to alkoxyl groups by reaction with alcohols at high temperatures[88], and by this method the hydroxyl content has been estimated for silica[89], γ-alumina[90], η-alumina, anatase, α-iron(III) oxide, cerium(IV) oxide, tin(IV), oxide and zinc oxide[87]. The influence of the reaction conditions on the extent of alkylation of the surface groups has been investigated[84], and independent evidence obtained from infrared spectroscopy[91] has shown that alcohols react not only with surface hydroxyl groups but also with oxide ion sites or oxygen 'bridges' in oxide surfaces.

Reactions with hydrides

It was suggested by Shapiro and Weiss[92] and Weiss *et al.*[93] that the reaction of silica surfaces with diborane could be used to differentiate between molecular water and silanol groups on the surface. With molecular water the reaction proceeds with the liberation of six molecules of hydrogen to each molecule of diborane according to the reaction:

$$B_2H_6 + 6H_2O \rightarrow 2B(OH)_3 + 6H_2 \qquad (5.7)$$

while with silanol groups, only two molecules of hydrogen are liberated according to the reaction:

$$2SiOH + B_2H_6 \rightarrow 2SiOBH_2 + 2H_2 \qquad (5.8)$$

The relative proportions of silanol groups and molecular water on the surface can be obtained from the ratio of hydrogen liberated to diborane consumed.

There is, however, considerable evidence that other side reactions occur beside reactions (5.7) and (5.8), including reaction with surface siloxane groups, and therefore this method cannot differentiate satisfactorily between hydroxyl groups and adsorbed water[94,95].

In this category, mention should be made to the work of Boehm[87], in which he measured the volume of hydrogen evolved from the reaction of lithium aluminium hydride with η-alumina to calculate the concentration of hydroxyl groups on the oxide surface.

Deuterium exchange reactions

Characterization of surface hydroxyl groups can also be carried out by the exchange with deuterium of hydrogen atoms on the surface. The technique involves contacting the oxide with deuterium or deuterium oxide, and when exchange is complete analysing the gas-phase products for H/D content. The composition of D_2/HD or H_2/HD mixtures can be determined by thermal conductivity measurements or by mass spectrometry[96]. The composition of $D_2O/HDO/H_2O$ mixtures in the gas phase has also been determined by thermal conductivity measurements[97]. Water mixtures may also be reduced to the corresponding hydrogen mixtures which are subsequently analysed.

Deuterium exchange experiments have been carried out to determine hydroxyl group surface concentration on several oxides, for example silica[97,98], silica-alumina[98], anatase[87,99], rutile[87], and magnesia[100]. Also, this method can enable distinctions to be drawn between the activities of hydrogen atoms on differing hydroxyl groups[98].

Reactions with metal halides

Aluminium trichloride and boron trichloride were used by Boehm et al.[101] for the determination of both molecular water and silanol groups on silica surfaces. For the same purpose, trimethylchlorosilane has also been used to differentiate between silanol groups and adsorbed water on silica[102,103]. Silanol groups react with the reagent to give $SiOSiMe_3$ groups on the surface, whereas water reacts to give volatile hexamethyldisiloxane. The reaction seems to be incomplete due steric hindrance affects[102,103] caused by the bulky nature of the reaction products. These effects are expected to be quite serious when dealing with microporous silica. Faure et al.[100] criticized the use of trimethylchlorosilane for estimating hydroxyl groups or water, because the hydrogen chloride formed as a reaction product is liable to be chemisorbed on oxide surfaces.

Reactions with metal alkyls

Fripiat and Uytterhoeven[104] used methylmagnesium bromide and methyllithium to estimate hydroxyl groups on silica. The same reagent was used by Boehm[87] to estimate hydroxyl groups on η-alumina. It was concluded by Sato et al.[105] that triethylaluminium chloride can be used to determine the total hydroxyl content on the surface of silica, alumina, or silica-alumina, and that this reagent is superior to ethylmagnesium bromide, ethyllithium, diethylaluminium chloride, or ethylaluminium chloride. The determinations were carried out by measuring the volume of methane produced in the reactions. Hanke[106] has described a method for the determination of the total number of hydroxyl groups in silica using the dimethylzinc-tetrahydrofuran complex $Zn(CH_3)_2 \cdot 2C_4H_8O$. However, the problem with bulky molecule reagents seems to be a common one, namely that the molecules may not get access to all of the surface due to the steric effects, preventing access of bulky reagents to functional groups contained within micropores. In one instance, a detailed study of the effect of pore size in silicas on the reaction between hydroxyl groups and methyllithium has been reported[107] and the reagent was found to be only reactive toward hydroxyl groups in pores of diameter greater than 5 nm.

235

References

1. M. S. Goldstein, in: R. B. Anderson (ed.), *Experimental Methods in Catalytic Research*, Ch. 9, Academic Press.
2. R. P. Bell, *Acids and Bases*, Methuen, 1952, p. 5
3. E. C. Franklin, *Am. Chem. J.*, **20**, 820 (1898); **47**, 285 (1912); *J. Am. Chem. Soc.*, **27**, 820 (1905); **46**, 2137 (1924)
4. J. N. Bronsted, *Rec. Trav. Chim.*, **42**, 718 (1923); *J. Phys. Chem.*, **30**, 777 (1926); *Chem. Rev.*, **5**, 231, 284 (1928); *Z. Phys. Chem.*, **A169**, 52 (1934)
5. A. E. O. Germann, *J. Am. Chem. Soc.*, **47**, 2461 (1925)
6. G. N. Lewis, *J. Frankline Inst.*, **226**, 293 (1938); *Valency and Structures of Atoms and Molecules*, Chemical Catalog Co., 1923
7. M. Ussanowitch, *J. Gen. Chem. USSR* (Eng. transl.), **9**, 182 (1939); H. Gehlen, *Z. Phys. Chem.*, **203**, 125 (1954)
8. J. Bjerrum, *Fys. Tidssk.*, **48**, 1 (1950); B. Sansoni, *Naturwissenschaften*, **38**, 46 (1951)
9. R. E. Johnson, T. H. Norris, and J. L. Huston, *J. Am. Chem. Soc.*, **73**, 3052 (1951)
10. H. Lux, *Z. Elektrochem.*, **45**, 303 (1939); H. Flood and T. Forland, *Acta Chem. Scand.*, *1*, 592, 781 (1947); J. W. Tomlinson, *The Physical Chemistry of Melts* (A symposium on molten slags and salts), Institution of Mining and Metallurgy, 1953
11. A. I. Shatenshtein, *Advances in Physical Organic Chemistry*, Vol. 1, Academic Press, 1963, p. 174
12. R. G. Pearson, *J. Am. Chem. Soc.*, **85**, 3533 (1963)
13. K. Tanabe, in: *Solid Acids and Bases—Their Catalytic Properties*, Kodansha, Tokyo, Academic Press, New York, London, 1970, p. 2
14. C. Walling, *J. Am. Chem. Soc.*, **72**, 1164 (1950)
15. L. P. Hammett, *Chem. Rev.*, **16**, 67 (1935); *Physical Organic Chemistry*, Ch. 9, McGraw-Hill, 1940
16. H. A. Benesi, *J. Am. Chem. Soc.*, **78**, 5490 (1956)
17. H. A. Benesi, J. Phys. Chem., **61**, 970 (1957)
18. R. I. Bertolacini, *Anal. Chem.* **35**, 599 (1963)
19. S. E. Voltz, A. E. Hirschler, and A. Smith, *J. Phys. Chem.*, **64**, 1594 (1960)
20. A. E. Hirschler, *J. Catalysis*, **2**, 428 (1963)
21. R. O. Clark, E. V. Ballou, and R. T. Barth, *Anal. Chem. Acta*, **23**, 189 (1960)
22. J. J. Chessik and A. C. Zettlemoyer, *Advan. Catalysis*, **11**, 263 (1959)
23. A. C. Zettlemoyer and J. J. Chessick, *J. Phys. Chem.*, **64**, 1131 (1960)
24. Y. Kubokawa, *J. Phys. Chem.*, **67**, 769 (1963)
25. A. N. Webb, *Ind. Eng. Chem.*, **49**, 261 (1957)
26. E. V. Ballou, R. T. Barth, and R. A. Flinn, *J. Phys. Chem.*, **65**, 1639 (1961)
27. C. E. Adams, C. N. Kimberlin, Jr., and D. P. Shoemaker, *Proc. 3rd. Intern. Congr. Catalysis, Amsterdam*, 1964, Vol. 2, Wiley, New York, 1965, p. 1310
28. Y. Amenomiya, J. H. B. Cherier, and R. I. Cvetanovic, *J. Phys. Chem.*, **67**, 54 (1964); **68**, 52 (1964); **67**, 144 (1963)
29. R. T. Barth and E. A. Ballou, *Anal. Chem.*, **33**, 1080 (1961)
30. M. W. Tamele, *Discussions Faraday Soc.*, **8**, 220 (1950)
31. O. Johnson, *J. Phys. Chem.*, **59**, 827 (1955)
32. Y. Trambouze, *Compt. Rend.*, **233**, 648 (1951); *Compt. Rend.* **236**, 1023 (1953)
33. K. V. Topchieva, I. F. Moskovskaya, and N. Y. Dobrokhotave, *Kinetics and Catalysis (USSR)* (Eng. trans.), **5**, 910 (1964)
34. K. Tanabe and T. Yamaguchi, *J. Res. Inst. Catalysis, Hokkaido Univ.*, **14**, 93 (1966)
35. Ref. 13, p. 17.

236

36. R. L. Richardson and S. W. Benson, *J. Phys. Chem.*, **61**, 405 (1957)
37. G. H. Mills, E. R. Boedecker, and A. G. Oblad, *J. Am. Chem. Soc.*, **72**, 1554 (1950)
38. T. H. Millikan, Jr., G. H. Mills, and A. G. Oblad, *Discussions Faraday Soc.*, **8**, 279 (1950)
39. E. Echigoya, *Nippon Kagaku Zasshi*, **76**, 1049 (1955)
40. H. Uchida and M. Temma, *Shokubai (Tokyo)*, **4**(4), 353 (1962)
41. R. L. Stone and H. F. Rase, *Anal. Chem.*, **29**, 1273 (1957)
42. Y. Tezuka and T. Takeuchi, *Bull. Chem. Soc. Japan*, **38**, 485 (1965)
43. A. Clark, V. C. F. Holm, and D. M. Blackburn, *J. Catalysis*, **1**, 244 (1962); A. Clark and V. C. F. Holm, *ibid.*, **2**, 16, 21 (1963)
44. T. Shirasaki, M. Mimura, and K. Mukaida, *Bunseki Kiki* (Japanese) **15**(7), 59 (1968)
45. S. Malinowski and S. Szezepanska, *J. Catalysis*, **2**, 310 (1963)
46. J. Take, N. Kikuchi, and Y. Yoneda, *Shakubai (Tokyo)*, **10** (23rd. Symp. Catalysis, Preprints of Papers), 127 (1968)
47. K. Tanabe and T. Yamaguchi, *J. Res. Inst. Catalysis, Hokkaido Univ.*, **11**, 179 (1964)
48. R. Stewart and D. Dolman, *Can. J. Chem.*, **41**, 925 (1967)
49. K. Nishimura, *Nippon Kagaku Zasski*, **81**, 1680 (1960)
50. K. Tanabe and M. Katayama, *J. Res. Inst. Catalysis, Hokkaido Univ.*, **7**, 106 (1959)
51. O. V. Krylov and E. A. Fokira, *Probl. Kinetiki, Kataliza*, Acad. Novk, USSR, Vol. 8, 1955, p. 248
52. A. King, *J. Chem. Soc.*, 1489 (1937)
53. S. Malinowski, S. Szezepanska, and I. Sloczynski, *J. Catalysis*, **7**, 67 (1964)
54. H. P. Boehm, *Adv. Catalysis*, **16**, 195 (1966)
55. W. J. de Bruin and Th. Van der Plas, *Rev. Gen. Caout*, **41**, 452 (1964)
56. B. R. Puri, in: P. I. Walker, Jr. (ed.), *Chemistry and Physics of Carbon*, Vol. 6, Marcel Dekker, New York, 1970, pp. 141–282
57. D. S. Villars, *J. Amer. Chem. Soc.*, **70**, 3655 (1948)
58. M. L. Studebaker, *Rubber Chem. Technol.*, **30**, 1401 (1957)
59. P. H. Given and L. W. Hill, *Carbon*, **7**, 649 (1969)
60. K. Kinoshita and J. A. S. Bett, *Carbon*, **11**, 403 (1973)
61. D. Rivin and J. Aron, U.S. Patent 3479300 (Nov. 18, 1969; to Cabot Corp.), 1969
62. D. Rivin, *Rubber Chem. Technol.*, **44**, 307 (1971)
63. D. Rivin, in: *Proceedings of the Fifth Conference in Carbon*, Vol. 2, Pergamon Press, New York, 1963, p. 199
64. H. P. Boehm, E. Diehl, W. Heck, and R. Sappok, *Angew. Chem.* (internat. ed.), **3**, 669 (1964)
65. H. P. Boehm, E. Diehl and W. Heck, *Rev. Gen. Caout.* **41**, 461 (1964)
66. M. L. Studebaker, E. W. D. Huffman, A. C. Wolfe, and L. G. Nabors, *Ind. Eng. Chem.*, **48**, 162 (1956)
67. B. R. Puri and R. C. Bonsal, *Carbon*, **1**, 451, 457 (1964)
68. J. B. Donnet and G. Henrich, *Bull. Soc. Chim. France*, 1609 (1960)
69. J. V. Hallum and H. V. Drushel, *J. Phys. Chem.*, **62**, 110 (1918)
70. J. B. Donnet and E. Papirer, *Rev. Gen. Caout.*, **42**, 389 (1965)
71. J. B. Donnet, *Carbon*, **6**, 161 (1968)
72. D. Rivin, *Rubber Chem. Technol.*, **36**, 729 (1963)
73. J. B. Donnet, *Bull. Soc. Chim. France*, 3353 (1970)
74. A. I. Medalia and D. Rivin, in: G. D. Parfitt and K. S. W. Sing (eds.), *Characterization of Powder Surfaces*, Academic Press, London, N.Y. and San Francisco, 1976, pp. 306–307

75. H. P. Boehm, E. Diehl, W. Heck, and R. Sappok, *Angew. Chem.*, **76**, 742 (1964)
76. J. B. Donnet, F. Hueber, C. Reitzer, J. Allaux, and G. Reiss *Bull Soc. Chim. France*, **8–9**, 1727 (1962)
77. J. B. Donnet, French Patent 1164786, July 1, 1958
78. G. Kraus and R. L. Collins, *Rubber World*, **139**, 219 (1958)
79. J. W. C. Speckman, *Chem. and Ind. (London)*, 1532 (1961)
80. J. B. Donnet, M. Rigant, and R. Furstenberger, *Carbon*, **11**, 153 (1923)
81. V. A. Garten and G. K. Sutherland, *Proc. 3rd Rubber Technol. Conf.*, 1954, p. 536
82. M. L. Deviney, *Adv. Colloid Interface. Sci.*, **2**, 237 (1969)
83. H. Devel, *Angew. Chem.*, **69**, 270 (1957)
84. H. P. Boehm and M. Schneider, *Z. Anorg. Chem.*, **301**, 326 (1959)
85. H. P. Boehm and M. Schneider, *Kolloid Zeits.*, **167**, 128 (1963)
86. H. P. Boehm, *Angew. Chem.*, **5**, 533 (1966)
87. H. P. Boehm, *Disc. Faraday Soc.*, **52**, 264 (1971)
88. M. Liefländer and W. Stöber, *Z. Naturforsch*, **15b**, 411 (1960)
89. W. Stöber, G. Bauer, and K. Thomas, *Ann. Chem.*, **664**, 104 (1957)
90. W. Stöber, M. Liefländer, and E. Bohn, *Beitr. Silikose-Forschung*, Special vol. **4**, 111 (1960)
91. C. H. Rochester and M. S. Scurrell, 'Surface and Defect Properties of Solids', Vol. 2, The Chemical Society, London, 1973, p. 114
92. I. Shapiro and H. G. Weiss, *J. Phys. Chem.*, **57**, 219 (1953)
93. M. G. Weiss, J. A. Knight, and I. Shapiro, *J. Amer. Chem. Soc.*, **81**, 1823 (1959)
94. M. Baverez and J. Bastik, *Bull. Soc. Chim. France*, 3226 (1964).
95. J. J. Fripiat and M. Van Tongelen, *J. Catalysis*, **5**, 158 (1966)
96. V. Y. Davydov, A. V. Kiselev, A. T. Zhuravlev, *Trans. Faraday Soc.*, **60**, 2254 (1965)
97. A. T. Zhuravlev and A. V. Kiselev, *Colloid Journal*, **24**, 16 (1962)
98. W. K. Hall, H. P. Leftin, F. J. Cheselske, and D. E. O'Keilly, *J. Catalysis*, **2**, 506 (1963)
99. H. P. Boehm and M. Herrmann, *Z. Anorg. Chem.*, **352**, 156 (1967)
100. M. Faure, J. Fraissard, and B. Imelik, *Bull. Soc. Chim. France*, 22867 (1967)
101. H. P. Boehm, M. Schneider, and F. Arendt, *Z. Anorg. Chem.*, **320**, 43 (1963)
102. W. Stöber, *Kolloid Zeits.*, **145**, 17 (1956)
103. H. W. Kohlschütter, P. Best, and G. Wirzing, *Z. Anorg. Chem.*, **285**, 236 (1956)
104. J. J. Fripiat and I. Uytterhoeven, *J. Phys. Chem.*, **66**, 800 (1962)
105. M. Sato, T. Kanbayashi, N. Kobayashi, and Y. Shima, *J. Catalysis*, **7**, 342 (1967)
106. W. Hanke, *Z. Anorg. Chem.*, **395**, 191 (1973)
107. K. Unger and E. Gallei, *Kolloid Zeits.*, **237**, 358 (1970)

Chapter 6

Solid Surfaces and their Characterization by Physical Means

As pointed out in previous chapters, any study of the properties of the gas–solid interface is plagued by a lack of knowledge of the geometry of the surface as well as its chemical nature. The latter is often obscure, even in the absence of an adsorbate or when there are no foreign substances present, and is still more so when impurities are present in small percentages, because they can be concentrated largely in the surface.

The differentiation between physical and chemisorption for example, is not always easy to make when the chemisorption is reversible. In the case of chemisorption, lack of a well-defined equilibrium can cloud the significance of isotherms. Some of the recently developed techniques hold considerable promise of elucidating some of the complicated and confusing situations that arise on surfaces in systems involving the gas–solid interface. Surface scientists have adopted convenient, but confusing, acronyms for these techniques (LEED, AES, PES, ESCA, FIM, etc.). However, it is widely accepted that the unambiguous description of a surface requires the application of several surface probes, preferably combined within a single experimental system. Electrons, with their very short escape depth from solids, are the most important probe for surface properties, both geometric and electronic. The most

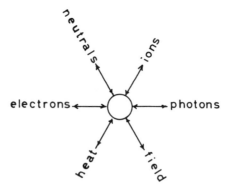

Fig. 6.1   The Propst diagram[1]. The circle represents the sample to be analysed. Ingoing arrows represent the various probes used to excite the sample. The possible responses to that excitation are indicated by the outgoing arrows, which convey information about the sample

useful of these techniques are described in this chapter with an adequate introduction to both the experimental procedures and the application at a level understandable to a physical chemist with no experience in the field.

Some idea of the number of techniques which can be adopted for the spectroscopic analysis of solid surfaces might be gained from a consideration of the diagram shown in Fig. 6.1. The circle represents the sample to be analysed. Arrows going in correspond to the possible surface probes, while outgoing arrows correspond to the secondary particles which convey information about the sample. Each combination of an in- and outgoing arrow seem to constitute a potential analytical technique. There are however, only 36 such combinations tried in the past, about half of which are in more or less common use[1].

6.1 Classification of surface spectroscopic techniques

There is no generally accepted taxonomy of surface spectroscopies, but Park[1] made a very successful trial to group them according to the properties that distinguish the desired spectrum from its background. Thus, for example, techniques relying on the energy analysis of emitted electrons to separate a discrete spectrum from a continuous background may be discussed together, although, depending on the energy range and the nature of the probe, they may supply quite different characterizations of the surface. Techniques are accordingly grouped according to the kind of information they provide. It will also be noticed that some spectroscopies might fall in more than one phylum.

Surface spectroscopic techniques can be divided into the following groups:

1. Electron spectroscopy (ESCA), with the following subgroups.
   (a) Low-energy characteristic loss spectroscopy.
   (b) Valence band electron spectroscopies—The direct methods, to include ion neutralization spectroscopy (INS); field emission energy distribution (FEED); and ultraviolet photoelectron spectroscopy (UPS).
   (c) Core level electron spectroscopies—The indirect methods, to include X-ray photoelectron spectroscopy (XPS) and X-ray excited Auger electron spectroscopy (XEAES).
2. Differentiation spectroscopy, with the following subgroups.
   (a) Electron-excited Auger electron spectroscopy (EEAES).
   (b) Core level characteristic loss spectroscopy (CLS).
3. Appearance potential spectroscopy, with the following subgroups.
   (a) Inelastic tunnelling spectroscopy.
   (b) Soft X-ray appearance potential spectroscopy (SXAPS).
   (c) Auger electron appearance potential spectroscopy (AEAPS).
   (d) Disappearance potential spectroscopy (DAPS).
4. Diffraction, with the following subgroups.
   (a) Low-energy electron diffraction (LEED).

    (b) Spatial filtering.

    (c) Reflection high-energy electron diffraction (RHEED).

    (d) Diffraction of atoms.

5. Photon spectroscopy, including the following subgroups.

    (a) Infrared spectroscopy.

    (b) Optical spectroscopy.

    (c) Bremsstrahlung isochromat spectroscopy.

    (d) Soft X-ray band emission.

    (e) Ion-excited X-rays.

6. Ion backscattering, including the following subgroups.

    (a) Binary scattering of noble gas ions.

    (b) Rutherford scattering.

7. Mass spectroscopy, including the following subgroups.

    (a) Thermal evaporation.

    (b) Electron-stimulated desorption (ESD).

    (c) Secondary ion mass spectroscopy (SIMS).

    (d) The field ion microscope (FIM).

    (e) The atom probe field ion microscope.

    (f) Field desorption spectroscopy (FDS).

The volume of the surface spectroscopic techniques, and the mass of technological advancements reached in the field make it quite impossible to summarize, even shortly, all the details, as well as the results obtained in one chapter of a book. As an alternative, only selected examples of these techniques will be discussed, namely those which have been more experienced by surface chemists rather than by surface physicists. In this attitude, more weight is intended to be put on experiment and application than on theory. Similar techniques are discussed in this context disregarding the above proposed classification.

6.2 Electron spectroscopy of solid surfaces

Electron spectroscopy in a variety of forms is now being used extensively in the study and characterization of solid surfaces. Electron spectroscopy may be defined quite generally as a technique with which spectroscopic information on the distribution and population of electronic energy states is determined by the measurement of the kinetic energy of electrons that are incident upon, have been scattered by, or have been emitted from the atomic system under investigation. In surface studies, the atomic system is the surface region of the solid.

The goals of various electron spectroscopies may differ widely. Some, for example, are directed toward chemical identification of surface atoms, and others to the determination of surface electronic structure; but in both cases the information is derived from knowledge of the energy level structure of the atoms in the surface region of the solid. Accordingly, electron spectroscopy can be used for both fundamental investigations of surfaces, and as a means of characterizing surfaces in experiments such as in chemisorption and catalysis.

Electron spectroscopies are, therefore, alternatively classified on a more practical basis into two types, which are also included in the more general classification presented earlier. These are *emission electron spectroscopy* and *scattering electron spectroscopy*. The former involves emission into vacuum of electrons excited in an electronic transition process caused by one of several perturbations, and the latter is one in which incident electrons are inelastically scattered from the surface in the basic electronic process.

Emission electron spectroscopies includes three fundamental classes. These are:

1. Photoemission spectroscopy (PES), which involves the absorption of a photon by an electron of the solid in a one-electron excitation process, followed by the emission into vacuum of a fraction of the excited electrons without energy loss. The kinetic energy distribution of these electrons is measured. According to the photon energy employed, there are two branches of PES, namely UPS and XPS; the latter is also known by the acronym ESCA.
2. The second class comprises those based on the two-electron, Auger type process by which a lower-energy hole is filled by a radiationless re-arrangement of higher-energy electrons. Excited electrons are produced, a fraction of which can leave the solid where their kinetic distribution is measured. The following categories of Auger spectroscopies can be identified: Auger electron spectroscopy (AES), where the low-energy hole is a core level of a surface atom, and ion neutralization spectroscopy (INS), where the hole is provided by an incident ion outside the surface of the solid.
3. The third class of emission electron spectroscopy used in surface study is field emission spectroscopy (FES), which involves emission of electrons by tunnelling through a surface potential barrier formed by a suitably large electric potential applied to a sample of appropriate geometry. The kinetic energy distribution of emitted electrons is then measured.

Regarding scattering electron spectroscopy, two basic types can be distinguished, namely energy loss spectroscopy (ELS), where the energies of the primary electron before and after scattering are measured, yielding a distribution of scattered electrons as a function of energy loss, and the appearance potential spectroscopies (APS). In this latter class, inelastic electron scattering involving core level ionization is detected as a function of energy of the primary electron via secondary processes made possible by the core ionization. In soft X-ray appearance potential spectroscopy (SXAPS), the soft X-rays produced in a secondary process of core neutralization are detected. In Auger electron appearance potential spectroscopy (AEAPS), electrons produced by Auger neutralization of the core are detected. In disappearance potential spectroscopy (DAPS), the change in partition between elastic and inelastic scattering as primary energy is varied has been used as the detector of the onset of the inelastic scattering.

Electron spectroscopy can, in general be thought to comprise three elements: (a) a perturbation, (b) an electronic transition process, and (c) an emission process. The perturbation is the agent that causes the electronic process to proceed. It may be an incident photon or electron, a surface electric field, or the presence of a hole in a core level or in an ion outside the surface. The electronic transition process can result in electron excitation, de-excitation, or tunnelling, and can involve one or two electrons. The emission process is the means by which the occurrence of the electronic transition process is detected. It may involve the emission of an electron from the solid, the scattering of an incident electron, or the emission of radiation or electrons produced in secondary de-excitation processes, which occur after and as a result of the basic transition process.

By definition, surface electron spectroscopy always requires the measurement of an electron kinetic energy. This may be the energy of an incident electron, a scattered electron, or an electron ejected from the energy level structure of the surface region. Spectroscopy, therefore determines a function, of which one component is proportional to the relative probability of occurrence of the basic electronic process.

6.2.1 Experimental methods

For the purposes of illustration rather than as a review, we shall largely limit ourselves to the main features of the apparatus of three of the emission spectroscopies: PES, AES, and INS.

Typical electron spectrometers for surface research consist of an ultrahigh vacuum (UHV) chamber (of pressure less than 10^{-7} Pa) that contains the sample, excitation sources for producing electron emission, and an energy analyser for measuring the kinetic energy distribution of the emitted electrons. A schematic diagram for an electron spectrometer is shown in Fig. 6.2[2]. Electron emission from the sample is generated by an electron gun (for AES), an ion gun (for INS), and X-ray source (for XPS), or a UV resonance lamp (for UPS). The emitted electrons are analysed in a field of applied magnetic and/or electric field so that only electrons in the narrow energy range $\Delta E \approx 0.1–0.5$ eV are detected. The applied field is varied linearly with electron energy so that a plot of detector signal versus field corresponds to the electron kinetic energy distribution. In some recently built apparatus, the vacuum chamber may contain electron diffraction apparatus for measuring the surface lattice structure.

A typical electron gun used for AES is shown in Fig. 6.3. For surface studies involving gas adsorption, the indirectly heated cathode is usually replaced by a tungsten cathode.

For INS an ion beam is required, and Hagstrum[3] developed the scheme

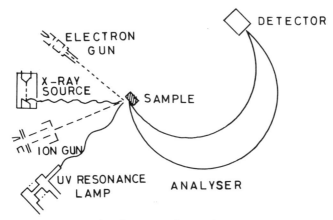

Fig. 6.2 Schematic diagram of an electron spectrometer showing excitation of the sample by an electron gun, X-ray source, ion gun, or UV resonance lamp. The electron kinetic energy distribution is obtained by detecting only those electrons with orbits corresponding to a narrow energy range[2]

shown in Fig. 6.4. The electron beam emitted from filament A_1 or A_2 is accelerated into an ionization chamber D generating ions from helium or neon gas coming through the gas inlet. These ions are extracted through electrodes E and F into a beam formed by the focusing lenses G, H, L, M, and N. The beam is deflected by cross-voltages applied to any symmetrical pair of electrodes having the same letter designation but different subscripts 1 and 2.

The common photon sources fall into two widely different energy ranges. The use of ultraviolet sources from 5 to 50 eV to study the valence shell electronic orbitals and shallow-core levels is a branch of PES known as UPS[4]. The other branch of PES, namely XPS, uses characteristic X-ray lines, usually $Al(K_\alpha)$ or $Mg(K_\alpha)$[5] used with their natural line width (~1 eV). The XPS sources do not have sufficient resolution for valence shell spectroscopy and are used mainly to study core level positions and relative intensities. Resolution has been improved in an appratus that monochromatizes the X-ray

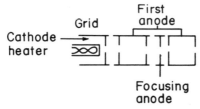

Fig. 6.3 Gun assembly used for producing the electron beam used in Auger electron spectroscopy[2]

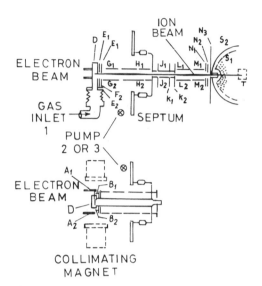

Fig. 6.4 Ion beam source used in ion
neutralization spectroscopy[3]

source[6]. Synchrotron radiation is increasingly being used to fill the energy gap between the ultraviolet and X-ray sources.

Electrons emitted from the sample surface may be energy analysed in one of two types of analysers. These are the retarding field analyser (RFA) and the velocity selection analyser (VSA). Rather large number of designs and geometries are used in electron spectroscopy, and some of the simpler designs are described by Hagstrum, Rowe, and Tracy[2].

Attention should be paid to sample preparation convenient for surface electron spectroscopy, and depending on needs this can be accomplished in several ways. The simplest is vacuum evaporation. However, this method does not always produce single-crystal surfaces, and for certain compounds and alloys which do not evaporate uniformly, non-stoichiometric surfaces are developed. Cleavage in UHV produces clean single-crystal surfaces but with a single orientation. A third method is to remove the outer layers of an oriented crystal by sputter etching with noble gas ions. This is followed by annealing to remove lattice damage and embedded ions introduced by sputtering. This last method is the most widely used, particularly in LEED studies, although one must carefully consider the possibility of selective sputtering from alloys and compounds as well as possible later contamination during annealing due to bulk and/or surface diffusion of impurities.

6.2.2 Applications of photoelectron spectroscopy

Photoelectron spectroscopy (PES) is a powerful method of directly observing electronic orbitals in atoms, molecules, solids, and surfaces. The main reason for the current wide application of PES is the extremely simple principle of interpretation of the photoelectron energy distribution $N_p(E_k)$. This is due to the fact that PES is a one-electron process. The kinetic energy E_k of the photoemitted electron is given by the equation:

$$E_k = E_{fi} - E_{vac} = \hbar\omega - (E_b + \phi_s) \tag{6.1}$$

where

$$\hbar\omega = E_{fi} - E_{in}. \tag{6.2}$$

E_{in} and E_{fi} designate initial and final levels of the photoexcited electron, E_b is the binding energy of the electron in its initial state relative to the Fermi level, and ϕ_s is the work function of the solid. In the one-electron approximation each energy eigenvalue is independent of its occupation and thus E_b is the true binding energy of the photoelectron relative to the Fermi level in the initial state before absorption of the photon. In this case the kinetic energy distribution of photoelectrons is just the one-electron density of initial states weighted by the transition probability and final-state density. For higher photon energy, $\hbar\omega > 10$ eV, the final states produce only a slowly varying contribution, which changes peak positions in $N_p(E_k)$ by about 0.1 to 0.3 eV.

The zero to which the energy scale is referenced is of major importance in surface studies since one would like to compare orbital binding energies of gas phase atoms or molecules with the analogous orbitals for the atom or molecule at the surface of a solid. One could then obtain a measure of the adsorbed atom binding energy to the surface from the shift in the electronic orbitals. An increase in binding energy is expected for the surface atom. However, recent experiments[2] have shown that the binding energy is actually smaller for the surface atom than for a gas phase atom. The solution to this apparent contradiction is the correction to the one-electron energy due to the polarization of the surface electrons by the final-state ion left behind. This is the classical image force polarization, shown in Fig. 6.5.

The curve for X^0 in Fig. 6.5 shows the potential energy as a function of distance d from the surface for a neutral molecule bound to a metal surface by about 1 eV by van der Waals' forces[7]. The curve for X^+ shows lowering by the image potential $- e^2/4(d + D)$, where D is the origin correction derived by Appelbaum and Hamann[8]. The repulsion energy term at $d < 0.1$ nm has been chosen to make the energy minimum fall at $d = 0.15$ nm for both curves. In order to see the effect of the lowering of the energy minimum by the image potential, one has to consider the total energy change in the photo-emission process. The initial state of ground-state atom plus photon has an initial energy that is taken to be

$$E_1 = \hbar\omega - E_{gd} - \phi_s \tag{6.3}$$

where E_{gd} is the orbital energy of the ground state. The final state comprising

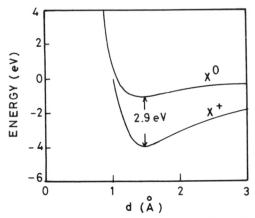

Fig. 6.5 Potential curves representing the
interaction of a neutral atom X^0 and an ion X^+
with a metal surface as discussed in the text[1]

photoelectron, polarized surface, and ion has the energy

$$E_2 = E_k - E_{im} \qquad (6.4)$$

where E_k is the kinetic energy of the photoelectron and $-E_{im}$ is the image
potential energy of the ion on the surface. By the energy conservation principle $E_1 = E_2$, and therefore

$$E_k = \hbar\omega - E_{gd} - \phi_s + E_{im} \qquad (6.5)$$

By comparison with Eq. (6.1) this gives the actual binding energy relative to
the Fermi level:

$$E_b = E_{gd} - E_{im} \qquad (6.6)$$

Thus the measured binding energy is lower than the ground-state binding
energy by the image polorization term E_{im}. It may be possible to determine
E_{im} experimentally from data from different adsorbed states obtained by PES
or other spectroscopies, or by comparing several different orbitals as shown
by Demuth and Eastman[9] for hydrocarbons on nickel surfaces. The assumption involved is that the surface atom position is the same in both states. Also,
the image term is a parameter to be calculated theoretically by constructing a
model of the surface atom binding.

In addition to the surface atom orbital energies and photon energy, which
determine the kinetic energy range in PES, one must consider the transition
probability matrix elements since these determine, in part, the relative
intensities or orbitals seen by PES. Further details are given by Hagstrum
et al.[2].

PES techniques have been used in a vast number of surface studies involving the bonding of foreign atoms to solid surfaces by chemisorption. Representative examples of the work done in this rapidly growing field are given below.

An example of chemisorption involving bonding orbital changes is the Si–O_2 system studied by UPS[10]. Due to the large nearest-neighbour spacing (0.384 nm) in the surface plane, this example provides a random site filling model with negligible adsorbate–adsorbate interaction. Results for $\hbar\omega$ = 21.2 eV are shown in Fig. 6.6. Curve 1 is for the clean surface, and curves 2–4 show the difference between the surface exposed to O_2 and the clean surface with the coverage θ (determined by AES) of 0.26, 0.52, and 1.0, respectively. Four orbitals are observed due to $2p$ electrons of O_2 at −8.3, −11.8, −15.1, and −18.4 eV, which are independent of coverage. This indicates that the O_2 molecule is not completely dissociated upon adsorption since no more than three $2p$ orbitals are possible for a single oxygen atom. Another example is the adsorption of cobalt on tungsten and molybdenum surfaces[11].

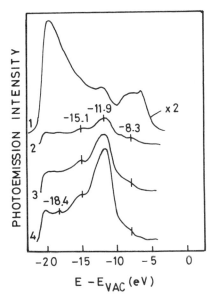

Fig. 6.6 Photoelectric spectra at $\hbar\omega$ = 21.3 eV from clean Si(111) and Si(111) surface (7 × 7 mm) exposed to various amounts of oxygen in the range zero to one monolayer (from Ibach and Rowe[10]); 1 kinetic energy distribution for the clean surface, 2–4 difference spectra of oxygen covered with the clean surface: 2 coverage 0.26, 3 coverage 0.52, 4 totally covered

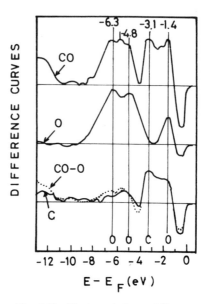

Fig. 6.7 Photoemission difference curves at $\hbar\omega = 21.2$ eV for chemisorbed CO, O, and C on W(100) shown as solid lines. The dotted line shows a 'best-fit' curve to C on W(100), which was obtained by subtracting the CO and O difference curves (from Plummer[11])

The UPS results shown in Fig. 6.7 indicate that dissociation takes place. The solid curves are difference curves for CO, O, and C on W(100), similar to those of Fig. 6.6. A detailed interpretation for each curve is not possible here but it is clear that every peak in the CO curve is reproduced in either the O curve or in the C curve. The dotted line is the weighted difference of the CO and O curves and is a good fit to the measured C curve. Brundle[12] has shown that if CO is adsorbed at low temperatures, a molecular state is found. His results are shown in Fig. 6.8, which shows difference curves for CO adsorption at room temperature and 80 K. The bands are broader than in Fig. 6.7. The 80 K curve indicates a molecular-like adsorption state.

Although XPS can also be used to study valence orbitals, the low intensity and relatively long escape depth have severely limited its application to surface studies. These limitations do not apply to core levels due to higher matrix elements and shorter escape depths for core level photoelectrons compared to valence shell photoelectrons at the same X-ray photon energy.

The core level shifts (i.e. chemical shifts) have been discussed by Siegbahn *et al.*[5,13], with the main idea that the electrostatic field of a core electron has an attractive component due to the positively charged nucleus and repulsive component due to the other electrons. If some valence electrons are removed

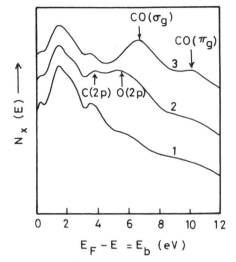

Fig. 6.8 Photoemission spectra at $\hbar\omega = 21.2$ eV for (1) clean Mo at 80 K, (2) Mo with CO adsorbed at 300 K, and (3) Mo with CO adsorbed at 80 K. At $T = 80$ K the adsorbed CO data are mainly due to molecular like orbitals. At 300 K the CO dissociates and has separate C(2p) and O(2p) orbitals (from Brundle[12])

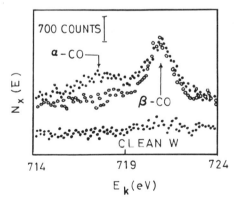

Fig. 6.9 X-ray photoemission spectra of CO on tungsten showing the α-CO and β-CO contribution. The α-CO was identified by thermal desorption, which left only the β-CO on the surface (from Madey et al.[14])

by changing the chemical bonding, the core potential becomes more attractive and the core level binding energy is increased.

Madey *et al.*[14] investigated the adsorption states of carbon monoxide on tungsten by means of XPS. Their results are shown in Fig. 6.9 for the $O(1s)$ core level. The $O(1s)$ for β-CO is at the same energy as for oxygen only adsorbed on tungsten, but α-CO is shifted by about 3 eV to higher binding energy, indicating a molecular state for α-CO but a dissociated state for β-CO. This is consistent with the UPS results for the valence orbitals. For adsorption at 80 to 100 K a third type of binding state is found, which is called 'virgin'-CO. Both the $O(1s)$ and $C(1s)$ core levels for this state are intermediate between the dissociated β-CO state and the more weakly bound α-CO states.

6.2.3 Applications of Auger electron spectroscopy

Auger electron spectroscopy (AES) is one of the most important techniques for determining the elemental composition of the outermost layers of a solid. The popularity of AES is based on its high sensitivity for all atoms except hydrogen and helium, the availability of energy analysers with high transmission, and the good lateral resolution afforded by electron beam excitation. The sensitivity of AES is such that less than 0.01 monolayer of a specific atom situated in the first few atom layers (0.5–1.0 nm) can be detected.

Auger electron spectroscopy is based on the property that each element of the periodic table will, when excited by the ionization of a core level, emit Auger electrons at characteristic energies that are usually only slightly influenced by chemical environment. The exact energies and the shapes of the lines in the Auger emission spectrum are determined by a number of factors, such as the energy and lifetime of the initial core hole, the pertubation, the energy distribution and lifetime of the two final hole states, and the dependence of the transition probability on initial and final states. The results of AES measurements can be used to derive properties of atomic ground states. For qualitative analysis, however, one is concerned with the presence of Auger peaks at their characteristic energies. For quantitative analysis, Auger surface analysis is based on detailed comparative measurements of unknowns with well defined standards.

The use of AES can be conveniently divided into two areas: the establishment of surface cleanliness and the measurement of the surface coverage of an impurity introduced under controlled conditions. The latter use has resulted in important new developments in areas such as adsorption kinetics, oxidation, and catalysis. Kinetics of adsorption depend on surface concentration, binding energy and structure of the adsorbed substance. LEED and work function measurements were combined with AES by Palmberg[15] to study the adsorption of xenon on Pd(100). The results are shown in Fig. 6.10, in which the xenon MNN Auger peak height, work function change, and LEED overlayer intensity are plotted as functions of exposure to Xe gas at 77 K. The linear increase in the Xe Auger signal implies a constant sticking

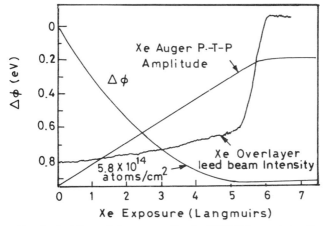

Fig. 6.10   Plots of Auger amplitude, LEED beam intensity, and $\Delta\phi$ measured during adsorption of Xe on Pd(100) (from Palmberg[15])

probability up to a saturation level at 6 L (Langmuirs), which correspond to a coverage of 5.8×10^{14} atoms/cm² as obtained from LEED experiment. The degree of coverage and the Auger signal strength of saturation yields a value of unity for the constant sticking probability below and on abrupt drop to zero above 6 L. This established the $\Delta\phi$-coverage relation, which agrees with a Topping model for dipole–dipole interactions[15].

Oxidation of a metal involves chemisorption of oxygen, the penetration of oxygen into the selvedge, and the growth of the oxide layer. Kinetics of the

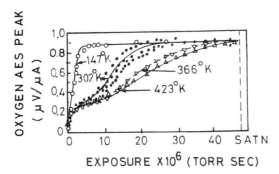

Fig. 6.11   Oxygen AES peak intensity versus exposure of a Ni(111) surface for very long times. Growth of NiO islands occurs in the range where the curves show an 'inverse' behaviour with respect to temperature. The lines through the data in this region are predictions of a model with adjusted parameters (From Holloway and Hudson[16])

initial oxidation of nickel single crystals was studied by Holloway and Hudson[16] using AES, LEED, and work function measurements. Initially a chemisorbed structure is formed on the nickel lattice, and after saturation, islands of NiO (a few layers thick) start nucleation and grow laterally till a continuous film is formed (Fig. 6.11). A third stage of very slow 'bulk' oxidation was also observed.

The high sensitivity of AES makes it also ideally suited for studies of catalytic reactions involving varying surface concentrations[2].

6.2.4 Applications of field emission and ion neutralization spectroscopies

Field emission and ion neutralization spectroscopies (FES, INS) have an important common feature which involves the tunnelling of an electron through a potential barrier at the surface of the solid. Both spectroscopies are surface sensitive and tend to favour the detection of electronic states from which electrons tunnel most easily. Both FES and INS require specific data reduction procedures in order to extract from the raw data the initial-state transition density functions that contain the desired information about surface electronic structure. In FES the data reduction is made necessary by the rapidly varying average tunnelling current caused by the rapid thickening of the barrier with energy below the Fermi level. The removal of this component is accomplished by dividing the measured energy distribution $j(E)$ by a calculated free-electron energy distribution $J_0(E)$[17]. This ratio is called the enhancement factor:

$$R(E) = j(E)/J_0(E) \qquad (6.7)$$

FES has been applied to the study of clean metal surface states on metals and the energy levels of adsorbed species, and Fig. 6.12 shows plots of the enhancement factor $R(E)$ of FES for the clean (111), (112), (100), and (110) faces of tungsten and the results indicate that the local density of states at the surface varies from one face of a clean crystal to another[17]. Also, Fig. 6.13 shows field emission and photoemission results demonstrating the disappearance of a surface-state peak as the surface adsorbs hydrogen[18]. Adatom energy levels have been observed for zirconium, barium, calcium, hydrogen, and oxygen on tungsten tips. It has been clearly demonstrated that the 'sensitivity volume' of FES may be considered to be the region near the classical turning point in which wave function magnitude governs the tunnelling characteristics.

INS has been applied in the study of clean metal[19] and semiconductor surfaces[20], and nickel surfaces having chalcogens adsorbed in a variety of surface arrays[21,22]. Evidence has been presented for band narrowing of the nickel d-band at the surface[19], and for the dependence of the molecular orbital spectrum of an adsorbed surface molecule on the local bonding possibilities[21]. INS has also been used in conjunction with UPS in the study of adsorbed species such as for tellurium adsorption on Ni(100)[23].

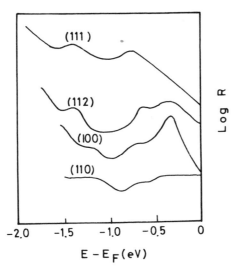

Fig. 6.12 Plots of the enhancement factor $R(E)$ of FES for the clean (111), (112), (100), and (110) faces of tungsten. Curves shifted vertically for clarity (From Gadzuk and Plummer[17])

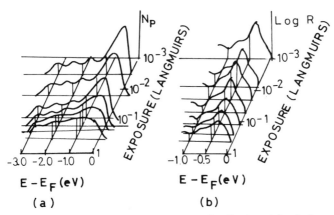

Fig. 6.13 Plots of the kinetic energy distribution (a) of electrons photoemitted from polycrystalline tungsten by light of energy $\hbar\omega = 7.7$ eV, and (b) of the field emission enhancement factor. Several curves are shown as the surface in each case is exposed to hydrogen (From Waclawski and Plummer[18])

6.2.5 Applications of appearance potential and energy loss spectroscopies

Appearance potential and energy loss spectroscopies (APS, ELS) are based on the same electronic process, in which an incident electron loses energy E and a bound electron in the solid gains the same amount of energy. They are also characterized by the fact that the kinetic energy of the excited or 'up'-electron is not measured. Thus for valence levels no direct determination is made of the energy levels between which the excited electron transits. If the initial state of the up-electron is a core level, it is usually possible to identify it and to pin down the transition.

These spectroscopies have been used as chemical identifiers and as probes of unfilled conduction and surface state as well as filled valence and surface states. In general, we would expect APS and ELS to complement AES because X-ray fluorescence increases and Auger emission decreases as atomic number increases. However, as pointed out by Park and Houston[24] in their review of the method, the insensitivity of SXAPS is not purely a matter of atomic number since elements as light as boron and as heavy as thorium give excellent spectra. Attention should be paid to the effects of the density of conduction band states, core hole lifetimes, final-state interactions, and other factors. As to the surface or bulk character of the final-state densities determined by ELS and APS, it has been pointed out by Park and Houston that APS yields a local density of unfilled levels in the vicinity of the atom whose core electron is excited. Determination of whether the atom lies on the surface or in the selvedge must be made in other ways. States found to lie in the energy gaps of semiconductors above the Fermi level E_F must clearly be surface states. But the determination as to whether an ELS or APS result applies to atoms in the surface monolayer is difficult in general.

The field is still growing rapidly, but one early example is the study of the vibrational modes of oxygen chemisorbed on the cleaved Si(111) surface, thoroughly investigated by Ibach et al.[25]. Figure 6.14 shows the variation of the energy loss spectrum with oxygen coverage. The 56-eV phonon peak largely disappears, being replaced with a weak structure at 48 eV, while two strong oxygen-related vibrations appear at 94 and 130 meV with a third weaker peak at 175 meV. Simply from the fact that three vibrational modes are observed, these investigators ruled out three possible structures for which the maximum number of vibrational modes is less than three. It is not possible

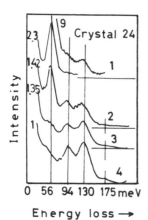

Fig. 6.14 Energy loss spectra of oxygen adsorbed on a cleaved Si(111) Surface at different coverages θ (from Ibach et al.[25]; 1 $\theta = 0.06$, 2 $\theta = 0.2$, 3 $\theta = 0.3$, 4 $\theta = 0.6$

to discriminate between two models involving two oxygen atoms bridged in two configurations between two silicon atoms. Adsorption kinetics as determined by the rate of growth of energy loss peaks is confirmed by the rates of change of oxygen surface concentration determined by AES and of surface optical properties measured by ellipsometry. High-resolution spectroscopy of electron energy losses at surfaces is obviously an important part of surface electron spectroscopy.

6.3 Diffraction

In crystals the primary concern is to determine the lengths and angles of the bonds between the atoms. The first assumption is that the crystal is made up of identical unit cells which repeat themselves. Of course, in practice, the situation is not that perfect. Electron diffraction techniques have been used extensively in studies of surfaces and of chemisorption[26,27].

In low-energy electron diffraction (LEED), the elastic scattering of electrons with energies below perhaps 200 eV reflects the surface properties of a solid because of the probability that electron–electron interactions will cause an electron to lose several electron volts before it penetrates more than a few atomic layers. Usually, atoms in this surface region of the solid are arranged differently than in parallel layers of the substrate, even in cases of clean solids[28]. Actually, therefore, two surfaces exist: the substrate surface, marking the disappearance of the bulk periodicity, and the selvedge surface, which is the actual physical surface. The term 'selvedge' usually describes the region 1–5 atomic layers thick. For most metal surfaces studied to date, however, the periodicity and symmetry parallel to the surface is the same as that of the substrate, and it is assumed that the periodicity perpendicular to the surface is changed, but this parameter is difficult to measure. On the other hand, increased amplitude of thermal vibration of selvedge atoms, reflecting the reduced energy of binding in this region, has been observed[26].

Because of the limited penetration and the variation of crystal parameters with depth in the selvedge, a useful model of the crystal surface is a stack of atomic layers. The directions of the diffraction beams are functions of the distances between rows of atoms in the various planes, and the geometry is described in terms of a two-dimensional 'net' of equivalent points which form a 'unit mesh'. The unit mesh may be described by unit vectors a_1 and a_2 and the interaxial angle γ. Five nets are used to describe diperiodic structures, namely the square, the rectangle, the centred rectangle, the hexagonal ($\gamma = 120°$), and the oblique or parallelogram. The surface atomic layer is represented by its reciprocal lattice (Fig. 6.15), with unit reciprocal mesh vectors a_1 and a_2 and angle γ^*, where

$$a_1^* \cdot a_j = 2\pi\delta_{ij} \quad \text{and} \quad \gamma^* = 180 - \gamma \qquad (6.8)$$

The diffraction geometry is visualized by the Ewald construction. For cubic crystals the reciprocal net plane is parallel to the real surface, in which the

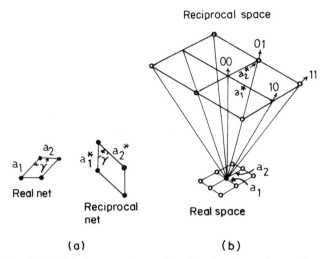

Fig. 6.15 (a) A comparison of real and reciprocal nets. In the example, a_1^* and a_1 are chosen equal. (b) For a cubic crystal the two-dimensional reciprocal net is parallel to the real surface[29]

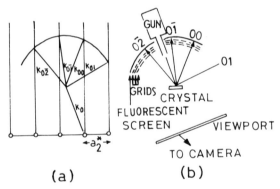

Fig. 6.16 (a) The Ewald construction in a plane perpendicular to the surface and parallel to a_2^* corresponding to a LEED pattern with primary energy of about 40 eV and a 20° angle of incidence. (b) A schematic diagram of the LEED apparatus for the conditions shown in (a). The grids are based to return inelastically scattered electrons to the crystal. The screen is maintained at a high positive potential (5 kV) giving the elastic electrons enough energy to produce fluorescence when they strike the screen[24]

incident beam makes the same angle with the surface normal as in real space and is represented by the wave vector $K_0 = 2\pi/\lambda$, terminating at the origin 00 of the reciprocal net. In Fig. 6.16(a), the Ewald sphere is drawn with k_0 as radius and normals are drawn through the points of the reciprocal net plane to intersect the sphere. Vectors K drawn from the centre of the sphere to these intersections represent the diffracted beams and they satisfy both the conditions of energy conservation,

$$k^2 = k_0^2 \qquad (6.9)$$

and momentum conservation, which due to the translational symmetry of the atomic layer, the momentum parallel to the layer is multivalued.

$$K_{11} = K_{011} + a_b{}^*_k \qquad (6.10)$$

where a_{bk}^* are reciprocal lattice vectors laying in the surface.

In the LEED apparatus (Fig. 6.16(b)), the diffracted beams are transmitted through the spherical grids and accelerated to approximately 5 kV to produce visible spots on the spherical fluorescent screen, and the inelastically scattered electrons are rejected by grids. The image is that of the two-dimensional reciprocal lattice net.

New diffraction beams appear when new periodic surface structures form. The superposition of two nets results in a pattern described by

$$\tilde{n}_a a^* + \tilde{n}_b b^* = \tilde{n}_c c^* \qquad (6.11)$$

where $\tilde{n}_a, \tilde{n}_b$ are integer row matrices and a^*, b^* two-element column matrices describing the substrate and surface reciprocal nets. If $\tilde{n}_a$ is zero, $\tilde{n}_c c^*$ describes the new surface structure beams, and if $\tilde{n}_b$ is zero, $\tilde{n}_c c^*$ describes the substrate beams.

In adsorption studies, the nets a and b are frequently related and the superposition can be described by a third net c, where

$$c = Pa = Nb \qquad (6.12)$$

where P and N are 2×2 transformation matrices chosen that det P and det N are integers with no common factor. The areas of the nets a and b, namely A and B, are related by

$$B/A = \det P/\det N \qquad (6.13)$$

Further details are given by Armstrong[29] and the review articles cited there.

Simple structures are frequently found in adsorption studies, especially if the adsorption is localized and takes place in an ordered array of adsorption sites. If one takes into account the adsorbate–adsorbent interaction energy (E_{AS}) and adsorbate–adsorbate interaction energy (E_{AA}), it follows that:

1. If $E_{AS} > E_{AA}$ independent of coverage, the adsorbed atoms should occupy the minimum of the surface potential and simple structures form.

2. If $E_{AA} > E_{AS}$, the ordering becomes characteristic of the adsorbate layer itself and close packing is common for certain metal coverage.

At present, there is no clear-cut method of determining the actual net b[29], and frequently several possible structures exist that could result in the observed reciprocal net c^*. To illustrate some of the possibilities Estrup and McRae[30] show six doubly spaced structures for a diatomic molecule such as hydrogen, which would give the same diffraction pattern (Fig. 6.17). The particles may be adsorbed as atoms (a) or as molecules (b). They may lie above (a) or between (c) surface atoms. The substrate may be reconstructed in a variety of ways (d–f). These different possibilities result in identical diffraction patterns that have different intensity distributions.

May[31] has collected several references for the adsorption of O_2, N_2, H_2, and CO on a whole series of metal surfaces. Somorjai[32] has arranged tables for numerous surface structures found on a large number of elemental crystal surfaces, arranged according to substrate symmetry, and he came to the conclusion that ordered adsorption is the common rule.

It must be mentioned here that the diffraction pattern alone does not permit a unique determination of the surface net b. Calibrated AES and/or thermal desorption are frequently used in conjunction with diffraction measurements to determine surface coverage, which normally will be equivalent to determining the area of unit mesh B, which will help in limiting the number of possible meshes.

It is not known to what extent such diffraction studies can be applied to real solids, that is, to high-area, polycrystalline alloy surfaces in the presence of high gas pressures of complex molecules. The nature and geometry of adsorption sites have only been determined in the simplest cases. Rearrangement of surfaces is difficult to measure, and departures from crystalline perfection such as steps, corners, pits, etc., can at best be detected but as yet cannot be assessed quantitatively.

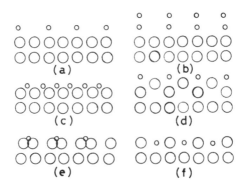

Fig. 6.17 Six different one-dimensional structures that give the same diffraction pattern[30]

Despite these shortcomings, the reader in the field can see the possibility that electron diffraction will become an important tool in determining the details of surface structure and surface reactions. This aspect of LEED is certain to be exploited in the next few years.

Reflection high-energy electron diffraction (RHEED) received initial enthusiasm on the hope that the same analytical methods that were known to suffice for transmission high-energy electron diffraction would render the solution of the surface structure problem more tractable than in the case of LEED. This optimism was quickly dispelled by the realization that the same considerations of momentum transfer govern both techniques. The authors are unaware of actual analysis of RHEED intensities that has been performed for even the clean-surface case.

One advantage of the RHEED technique is that a high-energy electron beam excites X-rays characteristic of the elements in the surface region, thus permitting simultaneous examination of both surface structure and composition[33]. A number of comparisons of LEED and RHEED have confirmed, however, that both methods provided information that is essentially equivalent[34]. Because of the grazing incidence, RHEED is more affected by surface morphology and hence may reveal islands of oxides or other impurities which do not show up in LEED.

6.4 Photon spectroscopy–Infrared Spectroscopy

The popularity of electron spectroscopies lies in the ease with which electrons can be manipulated by electrostatic or magnetic fields. Decay of the excited state is accompanied by the emission of photons as well as electrons, and for many purposes the indifference of photons to field is an advantage. Thus, for example, bond formation in chemisorption may be accompanied by emission of photons[35] at energies where electron emission is forbidden by the work function . Photon spectroscopies are therefore expected to have unique advantages at very low energies, although at all energies they offer an important source of surface information.

Infrared spectroscopy has proved to be the most popular technique in surface chemistry, among the other photon spectroscopies, and is widely used to identify species at solid surfaces. This popularity might be attributed to the relatively modest experimental requirements in comparison with many other methods of surface investigation, and also to the fact that it can provide more insight into the chemical nature of the surface layer.

6.4.1 Transmission spectroscopy

Eischens in his early work[36] showed that conventional transmission infrared spectrophotometers might be used to provide direct chemical information on the acidic character, Lewis or Brönsted, of silica-alumina cracking catalysts. This could be inferred from the spectrum of adsorbed ammonia, and was found to depend on the degree of surface dehydration.

Successful extension of surface infrared spectroscopy from these early applications to a wide variety of adsorption and chemisorption systems is summarized by Little[37] and Hair[38].

Most practical solids are transparent to infrared radiation, but the surfaces of high-area materials are often very heterogeneous. The spectra of molecules adsorbed at various sites may contribute to the measured spectrum and render it very difficult to interpret. Therefore reference spectra of well defined systems are highly desirable, and infrared spectra can be combined with results from LEED, photoelectron spectroscopy, etc., to extend our understanding of the fundamentals of surface interactions.

The identification of surface species by infrared spectroscopy has been based generally on the recognition of group frequencies by matching the surface spectra with those of known compounds. The frequencies in adsorbed molecules may be expected to parallel those of molecules in liquids and gases provided they are remote from the dense band of low-lying lattice vibrational frequencies of the solid adsorbent.

The ability to detect an absorption band in either transmission spectroscopy or reflection spectroscopy depends on the absolute magnitude of the intensity change as the peak is scanned.

Samples are usually handled by the pressed-disk technique, and extensive reviews of methods and results are available. In addition to the books already mentioned[37,38], the reader is referred to articles by Eischens and Pliskin[36], Blyholder[39], and Basila[40]. Practical aspects of sample preparation and cell construction are given by Parkyns[41]. The main advantage of the pressed-disk method is the large surface area available within the infrared beam, resulting in large concentrations of adsorbed species even at low surface coverages. A typical oxide disk may weigh about 20 mg cm^{-2} and possess a specific surface area of 100 m^2 gm^{-1}. The total surface area in a sample of size 1 cm^2 would then be 2 m^2. A supported metal sample may certain 10% metal by weight with an average particle size of 10 nm. Assuming a density of 10 gm cm^{-3}, we obtain a metal area of about 10^3 cm^2 per cm^2 of disk.

An important limitation of the method is set by the absorption of the oxide lattice. Silica disks lose transparency progressively below 2000 cm^{-1} and are opaque between 1300 and 200 cm^{-1}. This is a disadvantage for the study of supported metals. Alumina is somewhat better in this respect as it retains some transparency to about 1000 cm^{-1}.

A wide variety of cells has been designed for use with pressed disks. An example is shown in Fig. 6.18 for the cell designed by Avery[42] for the study of olefin adsorption on silica-supported palladium. The design permits rapid cooling of the nickel-plated copper sample container with liquid nitrogen as well as electrical heating for high-temperature treatment. With greased joints and stopcocks the typical ultimate vacua have been in the 10^{-4} Pa range, and were later replaced by Viton O-ring seals[43]. Fully bakable UHV cells can be constructed with sapphire or periclose windows sealed directly to glass, but these materials restrict the spectral range to frequencies above about 1800 or 1000 cm^{-1}.

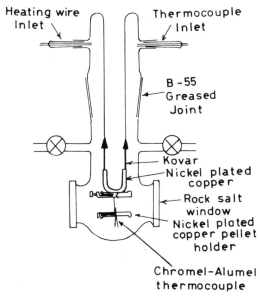

Fig. 6.18   Cell for transmission infrared spectroscopy by the pressed-disk method (after Avery[42])

The pressed-disk method is unsuitable for supported metals, and the main
problem is the possible incomplete reduction. This led to the exploration of
metals using evaporated films deposited on transparent substrates such as
CaF_2 or NaCl. Films produced by evaporating metal wires or beads and
allowing the vapour to condense on a cool substrate in an ultrahigh vacuum
have been extensively used for chemisorption investigations[44]. Porous fibres
of large specific surface area can be produced in this way, and as fresh surface
is created *in vacuo* the problems of reduction or of cleaning initially contaminated surface are avoidable. The infrared cell must be fully bakable.
Glass cells with periclase or sapphire windows are convenient but the windows restrict the wavelength range severely.

The large specific surface areas of porous films cannot be fully exploited in
transmission spectroscopy. Only very thin films ($\leq$ 10 nm) are suitable and
thicker films absorb or reflect two strongly. A simple glass cell with periclase
windows is shown in Fig. 6.19[45], and was used to study the adsorption of CO
and N_2 on nickel films.

In general, evaporated metal films gave results which agree with those on
supported metals, provided that the latter have not been strongly influenced
by impurities. In other respects films have little advantage[46]. Not only are the
spectra weak, but the very thin films, which are mostly discontinuous, are no
better defined structurally than the supported metals and they are much less
thermally stable, and are susceptible to sintering. One approach to reduce
sintering and to obtain thicker films with gain in sensitivity, is to evaporate the
metal in the presence of an adsorbable gas, usually CO[47].

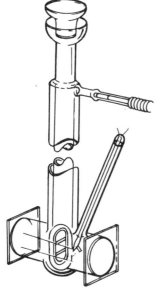

Fig. 6.19 UHV cell for evaporated films, with MgO windows sealed directly to the glass body. Films deposited from a shielded filament onto NaCl or CaF_2 plates clipped to the coolable re-entrant (after Bradshaw and Pritchard[45])

An interesting alternative to all the foregoing methods is that of matrix isolation, applied by Blyholder and Tanaka[48,49] to chemisorption studies. Metal vapour is first condensed with diluent argon on a salt plate at 44 K and a further layer of CO and argon is condensed on it. On warming, inter-diffusion leads to reaction of CO with small nickel particles in a clean environment. Temperature rise produces irreversible changes, but the technique is of particular promise for the characterization of small clusters of metal atoms with carbonyl ligands, etc., as models for the smaller metal particles in practical supported catalysts.

We have emphasized that evaporated metal films suitable for transmission spectroscopy have a poorly defined structure and the spectra of adsorbed species, similar to the case of supported metals, are likely to be complicated by surface heterogeneity. Much more homogeneous surfaces are obtained with alkali halide films, and because of the transparency of the alkali halide in the infrared region, much thicker films can be used in order to enhance the intensity of the spectrum. Such films have been used mostly for physical adsorption studies. Examples are the adsorption of H_2 on sodium chloride[50], of CO_2 on NaCl[51], and of CO on caesium halides[52].

6.4.2 Reflection spectroscopy

Reflection methods can only be applied to well-defined metal surfaces, including single crystals of 1 cm^2 in size[53]. The technique is complicated by the more demanding ultra-high vacuum necessary for clean single-crystal studies, the optical modifications necessary with the standard spectrometers, and particularly the sensitivity problem. In a single reflection, an infrared beam may interact with about 10^{15} adsorbed molecules, compared with 10^{18} in a typical transmission experiment. Multiple reflection certainly assists up to a point, and Pickering and Eckstrom[54] used up to 35 reflections at near normal incidence to detect weak bands of CO and H_2 adsorbed on rhodium and nickel-film mirrors. In their work, however, they used small angles of incidence. The advantage of large angles of incidence was pointed out in the analytical theory developed by Francis and Ellison[55]. This theory was restricted, however, by the approximations that were made to retain analytical expressions, and Greenler[56] extended the theory to define optimal conditions more clearly. The applications of multiple-reflection methods to the study of relatively thick films, including oxide films on aluminium, iron, and copper; corrosion inhibitors; and oil oxidation products on copper, have been reviewed by Poling[57].

The first observations of reflection-absorption spectra on metal surfaces were of CO chemisorbed on copper films at room temperature[58]. High angles of incidence were obtained by depositing the films on glass plates 70 mm in length and spaced 0.5 mm apart to form a light guide. Figure 6.20 shows the hinged glass plates that formed the light guide. Because of the angular range of the focused radiation, not all rays underwent the same number of reflections. Transmitted radiation that had undergone a given number of reflections corresponded to a narrow range of angles of incidence and could be separately collected and detected. In this way the intensity of absorption per reflection in several narrow angular ranges could be measured[59].

A disadvantage of this cell is the difficulty of controlling the film temperature, but this difficulty was overcome by using resistively heated tantalum ribbons as substrates for evaporated copper[60] and gold[61] films. Figure 6.21 shows the sensitivity of reflection-absorption spectroscopy for chemisorbed CO on gold, a measurable band being produced from 5% of monolayer

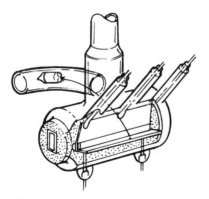

Fig. 6.20 Cell for multiple reflections between copper mirrors evaporated onto hinged glass plates (after Pritchard and Sims[59])

264

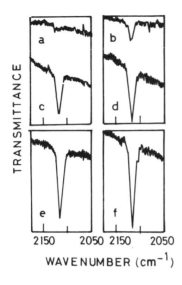

TRANSMITTANCE

a
b
c
d
e
f

2150   2050 2150   2050

WAVENUMBER (cm^{-1})

Fig. 6.21 Spectra showing the variation with pressure of the 2115-cm^{-1} band of CO adsorbed on gold: (a) 1 Pa, (b) 14 Pa, (c) 65 Pa, (d) 134 Pa, (e) 400 Pa, (f) 400 Pa (after Kottke et al.[61])

coverage. Obviously, single, narrow, and intense bands were obtained with chemisorbed CO. Spectra of CO on evaporated nickel fibres have also been recorded using a hinged glass plate cell[62], and good agreement was found with previous transmission spectra[45].

In most reflection-absorption studies the spectra have been recorded in a conventional way, with a single beam, and occasionally with a double beam. A baseline spectrum of the initial or clean surface is first recorded, and then, after introduction of the adsorbate, a sample spectrum is recorded. The difference is taken as the adsorbate spectrum. Digital recording facilitates accurate extraction of the adsorbate spectrum.

Wavelength modulation has been employed for measurements on single-crystal surfaces[63,64]. The techniques and advantages of wavelength modulation for the detection of weak spectral features in reflectance spectra of solids have been extensively described[65].

6.5 Internal reflection spectroscopy

The reflection methods described above are most appropriate for metals but not for solids that are transparent in the infrared region. Internal reflection spectroscopy has been applied to silicon surfaces[66] and to some oxide surfaces[67]. The method depends on the fact that radiation entering a parallel-sided crystal through a bevelled face is totally internally reflected at the parallel faces, if incident at above the critical angle, and the beam emerges, after several reflections, at another bevelled face. The phenomena have been extensively reviewed by Harrick[68] and Fahrenfort[69]. In spite of the fact that the method is attractive in principle, it has been very little used. Absorption of energy by the bulk solid restricts its application to rather narrower spectral ranges than the pressed-disk transmission method. One of its most successful applications is the study of water adsorption and surface hydroxyl species on alumina, magnesia, titania, and zinc oxide[66].

6.6 Raman spectroscopy

Vibrational spectra can also be obtained by Raman spectroscopy. Applications to surface spectroscopy have been reviewed by Hendra[70,71]. Most work has been carried out on high-area porous materials which carry the advantage of low Raman scattering due to the bulk vibrational modes of many oxides. For adsorption on metals, however, the same physical factors that limit infrared reflection-absorption spectroscopy also limit the exciting field in Raman scattering. Greenler and Slager[72] have discussed the optimization of angles of incidence and collection for the adsorption of benzoic acid on a silver film.

Raman studies have been reported for acetone adsorption on alumina[73], pyridine adsorption on silica, magnesium oxide, alumina, and titanium dioxide[74], and of the adsorption of several species on zeolites[75].

Raman spectra ($950-1100$ cm^{-1}) of pyridine adsorbed on several oxides[74,76] suggest that the spectral positions of the observed bands may be used as a means of characterizing acidic adsorption sites on the surfaces of solids. Raman bands at 1019, 1019, and 1020 cm^{-1} were observed following the adsorptions of pyridine on η-alumina, γ-alumina, and silica doped with Al^{3+} respectively. These bands are close to those for electron donor–acceptor complexes in which pyridine is behaving as a Lewis base and they therefore confirm the presence of Lewis acid sites in the surface of alumina or the aluminium-doped silica. The position (1016 cm^{-1}) of the corresponding band for pyridine on titania has been taken as indicating that Lewis sites on titania are more weakly acidic than those on alumina[76]. Pyridine adsorbs on Cab-O-Sil silica to give Raman bands at 1007 and 1034 cm^{-1}, and on silica gel to give bands at 1010 and 1036 cm^{-1} [77], which have been ascribed to hydrogen bonding interaction between surface hydroxyl groups and adsorbate molecules.

A Raman study of the adsorption of 2-chloropyridine on silica has confirmed that steric factors may influence the adsorptive properties of base molecules being used as probes for the characterization of surface acidity[77].

6.7 Nuclear magnetic resonance spectroscopy

Nuclear magnetic resonance (NMR) studies of surfaces may generally be divided into three categories, namely chemical shift measurements; relaxation time measurements; and studies of line-widths, line-shapes, and second moments. Aspects of theory relevant to surface studies have been summarized by Packer[78], Pfeifer[79], and Derouane et al.[80], but the analysis of NMR data relating to surface species is complex, especially when molecular motion is involved, and both Packer[78] and Fripiat[81] have stressed that NMR measurements are more useful when considered in conjunction with results obtained by other experimental techniques.

O'Reilly et al.[82] and Hall et al.[83] were among the first to study silicas, and they found that the hydrogen atoms of surface hydroxyl groups gave a proton magnetic resonance (PMR) signal, with a half-band width that did not vary over the temperature range −210 to 280 °C. These indications were taken to suggest that the hydrogen atoms are rigidly attached to hydroxyl groups which are randomly distributed over a small fraction of the total possible number of available sites in the surface. Thus, the chemical shift of −3 ± 2 ppm relative to water indicates that the hydrogen atoms are similar in character to alcoholic hydroxyl groups.

Bermudez[84] has suggested a method for evaluating the population of surface hydroxyl groups from the line widths of PMR signals, and a value of the surface concentration of silanol groups of 4.2 groups/nm^2 was obtained for a high area silica gel (800 m^2 gm^{-1}).

Measurements of line-widths, line-shapes, and second moments were used to gain information about hydroxyl groups on silica surfaces and the uptake of water by silica[85,86]. Second moments of the PMR signals due to three different types of hydroxyl groups on silica at 93 K were measured, and relative proportions of isolated hydroxyl groups, pairs of hydroxyl groups (vicinal or geminal), and hydroxyl groups with two or more neighbouring hydroxyl groups were deduced.

Second moment measurements were also used to follow the progressive dehydration of magnesium oxide prepared from the hydroxide[87]. The results are consistent with desorption by growth of vacant areas leaving clusters of hydroxyl groups.

Measurements of spin–spin and spin–lattice relaxation times using pulse (spin echo) NMR techniques were used to give information concerning the molecular mobility of adsorbed species. It could be shown that the protons of water adsorbed on silica gel exist in two distinct states characterized by different spin–spin relaxation times[88–90]. Spin–lattice relaxation data were also consistent with 'two-phase' behaviour[90], and that transfer of water molecules occurs between the two states on the surface. Studies of relaxation behaviour as a function of temperature gave information concerning the motional phenomena of protons in water molecules adsorbed in either state on silica[91,92].

A physical interpretation of the two-phase relaxation phenomena observed by Zimmerman et al.[88], was suggested by Winkler[93] who proposed that micropores in the silica samples were responsible for the experimental results. The detailed studies of Clifford and Lecchini[94] showed that the existence and size of micropores in silica had a profound influence on the PMR relaxation times for adsorbed water.

A comprehensive bibliography of systems studied by NMR techniques was given by Pfeifer[79]. NMR studies of adsorbates other than water can give information about the chemical nature of functional groups or sites on surfaces of solids. Thus, for example, results from investigations of the adsorption of ammonia[95] or other amines[96] have contributed to our understanding of the acid–base properties of oxide surfaces.

6.8 Electron spin resonance spectroscopy

Electron spin resonance (ESR) spectroscopy is well established for the study of free radicals, paramagnetic ions, and charge transfer interactions. The same technique has been widely used for the investigation of species on the surfaces of solids, such as paramagnetic ionic sites and electron donor or acceptor species on oxide surfaces. Free radical species on carbon surfaces have been largely characterized using ESR spectroscopy[97]. The technique has the advantage of being extremely sensitive, and therefore allows for the detection of extremely small concentrations of paramagnetic species at interfaces.

The use of ESR spectroscopy for the characterization of paramagnetic ionic species on solid surfaces is exemplified by studies of O^-, O_2^- and O_3^- ions on oxides. Results for magnesium oxide, tin(IV) oxide, anatase, rutile, and zinc oxide have been given by Lunsford[98], and for zinc oxide and titanium dioxide surfaces by Ivengar and Codell[99].

ESR spectroscopy can give information about the electron donor or electron acceptor properties of adsorption sites on oxide surfaces. The ESR spectra of the electron acceptor molecule TCNQ (tetracyanoquinodimethane) adsorbed on magnesia, γ-alumina, silica, anatase, zinc oxide and nickel oxide have been reported[100]. The electron donor properties of the oxides were compared by evaluation of the relative radical concentrations per unit area of surface (spin number metre^{-2}) from the observed signal intensities. One type of donor site in the surface may involve hydroxyl ions for which the electron transfer process may be represented by:

$$OH^- + TCNQ \rightarrow OH + TCNQ^- \tag{6.14}$$

It was therefore suggested[100] that the ESR results reflected in part the different electron donor properties of surface hydroxyl groups on oxides. The results were also probably a function of the semiconducting properties of the oxides since adsorption sites involving an anion deficiency may also donate electrons to TCNQ molecules.

The electron acceptor properties of surface sites may be characterized by measurement of the ESR spectra of adsorbed electron donor molecules. Thus, for example, ESR spectra of radical cations formed by adsorption of polynuclear aromatic hydrocarbons onto silica-alumina[101,102], mixed oxides[103], and zeolites[104] have been reported. The ESR technique provides a method for the characterization of Lewis acidic electron acceptor sites on oxide or other surfaces.

6.9 Mössbauer spectroscopy

Mössbauer spectroscopy[105] involves the recoil-free emission and resonant reabsorption of γ-rays by atomic nuclei. Early studies of surface species were reported in 1964[106,107,108], and since then the application in surface studies has been reviewed by Low[109], Delgass and Boudart[110], and Hobson[111].

Mössbauer spectra due to atoms or ions in the surface of solids can give information concerning the oxidation state and the stereochemical environment of the atoms, the nature of electric and magnetic fields around the atoms, and the motion of the atoms about their equilibrium sites. The effect is often too weak to be detectable experimentally, and experimental limitations have confined the majority of studies to about 10–15 elements. Iron happens to be the easiest of all elements to study by this technique. Very few studies of surfaces have involved elements other than iron or tin.

Work with iron is exemplified by experimental results for iron oxide supported on silica or alumina. Flinn et al.[112] assigned the observed spectral peaks to Fe^{3+} ions in octahedral sites on the alumina surface. Later on, it became accepted that the spectra are due to small crystallites of finely divided iron oxide within the samples[113–116]. The observation that the size of crystallites influences some of the parameters of the Mössbauer spectra led to a method of estimating the crystallite size from Mössbauer spectra[114]. Also the influence of particle shape and size on Mössbauer spectra of unsupported oxides is exemplified by the results of McNab et al.[117] for Fe_3O_4, and Takada et al.[118] for α-Fe_2O_3.

Mössbauer spectroscopy has been used for the observation of adsorption phenomena and for the characterization of adsorption sites. Ferric ions were reduced to ferrous ions by the chemisorption of ammonia[119] which suggests that the ferric ions are near the catalyst surface.

Information concerning the motion of ions about their equilibrium sites in surfaces can also be deduced from Mössbauer spectra. Thus, for example, Suzdalev et al.[120] deduced that for SnO surface species chemisorbed on silica gel, the root mean displacement of the tin atoms perpendicular to the surface (about 0.013 nm) is about twice the root mean square displacement parallel to the surface.

Information concerning the structure and properties of cationic sites in zeolites can be deduced from Mössbauer spectra. There have been some reports of Mössbauer studies of cations, particularly Fe^{2+} and Fe^{3+} ions in zeolites[111].

6.10 Desorption methods

These are methods which result in desorption of the adlayer and analysis of the desorbed material. There are as many different techniques available as there are methods of inducing desorption of the adlayer. These include thermal desorption, electron impact desorption, field desorption, ion impact desorption, and photon- and phonon-induced desorption. It should be pointed out that all desorption methods are structure-breaking techniques, and it will lead to a breakage of a surface complex into simpler gas-phase species on desorption. Different desorption methods, such as thermal and field desorption, are likely to break down the surface complex in different ways, and thus by using different methods it is more likely that the correct structure for the complex will be deduced. The chances of a correct analysis are increased even more if desorption is preceded by nondestructive analysis of the adlayer by the methods discussed earlier in this chapter. Also, as an alternative to analysis of the desorbed gas it is possible to follow the desorption process by following the change in some surface property of the solid accompanying the decrease in surface coverage.

Important information obtained from desorption methods includes surface analysis, namely surface concentration and stoichiometry, and sometimes the nature of the surface species. The information gained from some of the most commonly used techniques in this field will be discussed below.

6.10.1 Thermal desorption method

The thermal desorption method is probably more frequently used than any other single technique in the field. The desorption rate is extremely temperature sensitive, and is normally described by an Arrhenius (or Polanyi–Wigner) equation:

$$-\mathrm{d}n/\mathrm{d}t = k_\mathrm{d}n^x = v_* \exp(-E^*/RT)n^x \tag{6.15}$$

where n is the surface concentration of the desorbing species per unit area, k_d the rate constant for desorption, x the order of the desorption process, v_* the pre-exponential (or frequency factor), and E^* the activation energy for desorption.

Thermal desorption may be performed isothermally or by a temperature programme. Isothermal desorption experiments are simpler to analyse but more difficult to adjust experimentally. Also, if several desorption processes occur, it will be impossible to deduce the individual rates from the total rate, and a number of isothermal experiments at different temperatures need to be carried out. Clearly a programmed desorption technique in which the same information can be obtained in a single experiment has obvious advantages. In this technique, the temperature of the sample is varied with time in a controlled manner. Even in this technique, reliable rate parameters are obtained by carrying several experiments at different heating rates.

A typical thermal desorption apparatus contains an adsorbent sample that can be heated, a source of adsorbate gas, a detector capable of partial pressure analysis, usually a mass spectrometer, and a pump capable of attaining ultrahigh vacuum. The system must be constructed from components that are bakable to at least 250 °C. It should be mentioned that the key feature in

270

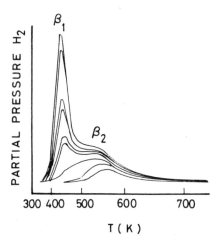

Fig. 6.22 Flash desorption of hydrogen from a (100) tungsten crystal. Each curve corresponds to a different initial coverage[122]

a thermal desorption experiment is the method used for heating and measuring the temperature of the sample. Essential details are given by Dawson and Walker[121].

In a thermal desorption experiment the adsorbent is exposed to the adsorbate and then heated in a programmed manner. The desorbed gases cause an increase in the partial pressure and the recorded pressure–time or pressure–temperature curve is known as a desorption spectrum. Typical spectra are shown in Fig. 6.22 for H_2 desorbed from a (100) tungsten crystal[122]. The rate of change of the partial pressure of a component is given by the balance between the desorption rate and the pumping rate,

$$\frac{dP}{dt} = -\frac{AkT}{V}\frac{dn}{dt} - \frac{SP}{V} \tag{6.16}$$

where n is the surface coverage of the desorbing species per unit area, A the area of the sample, S the pumping speed, and V the volume of the system. Equation (6.16) can also be written in the form

$$-\frac{dn}{dt} = \frac{V}{AkT}\left(\frac{dP}{dt} + \frac{P}{\tau}\right) \tag{6.17}$$

where $\tau = V/S$ is the characteristic pumping time. The desorption rate (Eqn. (6.15)) increases with temperature T, and decreases with decreasing surface coverage n, and thus the desorption rate passes through a maximum with increasing temperature, as shown in Fig. 6.22. The spectrum may contain several peaks if there are different binding energies for a given species with different E, or different desorption mechanisms for a single binding state.

The initial surface coverage prior to commencing desorption, n_0, can be determined from the desorption spectrum; thus for high pumping speed, such that $\tau \to 0$,

$$n_0 = \int_0^\infty (-\mathrm{d}n/\mathrm{d}t)\,\mathrm{d}t = \int_0^\infty cP\,\mathrm{d}t \qquad (6.18)$$

where c can be considered as a constant factor relating the partial pressure to the desorption rate. Determination of the relative surface coverage is obtained from the areas of the peaks, while determination of the absolute surface coverage requires the evaluation of c, which includes the total pumping speed. The total pumping speed, however, is a source of uncertainty, because it cannot always be regarded as constant, even for a single desorption spectrum. Normalization of the desorption spectra involves calibration by desorption under the same conditions of an adsorbed state of known surface coverage determined by an independent method such LEED, AES, or molecular-beam techniques.

On the other hand, desorption in a closed system, where $\tau \to \infty$. is more commonly employed in surface coverage determination. Calibration of the ion gauge or mass spectrometer gives the amount of gas desorbed, which can be converted to a surface coverage if the area of the sample is known.

Kinetic parameters can be calculated from the desorption spectra. We will consider, as a simple example, a single desorbing state with a coverage independent rate constant. In fast pumping ($\tau \to 0$), and with a linear temperature programme ($T = T_0 + \beta t$), the peak in the desorption spectrum occurs when the desorption rate is a maximum, and this condition can be found by setting $\mathrm{d}^2 n/\mathrm{d}t^2 = 0$.

$$\frac{E^*}{RT_m^2} = \frac{\nu_1}{\beta} \exp(-E^*/RT_m) \qquad (6.19)$$

and for $x = 2$,

$$\frac{E^*}{RT_m^2} = \frac{2n_m \nu_2}{\beta} \exp(-E^*/RT_m) \qquad (6.20)$$

where n_m is the surface coverage at $T = T_m$. Since a second-order desorption curve is fairly symmetric about T_m[121], $n_0 = 2n_m$ and Eqn. (6.20) can be rewritten

$$E^*/RT_m^2 = (n_0 \nu_2/\beta)\exp(-E^*/RT_m) \qquad (6.21)$$

From Eqns. (6.19) and (6.20) it is obvious that only for $x = 2$ does the peak maximum temperature depend on the initial coverage n_0. For first-order processes the peak maximum temperature is invariant. In Fig. 6.22, the peak β_1 can be seen to be first order, whereas β_2 is second order.

Activation energy and the pre-exponential factor can be determined from experiments in which the heating rate β is varied. For both first-order and second-order processes, with constant initial coverage, differentiation of Eqns. (6.19) or (6.21) give

$$\frac{\mathrm{d} \ln(T_m^2/\beta)}{\mathrm{d}(1/T_m)} = \frac{E^*}{R} \tag{6.22}$$

Thus the graph of $\ln(T_m^2/\beta)$ versus $1/T_m$ yields a straight line with a slope proportional to the activation energy. The pre-exponential factor v_* can then be found by substituting E^* into the rate equation (6.15).

For more detailed analysis of the shapes of desorption peaks and complex desorption spectra and their resolution, the reader is referred to the work of Dawson and Walker[121], and the references cited there.

Thermal desorption spectra have been successfully obtained in studies of the desorption of simple diatomic gases[123] and inert gases[124-126] from single-crystal surfaces. Thermal desorption methods have also been used to elucidate the mechanism of catalytic reactions, such as the decomposition of ammonia on a polycrystalline tungsten filament[127].

6.10.2 Electron-stimulated desorption (ESD)

When a surface is bombarded with low-energy electrons (< 500 eV) at low enough power densities to prevent thermal effects, desorption of neutral atoms, molecules, excited neutrals, and positive ions or conversion between binding states of the adsorbate may take place.

Measurement of the cross-section for desorption, the mass and kinetic energy distribution of the desorbed species, and the threshold electron energy for desorption help in the understanding of the complex interaction of gases on characterized surfaces, especially when the interaction is weak.

It is commonly observed in ESD experiments that: (a) more neutrals than ions are desorbed; (b) the cross-sections for ESD are much smaller than for similar gas phase processes; (c) metallic adsorbates on metals are not desorbed; and (d) different binding states exhibit different cross-sections. A model which explains the results of ESD experiments has been proposed[128,129]. Thus, in considering the potential energy diagram in Fig. 6.23, the lower curve represents the interaction between the metal surface M and the adsorbate atom A with binding energy $E_d(A)$. The upper curve represents the interaction of the metal surface and the ionized adatom. At large internuclear distances these curves are separated by the ionization potential of the adatom $I(A)$. Incident electrons may cause transition from the ground state M + A curve to the upper M + A$^+$ + e^- curve over the range of internuclear separations shown. It is assumed that the position and kinetic energy of the nucleus remain constant during the transition. This is based on the fact that the mass of the nucleus is much greater than that of the electron.

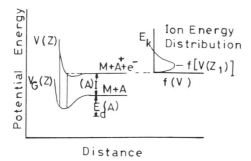

Fig. 6.23 A schematic potential energy diagram for a surface M and adsorbate A and the ion energy distribution resulting from ESD

The ions formed are repelled from the surface, and if all escape, their ion kinetic energy distribution is determined by reflection of the probability density distribution of the M + A ground state oscillator through the potential energy curve of the M + A$^+$ + e^- system[130]; that is,

$$f_0[V(z_i)] = nQ_{ex}^+ |\psi_G(z_i)|^2 (\partial V/\partial z)_{z=z_i}^{-1} \qquad (6.23)$$

where $f_0[V(z_i)]$ is the number of ions formed at initial separation z_i, n the surface density of atoms active in the ESD process, Q_{ex}^+ the cross-section for excitation from the ground state to the M + A$^+$ + e^- curve, $\psi_G(z)$ the wave function of the M + A oscillator, and $V(z)$ the potential energy function describing the M + A$^+$ + e^- curve.

While leaving the surface, some ions will be neutralized by Auger transitions. If neutralization occurs at separations $z \geq z_c$ the atom will have gained enough kinetic energy to overcome the remaining ground state potential barrier and a neutral atom will escape. At $z < z_c$ the atom is readsorbed. This critical distance z_c is defined by

$$\dot{V}(z_i) - V(z_c) = V_G(\infty) - V_H(z_c) \qquad (6.24)$$

(Fig. 6.23). With a rate of neutralization $R(z)$, the probability that an ion of velocity v moving through dz at z will be neutralized is $R(z)\text{d}z/v$. The ion at z has velocity v given by

$$v = \{2[V(z_i) - V(z)]/m\}^{1/2} \qquad (6.25)$$

and hence the probability $P_1(z_i)$ that an ion starts at z_i and moves to infinity without being neutralized is

$$P_1(z_i) = \exp\left\{-\int_{z_i}^{\infty} [R(z)/v]\,\text{d}z\right\} \qquad (6.26)$$

Now the ion kinetic energy distribution corrected for neutralization is

$$f[V(z_i)] = f_0[V(z_i)]P_1(z_i) \tag{6.27}$$

The total probability of desorption as an ion or atom is

$$P_T(z_i) = \exp\left\{-\int_{z_i}^{z_c} [R(z)/v] \, dz\right\} \tag{6.28}$$

In general, $P_T(z_i) \gg P_1(z_i)$ since more neutrals than ions are observed in ESD.

Other processes that might occur, such as antibonding or excited atomic states, may be detected by their different cross-sections, thresholds, or energy distributions.

If it is assumed that electron-stimulated transitions involve localized electrons, then their excitation cross-sections should be similar to those in gas phase molecules, i.e. about 10^{-16} cm^2. The observed cross-sections in ESD are smaller ($\leqslant 10^{-17}$ cm^2). This difference is due to rapid reneutralization at the metal surface and subsequent readsorption. Also, different binding states of the same adsorbate are expected to have different ESD cross-sections.

ESD experiments are carried out in ultrahigh vacuum, and they can be directed in two ways: either to observe changes in the surface layer under electron bombardment, to trace changes in work function, in flash desorption behaviour or in Auger signal; or to monitor the particle ejected from the surface. The first was reviewed by Madey and Yates[131], and the second by Dawson and Walker[121].

6.10.3 Secondary-ion mass spectroscopy (SIMS)

This method employs mass analysis of both negative and positive secondary ions emitted when the surface is bombarded by ions. Unlike ESD, substrate material is slowly removed from the surface. The SIMS method possesses the following features[132]:

1. Information in the monolayer range within limits after $<10^{-6}$ monolayers.
2. Detection of surface compounds by their fragment ions.
3. Differences in sensitivity for different surface structures (e.g. elements, compounds).
4. Detection of hydrogen and its compounds.
5. Isotope identification with high mass resolution.
6. Capacity for quantitative analysis.
7. Very small disturbance of the surface.

The technique is similar to the sputtering methods that have been used for analysing bulk materials, but by decreasing the primary ion current many orders of magnitude, the lifetime of the surface layer bombarded can be

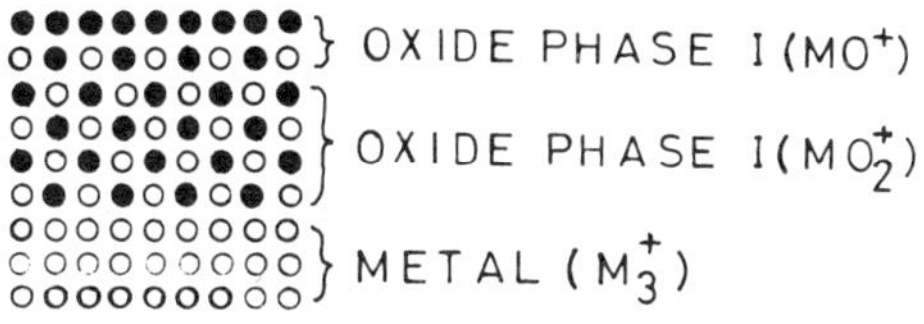

●●●●●●●●●} OXIDE PHASE I (MO⁺)
○●○●○●○●○}
●○●○●○●○●}
○●○●○●○●○} OXIDE PHASE I (MO₂⁺)
●○●○●○●○●}
○●○●○●○●○}
○○○○○○○○○}
○○○○○○○○○} METAL (M₃⁺)
○○○○○○○○○}

Fig. 6.24   Model of an oxide layer on a metal surface[132]

extended. A small fraction of primary ions with keV energies incident on a surface are reflected while the remainder penetrate the lattice and dissipate their energy. This energy causes sputtering of neutral atoms and clusters and lattice orders. Emission of photons and secondary electrons is observed as well as emission of positively and negatively charged ions. Ion emission can be treated as energy transfer to the surface particle, ionization of the particle during separation from the surface, followed by electron exchange between emitted particle and the surface, including reneutralization. A summary of experimental methods used in SIMS is given by Dawson and Walker[121].

Most of the SIMS work done involved studying the oxidation of metals, such as Mo[133], Cr[134], W(100)[135]; V, Nb, and Ta[136]; Mg, Ba, and Sr[137], Cu, Ni, and Ti[138]; and Si[139]. Simultaneous use of SIMS, ESD, and thermal desorption for studying the interaction of H_2 and O_2 chemisorbed on W(100) has been reported[135]. Also, Schubert and Tracy[140] have reported a SIMS investigation of the adsorption of Cs on GaAs and the composition of $Al_xGa_{1-x}As$ surfaces.

The SIMS investigation of oxidation of polycrystalline Cr by Benninghoven and Müller[134] provides a pioneer illustration of the utility of this method to study surface reactions. The details of the treatment do not fall within the scope of this book, but in general the conclusions reached from this study can be generalized for most metal oxidation reactions, and confirm a simple model used to explain the general oxidation behaviour of metals (cf. Fig. 6.24):

1. Oxidation begins only after a relatively high oxygen exposure.
2. Two phases of oxide are formed.
3. The first phase is characterized by the appearance of MeO_2^- ions, and with increasing oxidation MeO_n^- ions of increasing n are emitted.
4. At higher exposures a second oxide phase covers the first and is characterized by the emission of MeO^+ ions. The positive ion indicates the increasing oxidation state of the metal. The sputtering rate of the MeO^+ phase is about 10 times that of the MeO_2^- phase.
5. Oxide formation terminates at some hundreds of langmuirs exposure.

6.10.4 Field desorption mass spectroscopy (FDMS)

Under a very high positive electric field, adsorbed atoms and even substrate atoms may be removed as positive ions from a metal surface. The technique was first developed by Müller[141,142], in which the high field required is easily achieved in the field ion microscope (FIM). The microscope is capable of imaging a metal surface with a magnification of over a million times and a resolution of 0.2 to 0.3 nm, which allows neighbouring atomic positions to be viewed. In this technique, field desorption denotes removal of adsorbed foreign atoms, while field evaporation denotes the removal of the metal surface atom itself. During field evaporation, the surface structure may be examined by introducing an imaging gas (10^{-3} Torr of He or Ne) and lowering the electric field to a suitable value (He, 44 V/nm; Ne, 34 V/nm). In the high field regions above protruding surface atoms or the edges of closely packed net planes, the imaging gas is ionized by a tunnelling process known as field ionization[141,142]. These ions are repelled radially from the specimen to the phosphor screen where they form a weak image of the specimen surface. A wide variety of metals have been inspected by the FIM[141,143].

By combining a field ion microscope with a mass spectrometer of single-particle sensitivity, it is possible to analyse individual atoms field desorbed from a selected small area on the surface being imaged in atomic resolution. Such an instrument is known as the atom probe[144]. The atom probe is a field ion microscope with a probe hole in the screen. The specimen tip is manipulated to place the atom image spot over the probe hole and a short positive high-voltage pulse, of duration shorter than the instrument time resolution, is applied to the specimen in order to desorb the atom of interest. The desorbed ion quickly accelerates to a constant velocity, and travels through the probe hole and along a drift tube until it reaches an electron multiplier detector. The flight time between the high-voltage pulse and ion detection determines the ion mass to charge ratio. Flight times are typically in the range 1–20 μs. Review of current atom probe designs have been published by Müller[145] and by Panitz[146,147].

Atom probe determinations revealed the existence of multiple charges of field-evaporating metals and their compounds with residual gases like oxides and nitrides[144]. For example tungsten field evaporates as W^{3+} and W^{4+}, and iridium as Ir^{2+} and Ir^{3+} [148,149]. The interaction of N_2 and CO with several different metals has been investigated by Müller[150]. The results of Müller et al.[151] revealed that the inert imaging gas is adsorbed as a result of the high electric field at the surface, a fact important in understanding the detailed mechanism of field ion image formation[142].

Field desorption mass spectrometry has also been successfully applied in metallurgical studies[152,153]. Panitz[147] has studied the adsorption of H_2 on both tungsten and iridium, which makes FDMS most promising for studies of catalytic problems, and of the crystallographic distribution of adsorbates.

It should be pointed out that desorption methods consider surface studies from different approaches, but each can give suitable information about surface analysis and the identification of different adsorbate binding states. In general, desorption methods are all destructive, although in some cases (e.g. ESD, SIMS), the surface perturbation can be made nearly negligible.

References

1. R. L. Park, in: R. B. Anderson and P. T. Dawson (eds.), *Experimental Methods in Catalytic Research*, Vol. III, Academic Press, New York, San Francisco, London 1976, pp. 1–36.
2. H. D. Hagstrum, J. E. Rowe, and J. C. Tracy, in: R. B. Anderson, and P. T. Dawson (eds.), *Experimental Methods In Catalytic Research*, Vol. III, Academic Press, New York, San Francisco, London, 1976, pp. 42–118
3. H. D. Hagstrum, *Science*, **178**, 275 (1972)
4. J. A. R. Samson, *Techniques of Vacuum Ultraviolet Spectroscopy*, Wiley, New York, 1967
5. K. Siegbahn *et al., ESCA: Atomic, Molecular and Solid State Structure Studied By Means of Electron Spectroscopy*, Alonqwist and Wiksells, Uppsala, 1967.
6. K. Siegbahn *et al., Science*, **176**, 245 (1972)
7. E. J. R. Prosen and R. G. Sachs, *Phys. Rev.*, **61**, 65 (1942)
8. J. A. Appelbaum and D. R. Hamann, *Phys. Rev.*, **86**, 1122 (1972)
9. J. E. Demuth and D. E. Eastman, *Phys. Rev. Lett.*, **32**, 1123 (1974)
10. H. Ibach and J. E. Rowe, *Phys. Rev.*, **89**, 1951 (1974)
11. E. W. Plummer, in: E. Drauglis and R. I. Jaffee (eds.) *The Physical bases for Heterogeneous Catalysis*, Plenum, New York, 1975, pp. 203–230
12. C. R. Brundle, *J. Electron Spectrosc.*, **5**, 291 (1974)
13. K. Siegbahn *et al. ESCA Applied to Free Molecules*, North-Holland Publ., Amsterdam, 1969
14. T. E. Madey, J. T. Yates, and N. E. Erickson, *Chem. Phys. Lett.*, **19**, 487 (1973)
15. P. W. Palmberg, *Surface Sci.*, **25**, 598 (1971)
16. P. H. Holloway and J. B. Hudson, *Surface Sci.*, **43**, 123, 141 (1974)
17. J. W. Gadzuk and E. W. Plummer, *Rev. Mod. Phys.*, **45**, 487 (1973)
18. B. J. Waclawski and E. W. Plummer, *Phys. Rev. Lett.*, **29**, 783 (1972)
19. H. D. Hagstrum and G. E. Becker. *Phys. Rev.*, **159**, 572 (1967)
20. H. D. Hagstrum and G. E. Becker, *Phys. Rev.*, **B8**, 1580, 1592 (1973)
21. H. D. Hagstrum and G. E. Becker, *J. Chem. Phys.*, **54**, 1015 (1971)
22. G. E. Becker and H. D. Hagstrum, *Surface Sci.*, **30**, 505 (1972)
23. H. D. Hagstrum and G. E. Becker, in: E. Drauglis, and R. I. Jaffee (eds.), *The Physical Basis for Heterogeneous Catalysis*, Plenum, New York, 1975, pp. 173–187
24. R. L. Park and J. E. Houston, *J. Vac. Sci. Technol.*, **11**, 1 (1974)
25. M. Ibach, K. Horn, R. Dorn, and H. Luth, *Surface Sci.*, **38**, 433 (1973)
26. M. B. Webb and M. G. Legally, *Solid State Phys.*, **28**, 301 (1973)
27. J. B. Pendry, *Low Energy Electron Diffraction—The Theory and its Application of Determination of Surface Structure*, Academic Press, New York, 1974, p. 418
28. H. B. Lyon and B. A. Somorjai, *J. Chem. Phys.*, **46**, 2539 (1967)
29. R. A. Armstrong, in: R. S. Anderson and P. T. Dawson, (eds.), *Experimental Methods in Catalytic Research*, Vol. III, Academic Press, New York, San Francisco, London, 1976, pp. 121–148.
30. P. J. Estrup and E. G. McRae, *Surface Sci.*, **25**, 1–52 (1971)
31. J. N. May, *Advan. Catal.*, **21**, 152–268 (1970)
32. G. A. Somorjai, *Surface Sci.*, **34**, 156–176 (1973)
33. P. B. Sewell and M. Cohen, *Appl. Phys. Lett.*, **11**, 298 (1967)
34. G. W. Simmons, D. F. Mitchell, and K. R. Lawless, *Surface Sci.*, **8**, 130 (1967)
35. B. McCarroll, *J. Chem. Phys.*, **50**, 4758 (1969)
36. R. P. Eischens and W. A. Pliskin, *Advan. Catal.*, **10**, 1–56 (1958)
37. L. H. Little, *Infrared Spectra of Adsorbed Species*, Academic Press, New York, 1966.

278

38. M. L. Hair, *Infrared Spectroscopy in Surface Chemistry*, Dekker, New York, 1967.
39. G. Blyholder, in: R. B. Anderson (ed.), *Experimental methods in Catalytic Research*, Academic Press, New York, 1968, pp. 323–360
40. M. R. Basila, *Appl. Spectrosc. Rev.*, **1**, 289–378 (1968)
41. N. D. Parkyns, in: R. G. J. Miller and B. C. Stace (eds.), 'Laboratory Methods in Infrared Spectroscopy', Heyden and Son London, 1972, pp. 318–339
42. N. R. Avery, *J. Catal.*, **19**, 15–31 (1970)
43. F. Bozon-Verduraz, *J. Catal.*, **18**, 12–18 (1970)
44. J. R. Anderson, *Chemisorption and Reactions on Metallic Films*, Academic Press, New York, 1971.
45. A. M. Bradshaw and J. Pritchard, *Surface Sci.*, **17**, 372–386 (1969)
46. J. Pritchard and W. T. Catterick, in: R. B. Anderson and P. T. Dawson (eds), *Experimental Methods in Catalytic Research*, Vol. III, Academic Press, New York, San Francisco, London, 1976, pp. 281–316.
47. C. W. Garland, R. C. Lord and P. F. Froiano, *J. Phys. Chem.*, **69**, 1188–1203 (1965)
48. G. Blyholder and M. Tanaka, *J. Colloid Interface Sci.*, **37**, 753–759 (1971)
49. G. Blyholder and M. Tanaka, *J. Phys. Chem.*, **76**, 3180–3184 (1972)
50. M. Folman and Y. Kozirovski, *J. Colloid Interface Sci.*, **38**, 51–57 (1972).
51. J. Heidberg, S. Zhene, C. F. Chen, and H. Hartmann, *Ber. Bunsenges Phys. Chem.*, **75**, 1009–1017 (1971)
52. B. Rao and H. J. Dignam, *J. Chem. Soc., Faraday Trans.*, 2, **70**, 492–496 (1974)
53. J. G. Bullitt, F. A. Cotton and T. J. Marks, *Inorg. Chem.*, **11**, 671–676 (1972).
54. H. L. Pickering and H. C. Eckstrom, *J. Phys. Chem.*, **63**, 512–517 (1959)
55. S. A. Francis and A. H. Ellison, *J. Opt. Soc. Amer.*, **49**, 131–138 (1959)
56. R. G. Greenler, *J. Chem. Phys.*, **44**, 310–315 (1966)
57. G. W. Poling, *J. Colloid Interface Sci.*, **34**, 365–374 (1970)
58. A. M. Bradshaw, J. Pritchard, and M. L. Sims, *Chem. Common.*, 1519–1520 (1968)
59. J. Pritchard and M. L. Sims, *Trans. Faraday Soc.*, **66**, 427–433 (1970)
60. H. G. Tompkins and R. G. Greenler, *Surface Sci.*, **28**, 194–208 (1971)
61. M. L. Kottke, R. G. Greenler, and H. G. Tompkins, *Surface Sci.*, **32**, 231–243 (1972)
62. E. F. McCoy and R. St. C. Smart, *Surface Sci.*, **39**, 109–120 (1975)
63. K. Horn and J. Pritchard, *Surface Sci.*, **52**, 437–439 (1975)
64. J. Pritchard, T. Catterik, and R. K. Gupta, *Surface Sci.*, **53**, 1 (1975)
65. Y. R. Shen, *Surface Sci.*, **37**, 522–539 (1973)
66. G. E. Becker and G. W. Gobeli, *J. Chem. Phys.*, **38**, 2942–2945 (1963)
67. R. W. Rice and G. L. Haller, in: J. W. Hightower, (ed.), *Proc. 5th Int. Congr. Catal.*, North Holland, Amsterdam, 1973, pp. 317–325
68. N. J. Harrick, *Internal Reflection Spectroscopy*, Wiley Interscience, New York, 1967
69. J. Fahrenfort, in: P. Hepple, (ed.), *Molecular Spectroscopy*, Inst. of Petroleum, London 1968, pp. 111–130
70. P. J. Hendra, in: P. Hopple (ed.), *Chemisorption and Catalysis*, Inst. of Petroleum, London, 1970, pp. 80–94
71. P. J. Hendra, A. J. McQuillan, and I. D. M. Turner, *Moderne Verfahren der Oberflächenanalyse, Dechema-Monogr.*, **78**, 271–293 (1975)
72. R. G. Greenler and T. L. Slager, *Spectrochim. Acta.*, **29(A)**, 193–201 (1973)
73. H. Winde, *Z. Chem.*, **10**, 64 (1970)
74. P. J. Hendra, J. R. Horder, and E. J. Loader, *Chem. Comm.* 563 (1970)
75. C. L. Angell, *J. Phys. Chem.*, **77**, 222 (1973)
76. P. J. Hendra, J. R. Horder, and E. J. Loader, *J. Chem. Sec. (A)*, 1766 (1971)

77. R. O. Kagel, *J. Phys. Chem.*, **74**, 4518 (1970)
78. K. J. Packer, *Praga in NMR Spectroscopy* **3**, 87 (1967)
79. H. Pfeifer, *NMR*, **7**, 53 (1972), Springer-Verlag, Berlin
80. E. G. Derouane, J. Fraissand, J. J. Fripiat, and W. E. Stone *Catalysis Revs.*, **7**, 121 (1972)
81. J. J. Fripiat, *Catalysis Rev.*, **5**, 269 (1971)
82. D. E. O'Reilly, H. P. Leftin, and W. K. Hall, *J. Chem. Phys.*, **29**, 170 (1958)
83. W. K. Hall, H. P. Leftin, F. J. Cheselske, and D. E. O'Reilly, *J. Catalysis*, **2**, 506 (1963)
84. V. M. Bermudez, *J. Phys. Chem.*, **74**, 4160 (1970)
85. V. I. Kvilividze, *Dokl. Akad. Nauk SSSR*, **157**, 158, 673 (1964)
86. M. M. Egorov, V. I. Kvilividze, V. F. Kiselev, and K. G. Krassilinikov, *Kolloid Zeits.*, **212**, 126 (1966)
87. R. K. Webster, T. L. Jones, and P. J. Anderson, *Proc. Brit. Ceramic Soc.*, **5**, 153 (1965)
88. J. R. Zimmerman, B. G. Holmes, and J. A. Lasater, *J. Phys. Chem.*, **60**, 1157 (1956)
89. J. R. Zimmerman and W. E. Brittin, *J. Phys. Chem.*, **61**, 1328 (1957)
90. J. R. Zimmerman and J. A. Lasater, *J. Phys. Chem.*, **62**, 1157 (1958)
91. D. E. Woessner, *J. Chem. Phys.*, **39**, 2783 (1963)
92. D. E. Woessner and J. R. Zimmerman, *J. Phys. Chem.*, **67**, 1520 (1963)
93. H. Winkler, *Proc. Tenth Colloq. Ampere, Leipzig*, 1961, p. 219
94. J. Clifford and S. H. A. Lecchini, *Soc. Chem. Ind. Monograph.*, **25**, 174 (1967)
95. J. J. Fripiat, C. Van Der Meersche, R. Touillaux, and A. Jelli, *J. Phys. Chem.*, **74**, 382 (1970)
96. K. Hirota, K. Fueki, and T. Sakai, *Bull. Chem. Soc. Japan*, **35**, 1545 (1962).
97. M. L. Deviney, *Adv. Colloid Interface Sci.*, **2**, 237 (1969)
98. J. H. Lunsford, *Catalysis Revs.*, **8**, 135 (1973)
99. R. D. Ivengar and M. Codell, *Adv. Colloid Interface Sci.*, **3**, 365 (1972)
100. H. Hosaka, T. Fujiwara, and K. Meguro, *Bull. Chem. Soc. Japan*, **44**, 2616 (1971)
101. R. P. Porter and W. K. Hall, *J. Catalysis*, **5**, 366 (1966)
102. J. J. Rooney and R. C. Pink *Surface and Defect Properties of Solids*, **2**, 114 (1973), The Chemical Society London.
103. C. Naccade, J. Bandiera, and M. Dufaux, *J. Catalysis*, **25**, 334 (1972)
104. D. N. Stamires and J. Turkevich, *J. Amer. Chem. Sci.*, **86**, 749 (1964)
105. R. L. Mössbauer, *Z. Physik*, **151**, 124 (1958)
106. P. R. Brady and J. F. Duncan, *J. Chem. Soc.*, 653 (1964)
107. F. G. Allen, *Bull. Amer. Phys. Soc.*, **9**, 296 (1964)
108. P. A. Flinn, S. L. Ruby and W. L. Kehl, *Science*, **143**, 1434 (1964)
109. M. J. D. Low in: E. A. Flood (ed.), *The Solid–Gas Interface* Vol. 2, Edward Arnold, London, 1967, p. 947
110. W. N. Delgass and M. Boudart, *Catalysis Rev.*, **2**, 122 (1968)
111. M. C. Hobson, *Adv. Colloid Interface Sci.*, **3**, 1 (1972)
112. P. A. Flinn, S. L. Ruby, and W. L. Kehl, *Science*, **143**, 1434 (1964)
113. G. Constabaris, R. H. Lindquist, and W. Kündig, *Appl. Phys. Letters*, **7**, 59 (1965)
114. W. Kündig, H. Bommel, G. Constabaris, and R. H. Lindquist, *Phys. Rev.*, **142**, 327 (1966)
115. M. C. Hobson and A. D. Campbell, *J. Catalysis*, **8**, 294 (1967)
116. M. C. Hobson and H. M. Gager, *J. Catalysis*, **16**, 254 (1970)
117. T. K. McNab, R. J. Fox and A. J. F. Boyle, *J. Appl. Phys.*, **39**, 5703 (1968)
118. T. Takada, N. Yamamoto, T. Shinio, M. Kiyama, and Y. Bando, *Bull. Inst. Chem. Res. Kyoto Univ.*, **43**, 406 (1965)

280

119. M. C. Hobson, *Nature*, **214**, 79 (1967)
120. I. P. Suzdalev, V. I. Goldanskii, E. F. Makarov, A. S. Plachinda, and L. A. Korytoko, *Soviet Phys. JETP* (English trans.), **22**, 929 (1966)
121. P. T. Dawson and P. C. Walker, in: R. B. Anderson and P. T. Dawson (eds.); *Experimental methods in Catalytic Research*, Vol. III, Academic Press, New York, San Francisco, London, 1976, p. 211
122. T. E. Madey and J. T. Yates, *Actes Colloq. Int. Structure Properties Surface Solids*, Paris 1970, p. 155.
123. L. D. Schmidt, *Catal. Rev.*, **9**, 115 (1974)
124. E. V. Kornelson and M. K. Sinha, *Can. J. Phys.*, **46**, 613 (1968); *J. Appl. Phys.*, **39**, 4546 (1968); **40**, 2888 (1969)
125. E. V. Kornelson, *Can. J. Phys.*, **48**, 2812 (1970)
126. D. Edwards and E. V. Kornelson, *Surface. Sci.*, **44**, 1 (1974)
127. Y. K. Peng and P. T. Dawson, *J. Chem. Phys.*, **54**, 950 (1971)
128. D. Menzel and R. Gomer, *J. Chem. Phys.*, **41**, 3311 (1964)
129. P. A. Redhead, *Can. J. Phys.*, **42**, 1886 (1964)
130. M. Nishijima and F. M. Propst, *Phys. Rev.*, **B2**, 2368 (1970)
131. T. E. Madey and J. T. Yates, *J. Vac. Sci. Technol.*, **8**, 525 (1971)
132. A. Benninghoven, *Surface Sci.*, **35**, 427 (1973)
133. A. Benninghoven, *Chem. Phys. Lett.*, **6**, 626 (1970)
134. A. Benninghoven and A. Müller, *Surface Sci.*, **39**, 416 (1973)
135. A. Benninghoven, E. Loebach, C. Plog, and N. Treitz, *Surface Sci.*, **39**, 397 (1973)
136. A. Müller and A. Benninghoven, *Surface Sci.*, **39**, 427 (1973)
137. A. Benninghoven and L. Weidman, *Surface Sci.*, **41**, 483 (1974)
138. A. Müller and A. Benninghoven, *Surface Sci.*, **41**, 493 (1974)
139. A. Benninghoven and S. Storp, *Appl. Phys. Lett.*, **22**, 170 (1973)
140. R. Schubert and J. C. Tracy, *Rev. Sci. Instrum.*, **44**, 487 (1973)
141. E. W. Müller and T. T. Tsong, *Field Ion Microscopy, Principles and Applications*, American Elsevier, New York, 1969.
142. E. W. Müller and T. T. Tsong, *Progr. Surface Sci.* **4**, 1 (1973)
143. E. D. Boyes and M. J. Southon, *Vacuum*, **22**, 447 (1972)
144. E. W. Müller, J. A. Panitz and S. B. McLane, *Rev. Sci. Instrum.*, **39**, 83 (1968)
145. E. W. Müller, *Lab. Practice*, **22**, 408 (1973)
146. J. A. Panitz, *Rev. Sci. Instrum.*, **44**, 1034 (1973)
147. J. A. Panitz, Paper presented at the Hydrogen Econ. Miami Energy Conf. Miami Beach, 1974
148. E. W. Müller, *Quart. Rev.*, **23**, 177 (1969)
149. S. S. Brenner and J. T. McKinney, *Appl. Phys. Lett.*, **13**, 29 (1968)
150. E. W. Müller, *Ber. Bunsenges, Phys. Chem.*, **75**, 979 (1971)
151. E. W. Müller, S. V. Krishnaswamy, and S. B. McLane, *Surface Sci.*, **23**, 112 (1970)
152. J. P. Turner, B. J. Reagan, and M. Southon, *Vacuum*, **22**, 443 (1972)
153. S. S. Brenner and S. R. Gordman, *Scripta Met.*, **5**, 865 (1971)

Part 3

Thermogravimetry of Solid Surfaces

Introduction to Part 3

The extremely high sensitivity of balances with respect to the total sample mass under investigation enables the direct observation of mass changes of surface layers and thus the direct measurement of one important parameter of surface reactions. Fortunately, in many cases the interest is centred on materials exhibiting high surface areas. In this case the mass changes are big enough so that they can be measured without difficulty. The desire to extend the thermogravimetric studies to small mass changes gave the impact of the development of special balances (sorption balances, vacuum microbalances) and of special weighing techniques.

After a survey on applications of gravimetry for surface investigations and some related problems in the following chapters, the weighing techniques are described in more detail.

Chapter 7

Application of Thermogravimetry to Solid Surfaces

Thermal methods as applied to solid surfaces comprise calorimetry, differential thermal analysis (DTA), volumetric methods, and thermogravimetry. Examples of applications of calorimetry and DTA for the investigation of pore systems have been presented in Section 4.4. Calorimetry of surface reactions requires sensitive instruments and sophisticated experimental work and has so far met with the interest of relatively few specialized laboratories, e.g. the Centre de Microcalorimétrie et de Thermochimie du CNRS, Marseille[1,2]. The example of such institutions and the improvement of instruments may extend the application of these methods in future (see also the Bibliography at the end of the book). The widely used volumetric technique is briefly mentioned in this chapter. The gravimetric technique is then discussed in detail and illustrated by some examples, which in many cases can be transferred also to volumetric or calorimetric methods.

Volumetric apparatus has been described in Chapter 2, and its application for surface and pore analysis discussed in Chapters 2 to 4. Such apparatus can also be used for investigations of surface reactions as described below, using

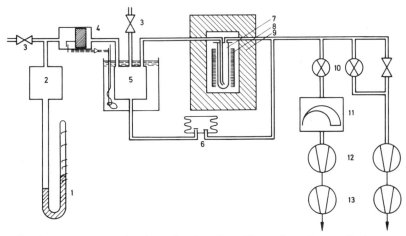

Fig. 7.1 Apparatus for investigating the effect of nuclear radiation on heterogeneously catalysed gas reactions; 1 mercury contact thermometer, 2 thermostatted volume for reference, 3 gas inlet valves, 4 diaphragm gauge, 5 thermostatted buffer volume, 6 circulation pump (see Fig. 8.30), 7 irradiated reaction vessel, 8 β source, surrounded by a thermostat, 9 lead shield, 10 needle valves, 11 mass spectrometer, 12 diffusion pumps, 13 rotary vane pumps

284

gravimetric methods. Ancillary equipment is generally required for the chemical treatment of the surface, e.g. reduction of a catalyst, or a circulation pump for the enrichment of the reaction gas over an extended period of time. A typical arrangement has been described by Emmett and Brunauer[3]. Further examples are given by Joy[4]. A more recent example is illustrated in Fig. 7.1, which shows an apparatus for investigating the influence of nuclear radiation on catalytic processes[5]. In the closed volume containing the β-radiating reaction source and a circulation pump, pressure variations have been observed by means of a diaphragm gauge, and the variation in the chemical composition of the reacting gas has been determined using a mass spectrometer.

Using this apparatus, various processes have been investigated, including the decomposition of methanol, ethanol, isopropanol, and formic acid; the hydrogenation of benzene and ethylene; and the oxidation of carbon monoxide at the surface of platinum, nickel, iron, copper, and activated carbon catalysts. As in the thermogravimetric corrosion experiments (section 7.2.2), no significant influence of the soft radiation could be observed. Thus, the results of these investigations contradict some results reported in the literature to have been obtained in tests with nuclear or ultraviolet radiation absorption mechanisms near the surface.

7.1 Gravimetric methods of surface investigation

Thermogravimetry[6] can be applied to surface layers in a similar way as for the bulk material.

Under *isobaric* conditions, thermogravimetric analysis (TGA) may be suitable for identifying the type of a surface layer and its mass. The slope of the mass loss curve changes rapidly, usually with linearly increasing temperature when a temperature is approached at which one phase becomes volatile or when the reaction velocity of a reaction involving production of a volatile phase becomes large. At this temperature the differential curve has a peak. As for bulk material these temperatures are often clearly defined; the TGA curve is typical of a certain material and can be used as a 'fingerprint'. Layers applied onto a surface in general have a lower bond strength, depending on the bulk material and the conditions of preparation, e.g. the cleanness of the original surface. Thus, the release of a surface phase may start at a lower temperature and extends over a wider temperature range. A reference book with 'fingerprints' for surface reactions or surface layers—as exists for bulk materials—therefore cannot be compiled.

A suitable gas pressure for TGA is between 1 and 10 kPa because the thermal gas flow in this pressure range is observed to be extremely small. To prevent any influence of diffusion restraint by the surrounding (nonreacting) gas on the kinetics of desorption, however, a vacuum is preferred. To avoid Knudsen forces (see section 9.4.6), the vacuum has to be held below 10^{-4} Pa. Average temperature changes are between 0.01 and 1 K/s. In special cases known as flash experiments with high resolution, however, low rates of

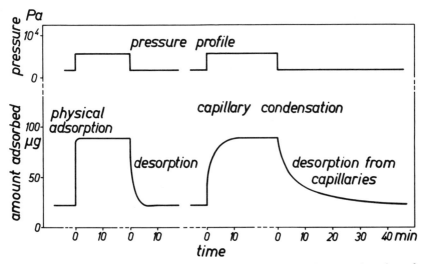

Fig. 7.2   Different types of isothermal/isobaric physisorption as a function of time

increase are preferred. A cyclic heating method has been proposed by F. and J. Rouquerol[7].

Isothermal measurements are used to determine adsorption isotherms in order to reveal the geometry of the surface and pore structure (as described in Part 1), the sorption capacity and the sorption kinetics. Of technical and economic importance are the measurement of isotherms and the kinetics of desorption in order to optimize drying processes and to investigate heterogeneous catalysis, corrosion and other chemical surface reactions[8]. Typical kinetic curves are shown in Figs. 7.2 and 7.3.

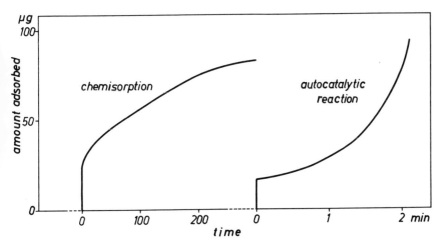

Fig. 7.3   Different types of isothermal/isobaric chemisorption as a function of time

Isothermal/isobaric measurements are being carried out for phase diagram determination, e.g. for solutions of hydrogen in palladium or in the case of special drying processes as described in section 7.2.1.

Of course, the gravimetric measurements for this purpose need to be supplemented by measurements using other methods, such gas analysis, mass spectrometry of released gases, or surface spectroscopy as described in Part 2. These additional measurements can be carried out either simultaneously or using a separate sample[9-34].

7.2 Examples

In the following, the gravimetric methods will be discussed by way of examples. Because in many of these examples more than one of the above gravimetric methods are being applied, the sections have been organized according to fields of application.

7.2.1 Drying and degassing

The investigation of drying processes is an important application of thermogravimetry. This is true also for surface thermogravimetry. Under atmospheric conditions all surfaces are covered with water layers which are troublesome in vacuum apparatus, space arrangements, electronic and electric parts, and many others, and which have to be removed from adsorbents, catalysts, etc., before use. The surface structure is also important for drying the bulk of materials, because the drying rate is often controlled by the surface area, by the pore system, and the desorption process, which depends on the chemistry of the surface.

Surface TGA is often used in context with degassing experiments with the aim of finding optimum conditions for cleaning the surface without damaging either the surface or the bulk structure. Such procedures, which are being applied to prepare sorption measurements, are described in Chapters 3 and 4. A distinction can be made between peaks due to activation processes involved in desorption and peaks due to the decomposition of hydrates or other volatile components. In the case of bulk drying, the concentration of volatile species can be calculated from the degassing curve at constant temperature as described in section 4.3.4.

Investigations into the processing of thermoplasts using a vent extruder

Thermoplastic resins are often processed by means of extruders with vents at the screw, where volatile constituents are withdrawn by a vacuum pump or a condenser. To find out the dimensions of vents and the vacuum required, the concentration of volatile species and the evaporation rate must be determined under processing conditions. This can be done using a thermogravimentric apparatus[35].

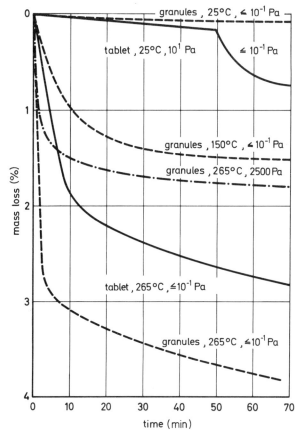

Fig. 7.4 Degassing of polyamide. Sample mass 1 g. Diameter of granules 3 mm

Typical degassing curves are shown in Figs. 7.4 and 7.5. It can be seen from these curves that the degassing rate depends not only on the temperature but also on the surface area: granules or powders are degassed much faster than compact tablets, which have a much smaller surface area. At gas pressures below 0.1 Pa, the amount of volatile constituents that can be removed is up to ten times as high as at 10 Pa. The curves of Figs. 7.4 and 7.5 can be used to calculate a formal diffusion coefficient according to section 9.5.1.

In a conventional vent extruder a plastic material stays in the degassing zone only for a few seconds. During this time only a small amount of volatile matter can be eliminated. Reducing the gas pressure at the vent to, say, 1 Pa will result in about double the amount and thus will lead to a saving of time and energy. More effective degassing can be achieved only by comprehensive changes in design.

288

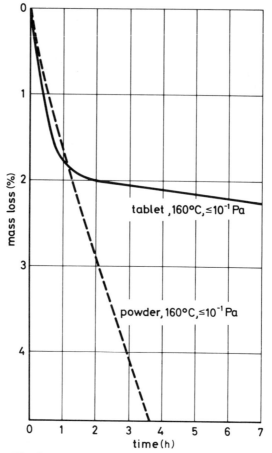

Fig. 7.5 Degassing of polyvinyl chloride. Sample
mass 1 g. Mean grain size of powder 0.05 mm

Investigations into the drying, freeze drying and critical point drying of organic materials

Many industrial techniques involve drying processes. Natural materials like wood or raw materials for food mostly consist of a heterogeneous porous matrix filled with water and other volatile constituents. In many manufacturing processes water and solvents have to be removed by time- and energy-consuming drying processes, the optimization of which is a general economic task.

Furthermore, rigorous drying is a very effective conservation method. When food is being dried, however, it should be taken into account that it must be possible to recover the original product by adding water. Thus, the pore system should not be destroyed by drying, which is often the case when drying rapidly at elevated temperatures or under vacuum. In addition, it should be noted that the high surface tension of water results in contraction of the pore walls during evacuation of the pores. This can be avoided by freeze drying which, however, proceeds slowly and requires much energy. Another problem is the destruction of vitamins and enzymes by the drying process. Here it is advisable to use a careful process. Odorous and taste-carrying components are volatile and are removed together with the water. Thus it will be necessary to find temperatures and pressures at which only a few of such constituents distil. On the other hand, the dried product (e.g. coffee extract) exhibits a large surface area which can be used to readsorb taste and odour molecules.

High demands have to be satisified when drying samples for electron-microscopic investigations. The freeze-drying method often fails here because the fine structure is damaged by expansion of the ice volume and by crystal growth. Therefore, the matrix is mostly stabilized by chemical means, and after that the water is replaced by alcohol or acetone in stepwise increasing concentrations and then the sample is evaporated[36]. Better results can be obtained by subsequently replacing the liquid by others in the order iso-pentene, amyl acetate, Freon 11, Freon 113, which are liquids with low surface tension. After this treatment the sample is embedded in resin. Because this method is not alway satisfying, the critical-point drying method is sometimes applied. Using this method, the water is first replaced by acetone, amyl acetate, or Freon 113, which is then replaced by a vapour above the critical point. Vapours normally used are Freon 11, Freon 23, Freon 13, CO_2, and N_2O; the pressures applied range between 30 and 75 bar, and the temperatures are between 298 and 308 K[37].

Suitable conditions for any drying process can easily be found by observing the drying process using a vacuum microbalance to determine the kinetic curves: mass loss as a function of time at constant and stepwise varied temperature and pressure. Milligram samples are sufficient to observe the original drying process because the pore and surface structure responsible for the diffusion and desorption process unalter in the sub-millimetre range. In some cases isosteric measurements are favourable, pressure and temperature being controlled by the mass value.

The pore and surface structures are basic parameters for the drying process. They can be determined by any method described in this book, most favourably by the gravimetric measurement of the nitrogen sorption isotherm of the sample under investigation. This method can also be used to determine the pore and surface structures of the dried material.

Another important parameter is the water sorption isotherm, which is preferably measured gravimetrically. The reversibility of the isotherm must be known in order to decide to what extent the material can be dried if it is desired to return to the original state. Reversible isotherms have been observed only with a few purified products. Rao[38] used inorganic materials as models for reversibility investigations: he demonstrated that the hysteresis loop may be crossed from the adsorption to the desorption branch (Fig. 7.6)

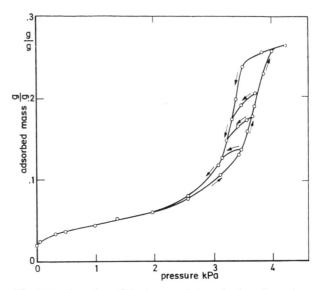

Fig. 7.6   Scanning of the hysteresis loop in the adsorption of water by titania gel according to Rao[38]. The loop may be crossed by moving from the adsorption to the desorption branch

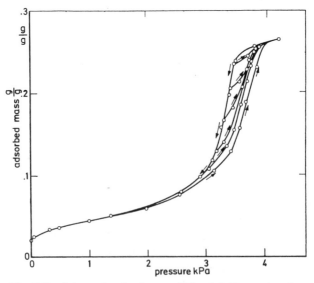

Fig. 7.7   Adsorption isotherm of Fig. 7.6. Returning from the desorption isotherm, a curve inside the hysteresis loop is reached, but not the adsorption branch

but not vice versa (Fig. 7.7). The results have been the basis for the explanation of curves observed on organic systems (Fig. 7.8). As in such investigations only mesopores and micropores are of interest, the sample mass may be as small as one milligram (Fig. 7.9)[39]. Numerous water isotherms have been published[40–46].

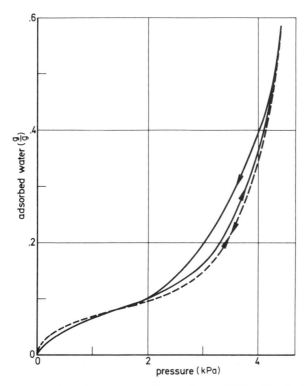

Fig. 7.8   Sorption of water on activated dhal at 303 K. The dhal grains were dried in vacuum at 338 K. ——— first run, – – – second run. The time required for two cycles was one month, and for each point two days. Both runs were found to be practically overlapping in the adsorption branch and reversible, but only the first one exhibited a hysteresis loop

Selection and pretreatment of vacuum and space parts

Materials to be used in spacecraft should not release too large an amount of volatile constituents because these might be hazardous at elevated concentrations, which may easily develop in the closed vehicle. Under space or vacuum conditions, volatile layers which impede cold welding of adjacent metal parts and maintain some lubrication of gliding planes may be lost by evaporation[47]. Extensive loss of monomers of plastics may result in the

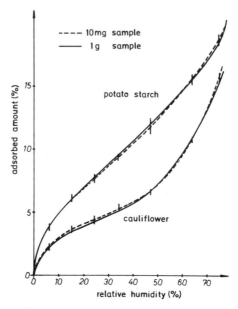

Fig. 7.9 Water sorption isotherm on food
according to Hofer and Mohler[39]

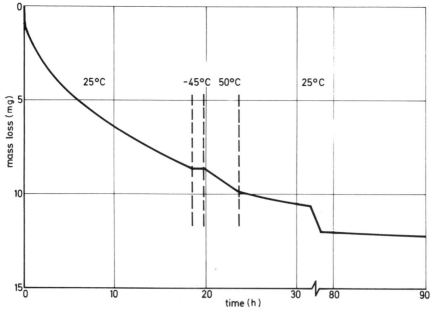

Fig. 7.10 Degassing of silicon rubber to be used as a mechanical damper in a
spacecraft. Sample mass 2 g

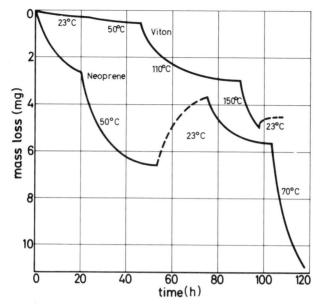

Fig. 7.11 Degassing and water sorption of vacuum sealing materials. Sample mass 2 g, ——— 10^{-3} Pa, – – – – – $2 \cdot 10^3$ Pa H_2O

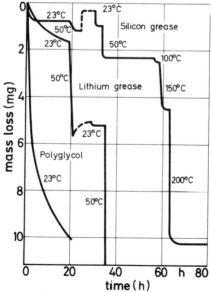

Fig. 7.12 Degassing and water sorption of vacuum greases. A thin layer of grease was applied to a 6 cm^2 stainless steel sheet, ——— 10^{-3} Pa, – – – – – $2 \cdot 10^3$ Pa H_2O

embrittlement of the material. As an example of such material testing, the degassing curve of silicon rubber for space conditions is shown in Fig. 7.10. Residual evaporation after baking could be reduced by coating the material.

Materials to be used for vacuum apparatus should not contain constituents of high vapour pressure and should only adsorb small amounts of gases. The parameters for evaluating materials are the relevant sorption isotherms and the degassing curves in vacuum at the service and baking temperatures. Results of the investigation of sealing materials[48] are shown in Figs. 7.11 and 7.12; the limiting baking temperatures and the necessary baking times can be gathered from these figures. Whereas only small amounts of water vapour are absorbed by lithium grease and silicon grease, polyglycol ether forms a solution with a large amount of water. If polyglycol ether must be used in a ground-glass joint, it should be covered on the outside with a mineral grease to prevent water diffusion through the joint.

The degassing conditions for metals and glass and also the uptake of water, pump oil and vapours can likewise be measured gravimetrically. Some examples are shown in Figs. 8.46, 9.4, and 9.11–24.

Investigations into the regeneration of adsorbents

Adsorbents and catalysts charged with a physisorbed liquid are regenerated by degassing at elevated temperature or at reduced partial pressure which is achieved by evacuation, by sweeping with a nonadsorbing gas, or by a combination of these methods[9]. Degassing always is an activated process. Furthermore, it should be noted that in catalysts, chemisorption processes take place, the original reaction gas being changed in its composition. The products may have a stronger bond to the surface. This may also occur in the case of materials designed only for adsorption: activated carbon, molecular sieves, and other highly porous adsorbents may exhibit catalytic activity. This increases the activation energy, the desorption process becomes complex, and many molecules remain which cannot be removed under appropriate conditions.

To investigate desorption processes from adsorbents it is recommended in addition to the gravimetric techniques to analyse the gas evolved by gas chromatography and/or by mass spectroscopy. A suitable arrangement is described by Seewald and Jüntgen[49]. They investigated the desorption of phenol and benzene from active carbon using the nonisothermal TGA technique with a temperature increases of 2 K min^{-1} and sweeped out the evolved gas with helium as a carrier gas. The dependence of the differential desorption dn/dT on the carrier gas velocity is shown in Fig. 7.13. Above a gas velocity of 13 l h^{-1} the shape of the curve remains unchanged. The situation of the peak was found to be dependent on the original charge and on the charging time.

To evaluate the curves, it is necessary to know the basic process, which may be controlled either by desorption or diffusion. Adsorption measurements

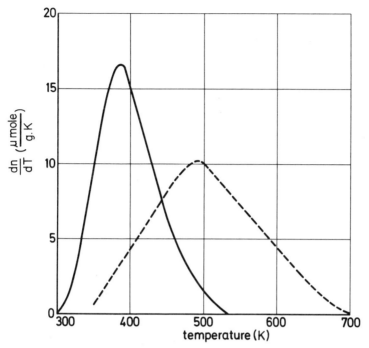

Fig. 7.13 Differential desorption of phenol from activated carbon as a function of the helium sweep gas stream velocity, according to Seewald and Jüntgen[49]. Temperature increase 2 K min^{-1}. ——— $\geqslant 13$ l h^{-1}, – – – – – 3 l h^{-1}. Above 13 l h^{-1} the curve remains stable

showed that the pore system contained only large pores. This suggest that the gas release is controlled by desorption rather than by diffusion.

The desorption process can be described as a first-order reaction:

$$\frac{dn}{dT} = \frac{k_0}{\tau} \exp\left(-\frac{E}{RT}\right) n \qquad (7.1)$$

with n the adsorbed amount, T temperature, R the gas constant, k_0 the frequency factor, and $\tau = dT/dt$ the temperature increase as a function of time. Integration results in

$$n = -n_0 \frac{k_0}{\tau} \exp\left(-\frac{E}{RT}\right) \exp\left(-\frac{k_0}{\tau} \int_{T_0}^{T} \exp\left(-\frac{E}{RT}\right) dT\right) \qquad (7.2)$$

with n_0 the initial adsorbed mass at initial temperature T_0. The first term represents the temperature dependence of the Arrhenius equation and the second the dependence of the desorption velocity on the concentration of the adsorbed molecules. The desorption rate curve plotted as a function of temperature exhibits a maximum which is shifted toward higher temperatures with increasing activation energy and decreasing factor k_0. For an extended discussion, it has to be taken into account that the experimental conditions may have a marked effect on the resulting curves, so that a theoretical description becomes difficult, as was pointed out by Donnelly et al.[50].

7.2.2 Corrosion

Corrosion is in most cases accompanied by a mass change of the material. This can be used as a measure of the extent of corrosion, even if the hazardous effect is due to a change of the structure of the material[51]. If the structural change results in generation of a pore system, this can be investigated by measuring the adsorption isotherm.

Investigations into the corrosion of fuel element graphite

The transport behaviour of fission products in fuel element graphite of a high-temperature reactor may be altered by changes in the pore structure of the graphite due to corrosion[52]. The corrosion of graphite in a CO_2 atmosphere at temperatures between 1120 and 1170 K results in the development of volatile species. Therefore the mass decreases, the bulk becomes porous, and the specific surface area increases.

The gravimetric method is well suited to investigate the corrosion behaviour of materials. All parameters of interest can be determined in the same apparatus, since it is possible to observe the weight loss during degassing, the weight loss during corrosion, and the corrosion rate. In addition, the specific surface area and the pore radius distribution in the micropore and mesopore range can be determined by measuring the sorption isotherm at low temperature before and after corrosion. Density determinations on the basis of buoyancy measurements allow the volume of closed pores and changes of their contents to be evaluated.

After degassing of the samples at 1300 K in high vacuum, the nitrogen adsorption and desorption isotherms were measured at 77 K. The specific surface area was determined using the simple BET equation, and the cumulative specific surface area was derived from the pore radius distribution. The samples were oxidized at temperatures between 1120 and 1170 K in high-grade (99.995%) CO_2 at 1.3 kPa.

A typical weight loss curve is shown in Fig. 7.14. The mass of the sample decreases linearly with time, i.e. the corrosion rate remained constant despite the increasing surface area and the change in the pore structure. The corrosion rate was about 0.5 $\mu g\ s^{-1}$ at 1170 K. A weight loss of only 0.55% resulted in an increase in the specific BET surface area from 0.7 to 5.3 $m^2\ g^{-1}$.

The isotherm before and after corrosion are shown in Fig. 7.15. All hysteresis loops obtained are of the B type shape according to the de Boer classification (Fig. 2.25). The hysteresis loop was markedly extended by the corrosion and in some cases even extended to very low relative pressures. The

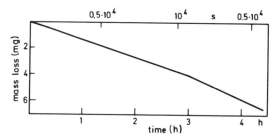

Fig. 7.14 Corrosion of graphite in CO_2 of 1.3 kPa at 1170 K. The sample mass is 1.3 g

pore width frequency is shown in Fig. 7.16 as a function of the pore radius. The most frequent radius is located at the lower limit of the mesopore range, which is the only range in which the calculation is valid. This means that the pore system consists mainly of micropores and small mesopores. Pores of the same size are generated in large numbers by the corrosion process.

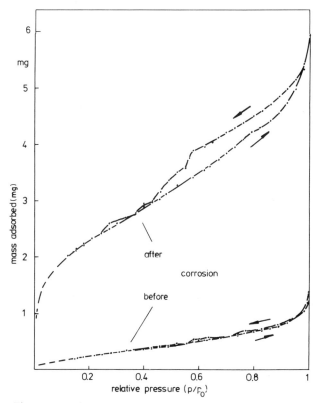

Fig. 7.15 Nitrogen isotherms of a graphite sample at 77 K before and after corrosion in CO_2 of 13 mbar at 1170 K

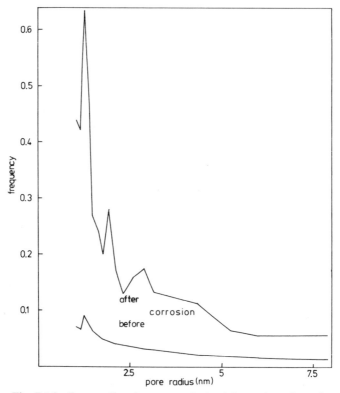

Fig. 7.16   Pore radius frequency derived from the adsorption
isotherm using a cylindrical pore shape model

In the mesopore range the comparison of the cumulative specific surface area with the BET value shows discrepancies. This is due to the high micropore content: the amount of N_2 adsorbed in micropores is not included in the cumulative calculation.

The extension of the hysteresis loop may be caused by other factors, i.e. by a pore blocking effect, as suggested by Doe and Haynes[53]: the depletion of the inner pore volume may be hindered by micropores in the outer region. In addition, swelling of the structure may occur.

The generation of micropores due to oxidation seems to be the reason for the almost constant corrosion rate which exists despite the increasing surface area. The narrow pore necks hinder exchange of the reacting species (CO_2, CO) during the corrosion process.

A comparison of the low density of 1.7 g cm^{-3} before corrosion, calculated from buoyancy with quartz counterweight, with the theoretical density of graphite of 2.25 g cm^{-3} suggested the presence of closed pores. During corrosion the density increased proportionally to the increase of surface area as a result of the opening of closed pores. Thus, the increase in pore volume and surface area is partly due to the opening of closed pores. Indeed, pore determinations by X-ray small-angle scattering, which covers both closed and open pores, showed that in the region examined the total pore content was only insignificantly varied by corrosion[54].

Investigations into the corrosion of metals in the presence of nuclear radiation

It has been assumed that β radiation is split into fractions of about 1 eV and that these energy quanta are physically active species which can accelerate corrosion processes. To verify this theory, the corrosion of various metals has been measured microgravimetrically[55]. Because of the precautions required owing to the nuclear radiation and the time-consuming measurements, six balances were used in parallel, one of which equipped with a dummy to determine the influence of gas flow. The specimens (foils 5 to 10 μm thick) were suspended from the balance into a stainless steel tube, in the middle of which a 30-curie Sr^{90}–Y^{90}–β source could be moved into different positions so that weighing in the presence and in the absence of radiation was possible.

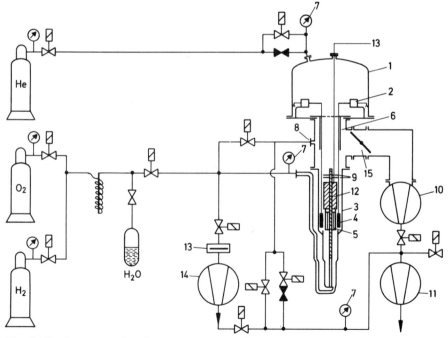

Fig. 7.17 Apparatus for the measurement of metal corrosion in the presence of nuclear radiation. Further details are shown in Figs. 8.37, 8.40, 9.43; 1 stainless steel vessel, 2 electronic balances, 3 reaction tube, 4 samples, 5 β source, 6 diffusion barrier, 7 pressure gauges, 8 combined exhaust for reaction and protecting gas, 9 heat shields, 10 turbo-molecular pump, 11 rotary vane pump, 12 radiation-protecting stainless steel block, 13 baffle, 14 oil-diffusion pump, 15 butterfly valve

300

The dose rate was about 10^5 rad h^{-1}, the temperatures range between 77 and 530 K and the pressure range between 10^{-3} and 10^5 Pa. The apparatus is shown in Figs. 7.17 and 8.37. One of the corrosion-resistant Gast-type balances is depicted in Fig. 8.40.

The gravimetric experiments were supplemented by microscopic and electron-microscopic investigations. The results may be summarized as follows. It appears that on a pure surface of iron and several other metals, an oxide film is instantaneously formed, even at room temperature. It is obviously due to this film that no further corrosive attack was observed at this temperature.

At higher temperatures, in the case of iron at about 473 K, this film becomes porous. This permits further attack on the metal; the reaction now proceeds according to the equation

$$\frac{dm}{dt} \sim t^n \qquad (\tfrac{1}{3} \leq n \leq \tfrac{1}{2}) \tag{7.3}$$

with m the mass and t the time, at rates which cannot be explained by ion diffusion in the oxide (Fig. 7.18). The oxide layer does not have uniform thickness. On reduction of this iron oxide film at 520 K the metal surface does not become smooth again; but at higher temperature (620 K) it is partly levelled again.

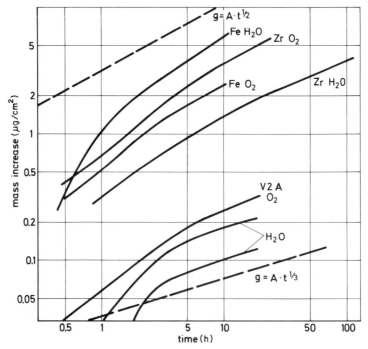

Fig. 7.18 Metal corrosion in $8 \cdot 10^4$ Pa oxygen and $1.7 \cdot 10^3$ Pa water vapour

In the case of the three materials investigated, irradiation with β rays (average energy 1.2 mev) at a dose rate of about 10^5 rad/h does not have any marked influence on these oxidation processes.

7.2.3 Preparation of materials

The preparation of materials starting from solids and involving gas reactions can be investigated gravimetrically. Observation of the temperature and pressure dependence of mass variations in the reactions involved is a favourable means to find out optimum conditions for the manufacturing process. The reactions with the gas phase always include surface reactions like adsorption or desorption and diffusion in the pore network. Thus, the surface properties of the solid are important parameters. The preparation of porous or finely divided samples is also discussed in the present section. In the latter case it is possible to observe not only the reaction, but also the development of the porosity and the increase in specific surface area.

Investigation into the production of tetraethyl lead

Tetraethyl lead, a motor fuel additive, is prepared from lead-sodium alloys and ethyl chloride. The reaction rate depends on the composition and on the conditions under which the PbNa alloy has been made, on the temperature applied, and on the pressure of ethyl chloride. Despite the high reaction rate to be expected even at room temperature[56], several progression types of the reaction have been observed in practice; thus, the overall reaction rate may be governed by the rate of reactions taking place at the surface of the alloy, which may be covered with an oxide layer. The surface reactions involve adsorption, reaction with the oxide, diffusion through the oxide layer, and reaction with the alloy surface.

Investigations into the reaction mechanisms with the aim of optimizing the production process have been made using gravimetric techniques in the following way. Ethyl chloride was distilled at 287 K after removal of the air by short-term evacuation. The intermediate fraction was filled into a vessel containing molecular sieves for drying. Residual impurities and air were removed by evacuation during repeated freezing and heating. Vapour pressures between 700 and 10^5 Pa could be kept constant by thermostatting the liquid down to 193 K using dry ice, or by means of a deep-freezer for higher temperatures. Lead-sodium alloy samples were prepared under oxygen-free conditions in the form of compact 1 g cubes exhibiting only a small surface area, because in some cases the reaction with ethyl chloride was very rapid. In some cases the surface was oxidized in oxygen at low pressures. The equipment to feed the PbNa into the balance consisted essentially of the plexiglass glove box shown in Fig. 9.3. In this box even surface layers could be removed from the sample using a scalpel.

At the beginning of the experiments the surface area was determined by

302

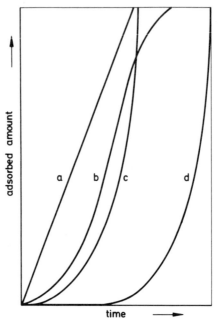

Fig. 7.19 Adsorption of ethyl chloride at 291 K, 69 kPa, on lead–sodium; (a) constant reaction rate due to oxide layer, (b) autocatalytic reaction, (c) autocatalytic reaction with reaction rate decrease after some time due to the limited surface area, (d) autocatalytic reaction after some initial time

measuring the nitrogen isotherm at 77 K. Within the margin of error, no internal surface was observed, even in the case of oxide layers. Subsequently, the sample was thermostatted, the balance was connected to the ethyl chloride, and the mass gain was recorded. Typical reaction curves are shown in Fig. 7.19: some of the oxide-covered samples are characterized by a linear mass increase, but most of the curves represent the autocatalytic reaction, in some cases after some initial delay. In some experiments the reaction rate was found to decrease after a certain time, most probably because of the limited surface area of the sample. At room temperature the reaction rate was between 0.1 and 100 mg s^{-1}.

Preparation and characterization of candidate catalysts for fuel cell electrodes

Catalytically active materials for fuel cell electrodes have to be electrically conductive and corrosion-resistant. So far these requirements are fulfilled satisfactorily only by noble metals which, however, are unsuitable for extensive use for reasons of price and availability. Therefore, it was hoped to find non-noble materials suitable as cathode catalysts for oxygen reduction[57]. The investigations were based on thermogravimetric methods on a microscale and were aimed at determining the conditions of preparation, analysing the chemical properties, and characterizing the pore structure of the catalysts candidates.

Using the 'Gravimat' (Fig. 2.14), the substances were chemically characterized by thermogravimetric analysis under vacuum or inert gas, and the results were compared with literature data. Furthermore, the mass loss of the sample was observed at linearly rising temperature and then at constant temperature. A temperature value within a defined range was chosen as the preparation temperature at which the weight of the sample did not change over an extended period of time after completed conversion of the substance. In a few cases, the substance prepared in the pan of the scales could be worked up directly to an electrode; more frequently, however, the catalysts were prepared separately in an oven on the basis of the temperature values determined gravimetrically.

In addition to the area of the surface in contact with the electrolyte, the pore radius is one of the main electrode parameters. The pores have to be large enough to enable transport of both the reacting species and the reaction products. The kinetics of the electrode reaction and thus its efficiency under load, as well as the limits of performance, can be influenced drastically by transport processes in the pores. An external electric field is distorted when penetrating into the interior of the electrode as a function of pore size. For this reason, measurements were made of specific surface area and pore size.

The methods described were used to investigate ammonium tungstates, chromates, vanadates, molybdate, and a permanganate. Typical degradation curves with plateaus are shown in Fig. 7.20. A very slight weight loss observed below 150 °C in the case of the chromates was neglected because it was due to evaporated water traces. For comparison, the chromate curve referring to the literature values[58] is reproduced. Plateaus were measured for the acid tungstate within a temperature range between 130 and 240 °C, and for the neutral tungstate at temperatures between 150 and about 210 °C. All the tungstate decomposition products were soluble in dilute sulphuric acid and are not suitable for the intended purpose.

Ammonium permanganate gave an insoluble oxidic substance which decomposed by explosion at temperatures 80 °C if the temperature was raised at a rate higher than 10 K h^{-1}. Since ammonia containing inorganic species is entirely unsuitable as a catalyst after thermal treatment, thermal degradation of organic polyamide nitrile was tried. Nearly no weight loss was encountered at temperatures up to 400 °C; even at 1000 °C, more than 30 per cent of the starting weight was retained. The pyrolysate showed some catalytic activity which, however, was not high enough for practical application. The pore size distribution analyses, the t-plots, and also the remarkable differences between the results of surface area determinations according to the BET and the cumulative method revealed a highly microporous structure of all the materi-

304

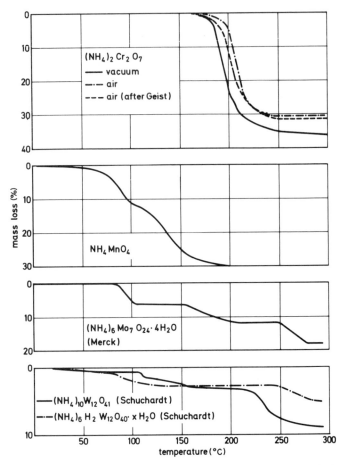

Fig. 7.20 Thermograms. Temperature increase 9.4 K h^{-1}
(Curve for comparison after Geist[58])

als (Fig. 7.21, 7.22). It can therefore be concluded that transport processes are also similar in both active and inactive samples of polyacenoquinone pyrolysates.

The reaction rate of the molecular electrocatalytic reduction process and the existence of 'active sites' may be assumed to be the reasons for the differences in activity. Some specualtive models of electrocatalytic oxygen reduction are described in the literature[58-61]. It is assumed that adjacent carbon atoms with special substituents (e.g. quinone structure) may be suitable for binding oxygen. After chemisorption and the subsequent electron transfer, the reduced (and negatively charged or protonated) oxygen molecule should be able to leave the chemisorption site.

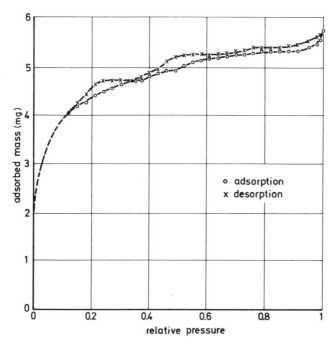

Fig. 7.21   Nitrogen adsorption isotherm of polyacenoquinone pyrolysate at 77.5 K

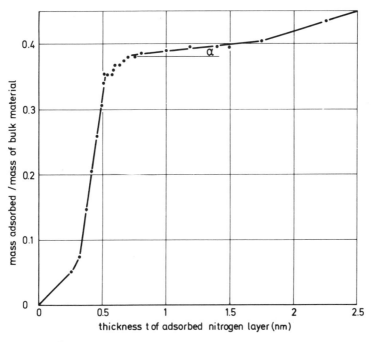

Fig. 7.22 t-plot corresponding to the isotherm in Fig. 7.21

7.2.4 Investigation of material systems

In the following, various gravimetric investigations are reported, in which the TGA techniques are combined with other surface measuring methods.

Investigations into the chemisorption of hydrocarbons at fuel cell catalysts

It is assumed that during chemisorption of saturated hydrocarbons on platinum surfaces some C–C and much C–H is dissociated at temperatures above about 350 k[62-67]. The present work was carried out to study how the chemisorption and the catalytic processes are affected by the presence of water[65,68,69] in a fuel cell.

Raney platinum was prepared by decomposition of the alloy $PtAl_3$ using potassium hydroxide solution. The alloy was made from 99.99% aluminium and 99.9% platinum. The BET surface area of the freshly prepared catalyst was 15.2 m^2/g. The apparatus is shown schematically in Fig. 8.54.

Prior to the experiment, the following oxidation–reduction treatment was applied to clean the catalyst surface: the specimen was outgassed in the load pan of the microbalance in vacuum at 420 K. After mass constancy has been attained, oxygen at 100 Pa was admitted and, 10 min later, the oxygen pressure increase to 10^3 Pa. After a further 10 min, oxygen was pumped off and, after 20 min of evacuation, hydrogen was admitted at pressures increased in steps of 0.1, 1, and 10^3 Pa, each pressure being maintained for about 10 min. Subsequently, the speciment was evacuated overnight at about 10^{-4} Pa. Finally, the temperature was raised to 573 K for 1 h and then reduced to 373 K, which was the temperature of the adsorption experiments. This treatment resulted in a decrease in specific surface area. After the adsorption experiments a BET surface area averaging 13 $m^2\ g^{-1}$ was obtained. The procedure of the adsorption experiments is illustrated in Fig. 7.23, which presents the mass record of one experiment in which oxygen, water, and propane were consecutively admitted to the catalyst.

After the pretreatment described above, a small amount of oxygen was admitted until the desired amount of oxygen had been adsorbed. Under evacuation, the temperature was raised to 570 K and maintained for 1 h. The latter treatment reduced the adsorbed quantity by a small amount. The specimen was then allowed to cool again to 370 K, and water vapour at 1400 Pa admitted. Thirty minutes later gaseous and weakly adsorbed water was removed by evacuation for 20 min. Subsequently, propane at a pressure of 100 Pa was admitted for 10 min. After removal of gaseous and weakly adsorbed propane by evacuation, oxygen at 120 Pa was admitted. Under these conditions, the chemisorbed carbonaceous species are completely converted to CO_2, CO, and H_2O[65,69]. The amount of CO_2 and CO present in the product gas was used to calculate the chemisorbed proportion of propane.

Each experiment of the type described above yields four values. Gravimetric measurements yield the amount of chemisorbed oxygen, m_o, the amount of chemisorbed water, m_w, and the weight change upon propane

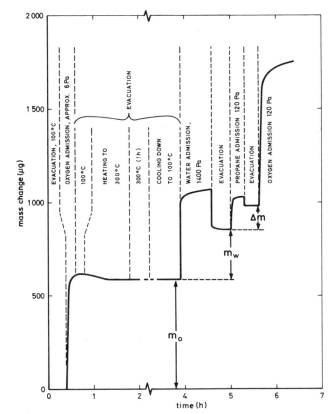

Fig. 7.23 Mass record of an adsorption experiment with consecutive oxygen, water, and propane adsorption

chemisorption, Δm (see also Fig. 7.24). The amount of chemisorbed propane, m_p, is determined by mass-spectrometric analysis.

As discussed by Bond[70], water is chemisorbed on platinum following

$$H_2O + 2^* \longrightarrow \underset{*}{O}H + \underset{*}{H} \tag{7.4}$$

where the asterisk denotes an adsorption site, e.g. a platinum surface atom. While in the case of a bare platinum surface propane is chemisorbed via

$$C_3H_8 + 2^* \longrightarrow \underset{*}{C_3H_7} + \underset{*}{H} \tag{7.5}$$

we assume that the water-covered surface reacts as follows:

$$C_3H_8 + \underset{*}{O}H + \underset{*}{H} \longrightarrow \underset{*}{C_3H_7} + \underset{*}{H} + H_2O \tag{7.6}$$

The sites covered by chemisorbed hydrogen atoms are blocked against hydrocarbon chemisorption, as has been shown for the case of the nickel surface by Galwey[71] and for the case of the platinum surface, from electrochemical evidence, by Brummer et al.[72] and Shropshire et al.[73]. With this in mind, comparison of processes (7.5) and (7.6) explains why the amount of hydrocarbon to be chemisorbed is not affected by the presence of preadsorbed water. A particular feature of reaction (7.6) is that one water molecule is released per chemisorbed propane molecule. In fact, with increasing coverage of the platinum surface with preadsorbed water, the amount of water released upon propane chemisorption increases from 0 to 1 water molecule per propane molecule.

The state of the oxygen-covered platinum surface is not completely known; however, from the similarity of the conditions in pertinent experiments carried out by Gruber[74] it may be inferred that the prevailing adsorption state is

$$-Pt\underset{|}{\overset{\displaystyle \overset{O}{\diagup \diagdown}}{\rule{1cm}{0.4pt}}}Pt-\quad \text{or, in short } {}_*O_* .\qquad\qquad (A)$$

With this surface configuration, the strong enhancement of propane chemisorption may be interpreted by the surface reaction

$$ {}_*^{}O_*^{} + C_3H_8 \longrightarrow {}_*OH + {}_*C_3H_7 \qquad\qquad (7.7)$$

The OH surface groups generated in this process are capable of reacting with further propane molecules via reaction (7.6), with formation of propyl groups, thus increasing the amount of propane finally chemisorbed.

The interaction of water with configuration (A) is suggested to be of the type

$$ {}_*^{}O_*^{} + H_2O \longrightarrow 2\,{}_*OH \qquad\qquad (7.8)$$

Hence, oxygen preadsorption, followed by water adsorption, leads to generation of more OH groups than would be produced by water adsorption alone. Increased OH surface concentration has two effects:

1. More propane is chemisorbed than in the case of the oxygen-free surface; this is shown in Fig. 7.24(a).
2. The strong accumulation of OH groups permits further reaction of chemisorbed propyl radicals with OH. This effect is manifested in Fig. 7.24(b) by the strong increase in the number of water molecules released per chemisorbed propane molecule.

7.2.5 Investigations into the characterization of galvanic electrodes

The processes occurring at galvanic electrodes are rather complex. An electric field between the electrodes, which depends on the voltage applied and the

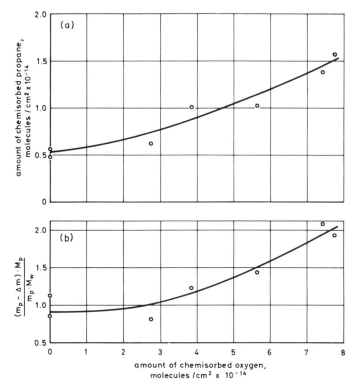

Fig. 7.24   (a) Amount of chemisorbed propane as a function of the amount of previously chemisorbed oxygen. (b) Number of water molecules released per chemisorbed propane molecule as a function of the amount of previously chemisorbed oxygen. The amount of water chemisorbed on top of the oxygen layer before propane admission was kept approximately constant (about 0.5×10^{15} water molecules per cm^2)

outer geometry of the electrodes, forces the ions to travel across the electrolyte. The ions are adsorbed and discharged at the outer surface because the internal voids of pores are field-free. Subsequently, a catalytic process takes place in which the total inner and outer surface participates. It should be noted, however, that reactions at the inner surface are delayed by the diffusion process. If a gas is added as reactant (O_2, H_2), the porous electrode must be permeable for gases but not for the liquid electrolyte.

Thus, various geometric properties of the surface are of interest and it is not clear which method of investigation of the surface area and the pore structure will give relevant results. As it is possible to determine the specific surface area by cyclic voltammetry (Section 3.5), results of measurements at platinum fuel cell electrodes have been compared with those obtained by means of nitrogen sorption method[75,76]. Figures 7.25 to 7.27 depict the isotherms and the pore size distributions. In the cumulative distributions (Fig. 7.27), the final value of the curve denotes the cumulative surface area; the correspond-

310

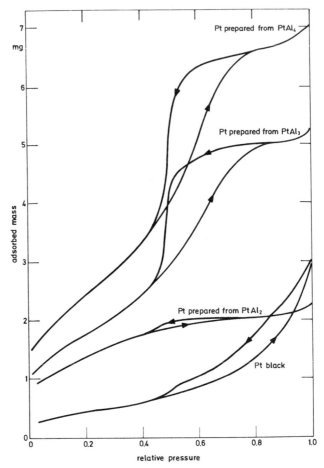

Fig. 7.25   Nitrogen adsorption isotherms measured at 77 K
on electrodes of Raney platinum prepared from alloys of
different aluminum content, and of platinum black

ing BET values and those from triangle voltammetry are also indicated. It can be seen that surface areas resulting from adsorption measurements are a suitable measure of the electrode activity. This result was obtained for all systems investigated but may not hold good for special cases. After long-time testing, the electrode showed a loss of activity, which was not accompanied, however, by a remarkable decrease in surface area. The pore size distribution, on the other hand, was shifted towards larger pores as shown in Fig. 7.26.

Investigations into the germanium—oxygen system

As germanium is an important semiconductor material, methods for the production of this material with atomically clean surfaces have been elaborated.

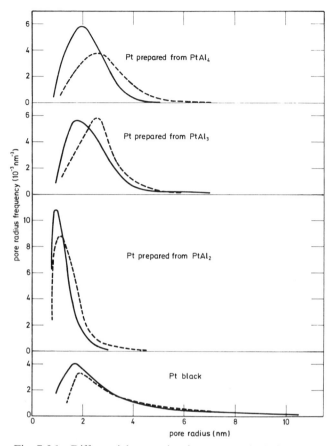

Fig. 7.26 Differential pore size frequency of platinum electrodes. Solid lines correspond to the isotherms of Fig. 7.25; dashed lines are results obtained from electrodes after extended use

The surface properties of germanium are of high interest for its technical application in microelectronic devices; besides, its clean surface has made germanium a good model substance for the investigation of chemical surface reactions.

Thermogravimetric equipment combined with a molecular beam apparatus has been described by Madix and Boudart[77], who determined the sticking probability of oxygen on the surface. This parameter permitted fundamental knowledge of adsorption kinetics to be derived. The apparatus is shown schematically in Fig. 7.28.

The effusive beam constructed for this investigation allowed independent control of the reaction variables. Oxygen in effusive flow was directed on a heated single-crystal germanium wafer cut parallel to the desired crystal plane; the wafer temperature was varied independently of the oxygen

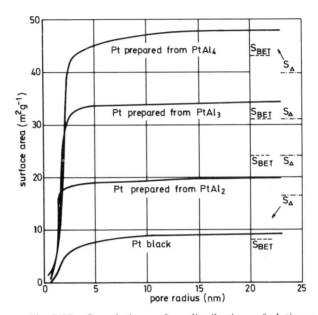

Fig. 7.27 Cumulative surface distributions of platinum electrodes calculated from the isotherms in Fig. 7.25, the final values of the curves denoting the cumulative surface areas. The corresponding BET values S_{BET} and those obtained from triangle voltammetry, S_Δ, are also indicated. All values are related to the total electrode mass, including matrix materials

temperature. The molecular flux of oxygen was altered simply by changing the pressure in the source chamber. The sticking probability was calculated from the known beam flux and the weight loss of the germanium wafer due to the evaporation of GeO formed as a result of the adsorption of beam and background oxygen molecules.

The germanium wafer as suspended from a microbalance that was mounted in the chamber on top of the main vacuum chamber, aligned with the effusion hole as shown in Fig. 7.28. Suspension wires were made of tungsten. The wafer was supported by a tungsten wire harness. Due to the vibration noise, the sensitivity of the balance was reduced to 4.10^{-7} g/scale division. A mass loss of 10^{-5} g h^{-1} could be measured with 10% accuracy. Because of this high sensitivity a high intensity of the supersonic beam could be avoided.

As shown in Fig. 7.29, the apparent sticking probability increased from zero to 0.045 over a period of 118 h. The apparent sticking probability increased initially from 1.6×10^{-3} to 1.0×10^{-2}. This change amounted to a rate of increase in the apparent sticking probability of 7.1×10^{-4} h^{-1}. the sharp decrease in $\alpha_{apparent}$ to 2.4×10^{-3} was followed by an increase rate in $\alpha_{apparent}$ of 7.9×10^{-4} h^{-1}.

The main result of this investigation was that the sticking probability α of

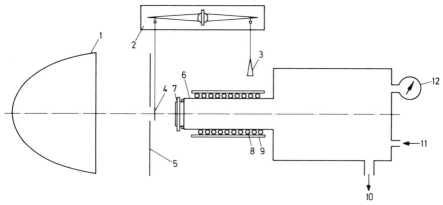

Fig. 7.28 Schematic representation of the molecular beam/microbalance apparatus according to Madix and Bourdart[77]; 1 reflector, 2 electrobalance, 3 counterweight, 4 wafer, 5 heat shield, 6 thermocouples, 7 foil assembly, 8 copper cooling coils, 9 heating tape, 10 to vacuum pump, 11 oxygen inlet, 12 Pirani gauge

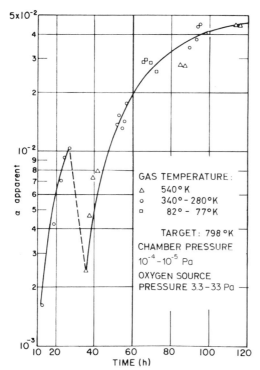

Fig. 7.29 Plot of apparent sticking probability of oxygen at germanium (100) against exposure time at various oxygen temperatures; wafer temperature 800 K

oxygen molecules on germanium surfaces increases with the gas and the sample temperature. Values of α went up from 0.00091 at 85 K to 0.020 at 283 K, to 0.042 at 536 K. Thus, α changes by a factor of about 40 when the absolute temperature increases sixfold.

Investigations into the mechanism of glueing and lubrication

In many cases good adherence (e.g. of adhesives and lubricants) to metal surfaces can be attributed to the binding of certain molecule groups of the substance at oxide layers of the metal. For carboxyl-containing lubricants and adhesives this hypothesis has been proved using acetic acid vapour as a model substance for sorption experiments with a vacuum microbalance[78]. At ambient temperature, adsorption isotherms were measured on clean and on oxide-covered surfaces of gold and aluminum. A resulting series of isotherms is shown in Fig. 9.21: at a clean metal surface only fast and reversible physisorption takes place. At an oxide-covered surface the physical adsorption is followed by slow, irreversible chemisorption, and reversible physisorption can occur at the chemisorbed layer.

7.3 Thermogravimetry under Extreme Conditions

'Extreme conditions' are here understood to include extreme temperatures, extreme pressures, and suspension.

7.3.1 Very low temperatures

Many examples discussed in this book, especially the surface area and pore size determination from the nitrogen isotherm (Chapters 3 and 4), are concerned with temperatures down to the liquid nitrogen temperature. The measuring technique is therefore well known. Extending the temperature range down to liquid helium and liquid hydrogen temperatures does not involve any serious problems. In this case the sample must be suspended on long thin wires, e.g. nickel-chromium alloy wires, 25 μm in diameter, 1 m in length, and shielded by several thin reflecting metal shields that are fastened to the suspension wires, as shown in Fig. 9.10. Additionally, diaphragms fastened to the wall of the hand-down tube must prevent any temperature radiation from the balance system. To prevent gas flows, the whole apparatus must be operated at ultrahigh vacuum, and the gases to be applied to the sample must be conveyed by a molecular beam technique. Thermostating is effected by metal helium cryostats. The sample can be observed through a window which can be closed with an internal shutter.

The investigation of the influence of adsorbed layers on superconductivity is an example of low-temperature adsorption measurements. Similar amounts of oxygen are applied to a sample suspended on the balance and to a second sample equipped with leads for voltage/current measurements. With the bal ance the adsorption/desorption is controlled and at the same time the electric conductivity is measured at the other sample.

7.3.2 High temperatures

Temperatures up to 2100 K (using a platinum oven) are commonly used in thermogravimetry. Apparatus equipped with a milligram balance, where the sample is above the beam, are being replaced by microgram balances with the sample suspended from the beam. The design of the apparatus is governed by the type of oven used. Typical thermogravimetric analysis applications of the high temperature techniques are investigations of the oxidation and reduction of metals and carbon. Experimental details and many examples are found in Gulbransen et al.[79].

For temperatures up to 2500 K, Tamman graphite ovens can be applied. Up to temperatures of 3300 K a thermogravimetric apparatus incorporating a

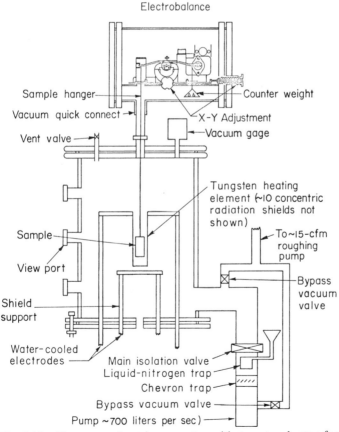

Fig. 7.30 Thermogravimetric apparatus with tungsten heater for temperatures up to 3300 K developed by Battelle-Columbus[59]

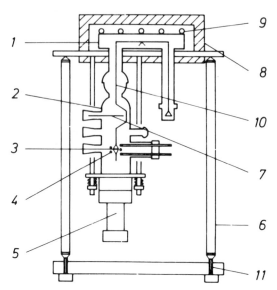

Fig. 7.31 Microbalance with induction heater up to 3300 K according to Steinheil[81]; 1 cast microbalance, 2 quartz vessel, 3 sample, 4 induction coil, 5 adjustment for sample vessel and heater, 6 balance support, 7 radiation shield, 8 metal box, 9 thermostat, 10 suspension, 11 adjusting screws

tungsten radiation heater for TGA, effusion, and transpiration experiments in high vacuum and inactive gases as described by Treweek[80] can be used. The apparatus is schematically represented in Fig. 7.30. The furnace consists of a tungsten mesh heater element, tungsten and molybdenum radiation shields, double-wall, water-cooled stainless steel containment vessel equipped with ports for viewing, electrical connections, or for mechanical connections or manipulations.

Steinheil[81] described an apparatus (Fig. 7.31) equipped with an induction oven for temperatures up to 3300 K. He used it for investigating reactions of refractory metals with the environmental atmosphere. The materials are destined for nuclear reactors, jet and rocket engines, and space technology. When using an induction heater, there are problems to be overcome not only with respect to high temperatures, but also with respect to high magnetic fields. Nevertheless, Steinheil achieved an accuracy better than 1 μg.

7.3.3 Ultrahigh vacuum

Ultrahigh vacuum (UHV) is common practice today. As regards the balances to be used, they should contain only few organic materials with high vapour pressure and be able to dissolve gases. For notes concerning the construction of UHV apparatus, see Section 8.6. The magnetic suspension balance after

Gast, the UHV balances after Czanderna and Rodder, and quartz spring balances (Chapter 8) are the most favourable. Applications of UHV include investigations of adsorption in the sub-monolayer region, desorption processes from 'clean' surfaces, and vapour pressure measurements.

7.3.4 High pressure

The application of high pressures requires rigid balance containers and thick-walled hang-down tubes made of metal. Balances and ancillary equipment for high pressure work are commercially available (see list in Appendix D). Heating of the sample becomes difficult; special heating devices are necessary. Buoyancy becomes a pronounced problem.

There are many technical processes in which high-pressure gas reactions are involved: selective adsorption at porous adsorbents at higher pressures is of considerable interest for the separation and purification of the lower alkanes and other gases. Many heterogenic catalytic processes take place under high-pressure conditions.

With compressed gases in excess adsorption is observed above the critical temperature, as shown in Fig. 7.32. This effect has been investigated by Specovius and Findenegg[82] using a commercial electronic balance (Fig. 7.33).

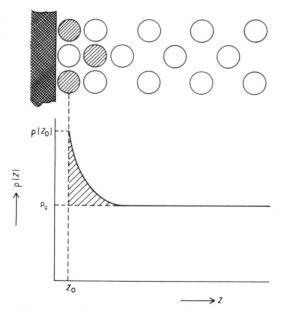

Fig. 7.32 Schematic representation of a compressed gas near an adsorbing surface above the critical temperature of the gas. Excess molecules are indicated by shading. The corresponding density profile shows an exponential decrease to the bulk density of the gas

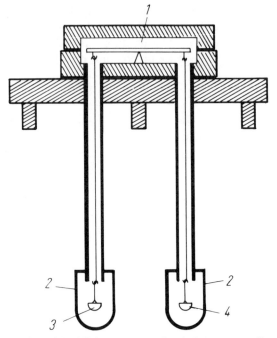

Fig. 7.33 High-pressure microbalance according to Gast; 1 balance, 2 sample container, 3 sample pan, 4 counterweight pan

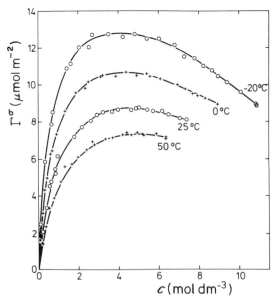

Fig. 7.34 Surface excess concentration as a function of the bulk density of methane (critical density 10.1 mole dm^{-3}) on graphon according to Specovius and Findenegg[82]

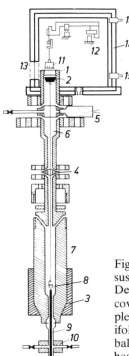

Fig. 7.35 High-pressure autoclave for a Gast suspension balance according to Sabrowsky and Deckert[83]; 1 window, 2 suspension magnet, 3 cover, 4 lens, 5 pressure gauge, 6 gold wire, 7 sample space, 8 sample pan, 9 thermocouples, 10 manifold with valves, 11 electromagnet, 12 electronic balance, compensating and measuring system, 13 heater, 14 connection for the water thermostat, 15 window

Typical isotherms of methane on graphon are shown in Fig. 7.34. When plotting the adsorbed amount against the bulk density of methane, the isotherms exhibit a maximum at about 0.4 to 0.5 of the critical density.

Sabrowsky and Deckert[83] used the Gast magnetic suspension balance (Fig. 7.35) for investigations with corrosive gases at pressures up to 150 bar and temperatures up to 900 K.

7.3.5 Thermogravimetry with suspended particles

The foregoing describes examples of measurements with suspended samples using the magnetic suspension balance. Straubel's method[84] of trapping and stabilizing charged particles in an inhomogeneous a.c. field (see section 8.1.3) permits thermogravimetric measurements on suspended particles. The application of the method is limited because the total pressure should not be varied too much and a vacuum, in which a gas discharge occurs, must be avoided because this would mean that the particle is discharged. Thus, measurements in UHV are possible but evacuation during the measurement is not feasible. It is, however, possible to vary the relative pressure of a gas component, e.g. the relative humidity.

Results of measurements of the sorption of water by an $Mg(ClO_4)_2$ particle and formation of a solution drop are shown in Fig. 7.36. The plot has been

320

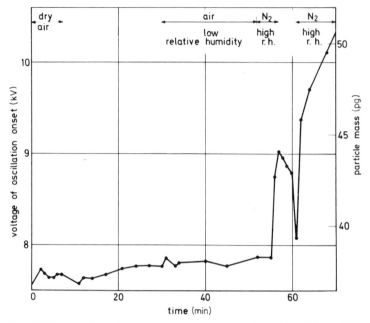

Fig. 7.36   Sorption of water vapour by a suspended $Mg(ClO_4)_2 \cdot xH_2O$
particle as a function of time

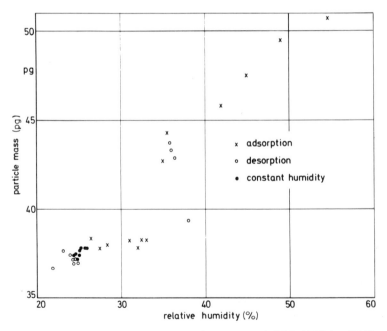

Fig. 7.37   Sorption of water vapour by a suspended $Mg(ClO_4)_2 \cdot xH_2O$
particle as a function of relative humidity

converted into an isotherm plot (Fig. 7.37). Note that mass differences of 0.1 pg could be observed.

7.4 Other applications of vacuum microbalances

A number of 'unusual' applications of microbalances have been compiled by Gast[85] and Eyraud[86]. They are briefly mentioned here, together with some additional examples.

7.4.1 Measurement of density and pressure

Using the buoyancy effect on a beam balance loaded on either side with bodies of equal mass but very different volume (a piece of glass and a glass balloon), the balance can be used for sensitive density measurements. Gast[87] recorded density variations in a multi-component gas stream with such a balance.

If the specific density of the gas is known or has been determined by calibration it is possible to use such an instrument as pressure gauge, as described in Section 8.3 and illustrated in Fig. 8.26. Knudsen forces have been used to extend the range of this pressure gauge (Section 8.3).

7.4.2 Measurement of vapour pressure

By means of a thermobalance the vapour pressure of solids and liquids can be measured using either the Langmuir or the Knudsen method[79]. In the Langmuir method, the mass loss from a body of known surface area is determined as a function of time and temperature. In the Knudsen method, the specimen is placed in a platinum bucket which contains a small orifice for the effusion of the vapour. The force exerted by the gas stream on a plate before the orifice, or the reaction force if the Knudsen cell is suspended from the balance, or the mass loss with time, is measured. The Knudsen method is the more accurate; however, higher temperatures must be used to achieve the same mass loss as in the Langmuir method.

7.4.3 Measurement of flow

Microbalances, often in the form of multicomponent balances, can be used to measure gas flows (see Chapter 8). Straubel[88] used an electrostatically suspended particle as a sensor. Krüger and Scharmann[89] determined the mean velocity of particles that are emitted upon sputtering of metals by ions, using a microbalance[9].

7.4.4 Measurement of permeation

For the measurement of permeation and the determination of the permeation coefficient, the membrane under investigation separates a space connected with a thermostatted container with a liquid, e.g. water, whose vapour should diffuse through the membrane from the other space equipped with a balance. The balance is charged with a dessicating agent, e.g. P_2O_5.

7.4.5 Measurement of temperature

Wiedemann and van Tets[90] described experiments in which a molecular beam has been reflected on the balance pan. The force exerted on the pan by the beam depends linearly on the temperature. Temperatures between 300 and 1300 K have been measured in this way. The measurements have to be carried out in high vacuum, the gas and the balance pan being at the same temperature.

7.4.6 Measurement of dust concentration

Here the balance must be combined with a precipitating device, either electrically or mechanically, using a filter through which the loaded gas will be sucked. A very elegant method is the use of vibrating thin band as mass indicator.

7.4.7 Measurement of grain size distribution by sedimentation

This can be done either by sedimentation from a liquid suspension, from an aerosol or in vacuum. Some commercial sedimentation balances are available.

7.4.8 Measurement of surface tension and contact angle

Surface tension is measured by dragging a body of known geometry (e.g. platinum ring, frame, or plate) out of a liquid. The surface resists against its extension, and this force can be directly determined.

Langbein[91] extended the method to the measurement of contact angles. Compared with direct microscopic observation of the contact angle, this method is more sensitive and gives objective results.

7.4.9 Measurement of spreading pressure

Langmuir[92,93] describes a balance which makes it possible to measure the force of a monolayer film spreading on the surface of a liquid. He confined the film by an adjustable barrier on one side and a floating one on the other. The film was prevented from leaking past the ends of the floating barrier by means of small air jets. The actual force on this barrier was then measured using a torsion balance system which indicates directly the film or spreading pressure.

7.4.10 Measurement of magnetic permittivity

According to the Faraday method, the sample is suspended from a balance between the pole faces of a high-power electromagnet[98,99]. If a powder, it may be placed in a quartz bucket. The electrobalance measures the force F which is exerted on the sample by the magnetic field of strength H. The dimensionless magnetic permittivity is determined from

$$\mathscr{X} = \frac{F\rho}{\mu_0 mH(dH/dz)}$$

where m is the mass of the sample, ρ is the density, dH/dz is the field gradient, z is the vertical distance from the pole horizon, and μ_0 equals 4.10^{-7} J m^{-1} A^{-2}.

7.4.11 Measurement of dielectric constant and loss factor

For the measurement of the dielectric constant, the sample is suspended from the balance into a thermostatted spherical condensor applied with an a.c. voltage of about 1 kV and frequencies between 50 Hz and 100 MHz. To determine the dielectric loss factor the torque is measured which a rotating electric field exerts on a sample.

References

1. J. Rouquérol, in: *Thermochimie Marseille 1971*, CNRS, Paris, 1972, p. 537
2. J. Rouquérol, F. Rouquérol, C. Pérès, Y. Grillet, and M. Boudellal, in: S. J. Gregg, K. S. W. Sing, H. F. Stoeckli (eds.), *Characterisation of Porous Solids*, Society of Chemical Industry, London, 1979, p. 107
3. P. H. Emmett and S. J. Brunauer, *J. Amer. Chem. Soc.*, **56**, 35 (1934)
4. A. S. Joy, *Vacuum,*. **3**, 254 (1953)
5. W. H. Kuhn, G. Walter, and G. Wurzbacher, *Studies on the Effect of Nuclear Radiation on Heterogeneously Catalyzed Gas Reactions*. Report EUR 2455.e. Presses Académiques Européennes 1965
6. E. Robens and G. Walter, *Sprechsaal*, **104**, 426, 489 (1971)
7. F. Rouquerol and J. Rouquerol, in: H. G. Wiedemann (ed.), *Thermal Analysis*, Vol. 1, Birkhäuser, Basel, 1972, p. 373
8. F. Paulik and J. Paulik, in: H. G. Wiedemann (ed.), *Thermal Analysis*, Vol. 1, Birkhäuser, Basel, 1972, p. 161
9. D. Dollimore and G. Rickett, in: H. G. Wiedemann (ed.), *Thermal Analysis*, Vol. 2, Birkhäuser, Basel 1972, p. 43.
10. H. J. Seifert, G. Thiel, and R. Schmitt, in: W. Hemminger (ed.), *Thermal Analysis*, Vol. 2, Birkhäuser, Basel 1980, p. 81.
11. H. Förster and V. Meyn, in: C. Eyraud and M. Escoubes (eds.), *Progress in Vacuum Microbalance Techniques*, Vol. 3, Heyden, London 1975, p. 370
12. M. Escoubes and R. Blanc, in: C. Eyraud and M. Escoubes (eds.), *Progress in Vacuum Microbalance Techniques*, Vol. 3, Heyden, London 1975, p. 388
13. M. Brun, A. Lallemand, J. F. Quinson, and C. Eyraud, in: C. Eyraud and M. Escoubes (eds.), *Progress in Vacuum Microbalance Techniques*, Vol. 3, Heyden, London, 1975, p. 428

14. N. Pernicone, G. Liberti, and G. Servi in: C. Eyraud and M. Escoubes (eds.), *Progress in Vacuum Microbalance Techniques*, Vol. 3, Heyden, London, 1975, p. 304
15. M. Grunze and W. Hirshwald, in: C. Eyraud and M. Escoubes (eds.), *Progress in Vacuum Microbalance Techniques*, Vol. 3, Heyden, London, 1975, p. 233.
16. H. Bentlage and W. Wilkens, in: C. Eyraud and M. Escoubes (eds.), *Progress in Vacuum Microbalance Techniques*, Vol. 3, Heyden, London, 1975, p. 114
17. D. Shamir and M. Steinberg, in: S. C. Bevan, S. J. Gregg, and N. D. Parkyns (eds.), *Progress in Vacuum Microbalance Techniques*, Vol. 2, Heyden, London, 1973, p. 19
18. M. Breysse, L. Faure, B. Claudel, and J. Veron, in: S. C. Bevan, S. J. Gregg, and N. D. Parkyns (eds.), *Progress in Vacuum Microbalance Techniques*, Vol. 2, Heyden, London, 1973, p. 229
19. W. E. Gardner and A. K. Gregson, in: S. C. Bevan, S. J. Gregg, and N. D. Parkyns (eds.), *Progress in Vacuum Microbalance Techniques*, Vol. 2, Heyden, London 1973, p. 183
20. H. Charcosset, C. Bolivar, R. Fréty, R. Gomez, and Y. Trambouze, in: S. C. Bevan, S. J. Gregg, and N. D. Parkyns (eds.), *Progress in Vacuum Microbalance Techniques*, Vol. 2, Heyden, London, 1973, p. 175
21. H. Ewe, E. W. Justi, A. F. Schmitt, and H. Willigeroth, in: S. C. Bevan, S. J. Gregg, and N. D. Parkyns (eds.),. *Progressin Vacuum Microbalance Techniques*, Vol. 2, Heyden, London, 1972, p. 113
22. A. J. Hegedüs, in: Th. Gast and E. Robens (eds.) *Progress in Vacuum Microbalance Techniques*, Vol. 1, Heyden, London, 1972, p. 365
23. K. Martin, in: Th. Gast and E. Robens (eds.), *Progress in Vacuum Microbalance Techniques*, Vol. 1, Heyden, London 1972, p. 369
24. J. J. Nickl, and Chr. v. Braunmühl, in: Th. Gast and E. Robens (eds.), *Progress in Vacuum Microbalance Techniques*, Vol. 1, Heyden, London 1972, p. 323
25. A. J. Ashworth, in: Th. Gast and E. Robens (eds.), *Progress in Vacuum Microbalance Techniques*, Vol. 1, Heyden, London, 1972, p. 313
26. E. L. Fuller, Jr., H. F. Holmes, R. B Gammage, and C. H. Secoy, in: Th. Gast and E. Robens (eds.), *Progress in Vacuum Microbalance Techniques*, Vol. 1, Heyden, London 1972, p. 265
27. G. Dickel and D. Fiederer, in: Th. Gast and E. Robens (eds.), *Progress in Vacuum Microbalance Techniques*, Vol. 1, Heyden, London, 1972, p. 119
28. J. Nixdorf, E. Poeschel and R. Skoutajan, in: Th. Gast and E. Robens (eds.), *Progress in Vacuum Microbalance Techniques*, Vol. 1, Heyden, London, 1972, p. 63
29. E. Clarke, *Thermochimica Acta*, **51**, 7 (1981)
30. A. J. Ashworth, *Thermochimica Acta*, **51**, 17 (1981)
31. H. L. Eschbach, I. V. Mitchell, and E. Louwerix, *Thermochimica Acta*, **51**, 33 (1981)
32. E. C. Brown, D. R. Glasson, and S. A. A. Jayaweera, *Thermochimica Acta*, **51**, 53 (1981)
33. N. Chakrabarti, D. R. Glasson, and S. A. A. Jayaweera, *Thermochimica Acta*, **51**, 77 (1981)
34. Th. Gast and K. P. Gebauer, *Thermochimica Acta*, **51**, 1 (1981)
35. H. Czabon, E. Robens, G. Walter, M.-L. Welling, and G. Hild, *I&EC Product Res. and Dev.*, **9**, 27 (1970)
36. D. Schroeter and W. Liebrich, *Analyse*, **K1**, 4 (1975)
37. T. F. Anderson, *Trans. N.Y. Acad. Sci.*, Ser. II, **13**, 130 (1951)
38. K. S. Rao, *J. Phys. Chem.*, **45**, 506, 517 (1941)
39. A. A. Hofer and H. Mohler, *Helvetica Chimica Acta*, **45**, 1415 (1962)

40. L. M. Nikitina, Tables of mass transport coefficients in humid materials. *Nauka i Technika*, Izdatelstvo, Minsk, 1964
41. L. M. Nikitina: Thermodynamic parameters and mass transport coefficients in humid materials. *Chimija-Energija*, 1968
42. S. Gál, *Die Methodik der Wasserdampf-Sorptionsmessung*, Springer, Berlin, 1967
43. F. Kneule (ed.), *Sorptions- und Desorptionsisothermen. Berichstsheft 6 der Fachgemeinschaft Lufttechnische und Trocknungsanlagen im VDMA*, Maschinenbau-Verlag, Frankfurt am Main, 1964
44. E. Berlin, B. A. Anderson, and M. J. Pallansch, *J. Dairy Sci.*, **51**, 1339 (1968)
45. *Wasserdampf-Sorptionsisothermen von Lebensmitteln. Berichtsheft 18 der Fachgemeinschaft Allgemeine Lufttechnik im VDMA*, Frankfurt am Main, 1968
46. K. Mahler, *Chem.-Ing.-Techn.*, **33**, 627 (1961)
47. D. H. Buckley, *Surface Effects in Adhesion, Friction, Wear, and Lubrication*, Elsevier, Amsterdam 1981
48. E. Robens, G. Robens, and G. Sandstede, *Vacuum*, **13**, 103 (1963)
49. H. Seewald and H. Jüntgen, *Berichte Bunsen-Ges. Phys. Chem.*, **81**, 638 (1977)
50. S. E. Donnelly, D. C. Ingram, R. P. Webb, and D. G. Armour, *Vacuum*, **29**, 303 (1979)
51. J. M. Ferguson, R. J. Fuller, and D. Mortimer, in: H. G. Wiedemann (ed.), *Thermal Analysis*, Vol. 1, Birkhäuser, Basel, 1972, p. 197.
52. E. Hoinkis, H. Behret, D. Hartmann, A. Köhling, and E. Robens, *Thermochimica Acta*, **29**, 345 (1979)
53. P. H. Doe and J. M. Haynes in: S. J. Gregg, K. S. W. Sing, and H. F. Stoeckli (eds.), *Characterisation of Porous Solids*, Society of Chemical Industry, London, 1979, p. 253
54. P. Krautwasser: Über die röntgenographisch bestimmte Mikroporosität. Dissertation, TH Aachen 1975; Bericht Jül-1202, KFA Jülich 1975
55. W. H. Kuhn and G. Walter, *Microgravimetric Investigation into the Mechanism of Corrosion of Reactor Materials in the Presence of Nuclear Radiation*. Euratom Report 1474.e., Presses Académiques Européennes, Brussels, 1964
56. V. A. Susunov and Ju. N. Barysnikov, *Zurnal fiziceskoy chimii*, **27**, 830 (1953)
57. H. Behret, H. Binder, and E. Robens, *Thermochimica Acta*, **24**, 407 (1978)
58. R. Geist, Dissertation, Heidelberg, 1968
59. V. A. Garten and D. E. Weiss, *Rev. Pure Appl. Chem.*, **7**, 69 (1957)
60. R. E. Panzer and P. J. Elving, *Electrochim. Acta*, **20**, 635 (1975)
61. B. P. Bering, E. G. Zukovskaja, B. C. Rachmukov, and V. V. Serpinski, *Z. Chem.*, **9**, 13 (1969)
62. L. Riekert, *Ber. Bunsenges. Phys. Chem.*, **63**, 198 (1959)
63. D. Menzel and L. Riekers, *Ber. Bunsenges. Phys. Chem.*, **66**, 432 (1962)
64. O. M. Poltorak and V. S. Boronin, *Russ. J. Phys. Chem.* (Engl. tran.), **40**, 1436 (1966)
65. G. Walter and G. Wurzbacher, *Final Technical Report*, European Research Office, United States Army, Contract No. DA-91-591-EUC-3432, July 1965, AD 467849, CFSTI
66. R. W. Roberts, *Brit. J. Appl. Phys.*, **14**, 485 (1963)
67. D. W. McKee, *J. Amer. Chem. Soc.*, **87**, 1618 (1965)
68. G. Walter, G. Wurzbacher, and B. Krafczyk, *J. Catalysis*, **10**, 336 (1968)
69. G. Walter and G. Wurzbacher, *Final Technical Report*, European Research Office, United States Army, Contract No. DA-91-591-EUC-4035, Sept. 1967
70. G. C. Bond, *Catalysis by Metals*, Academic Press, London & New York, 1962, p. 217 ff.
71. A. K. Galwey, *Proc. Roy. Soc. (London)*, **271**, 218 (1963)
72. S. B. Brummer, J. I. Ford and M. Turner, *J. Phys. Chem.*, **69** 3424 (1965)

326

73. J. A. Shropshire and H. H. Horowitz, *J. Electrochem. Soc.*, **113**, 490 (1966)
74. H. L. Gruber, *J. Phys. Chem.*, **66**, 48 (1962)
75. H. Binder, A. Köhling, K. Metzelthin, G. Sandstede, and M.-L. Schrecker, *Chemie-Ing.-Technik*, **40**, 586 (1968)
76. E. Robens, G. Sandstede, and G. Walter, *Vide*, **24**, 266 (1969)
77. R. J. Madix and M. Boudart, *J. Catalysis*, **7**, 240 (1967)
78. G. Sandstede, E. Robens, and G. Walter, *Proceedings of the III. Int. Kongress für Grenzflächenaktive Stoffe*, Vol. II, Section B, Verlag Universitätsdruckerei Mainz, 1960, p. 409
79. E. A. Gulbransen and F. A. Brassart, in: A. W. Czanderna and S. P. Wolsky (eds.), *Microweighing in Vacuum and Controlled Environments*, Elsevier, Amsterdam 1980, Ch. 9
80. D. Treweek, in: *Materials Thermodynamic Capability Report*, Battelle Memorial Institute, Columbus, Ohio, 1969
81. E. Steinheil, in: H. W. Wiedemann (ed.), *Thermal Analysis*, Vol. 1, Birkhäuser, Basel, 1972, p. 187.
82. J. Specovius and G. H. Findenegg, *Ber. Bunsenges. Phys. Chem.*, **82**, 174 (1978)
83. H. Sabrowsky and H. G. Deckert, *Chem.-Ing.-Techn.*, **50**, 217 (1978)
84. G. Böhme, E. Robens, H. Straubel, and G. Walter, in: S. C. Bevan, S. J. Gregg, and N. D. Parkyns (eds.), *Progress in Vacuum Microbalance Techniques*, Vol. 2; Heyden, London 1973, p. 169
85. Th. Gast, in: A. W. Czanderna and S. P. Wolsky (eds.): *Microweighing in Vacuum and Controlled Environments*, Elsevier, Amsterdam, 1980, Ch. 10
86. C. Eyraud, M. Cronenberger, and M. Cogniat, *Techniques de l'Ingenieur*, **K870**
87. Th. Gast., *Feinwerktechnik*, **53**, 167 (1949)
88. H. Straubel, in: *Dechema-Monographien*, Vol. 43, Dechema, Frankfurt am Main 1962, p. 375
89. W. Krüger and A. Scharmann, in: Th. Gast and E. Robens (eds.), *Progress in Vacuum Microbalance Techniques*, Vol. 1, Heyden, London, 1972, p. 77
90. H. G. Wiedemann and A. van Tets, *Naturwissenshaften*, **56**, 278 (1969)
91. D. Langbein and E. Robens: German Patent Application P 29 02 561.4 (1979)
92. I. Langmuir, *J. Am. Chem. Soc.*, **39**, 1848 (1917)
93. A. W. Adamson, *Physical Chemistry of Surfaces*, Interscience, New York, 1960
94. S. Ladas, R. A. Dalla Betta, and M. Boudart, *J. Catalysis*, **53**, 356 (1978)
95. D. Shamir and M. Steinberg, in: S. C. Bevan, S. J. Gregg, and N. D. Parkyns (eds), *Progress in Vacuum Microbalance Techniques*, Vol. 2, Heyden, London, 1973, p. 19
96. J. Vansummeren and A. van den Bosch, in: S. C. Bevan, S. J. Gregg, and N. D. Parkyns (eds.) *Progress in Vacuum Microbalance Techniques*, Vol. 2, Heyden, London, 1973, p. 147
97. A. van den Bosch, in: C. Eyraud and M. Escoubes (eds.), *Progress in Vacuum Microbalance Techniques*, Vol. 3, Heyden, London, 1975, pp. 361, 398.
98. W. E. Gardner and A. K. Gregson, in: S. C. Bevan, S. J. Gregg, and N. D. Parkyns (eds.), *Progress in Vacuum Microbalance Techniques*, Vol. 2, Heyden, London 1973, p. 183
99. V. J. Perrichon, J. P. Candy, and P. Fouilloux, in: C. Eyraud and M. Escoubes (eds.), *Progress in Vacuum Micro-balance Techniques*, Vol. 3, Heyden, London 1975, p. 18

Chapter 8

Instrumentation

This chapter deals with the instrumentation indispensable for gravimetric apparatus and with some ancillary equipment. It chiefly considers commercially available parts. Essential parts include the balance, pressure, and temperature instruments and controls, manostats, thermostats, and vacuum equipment. Differential thermoanalysis, dilatometry, and gas analysis are included as supplementing measuring techniques. Additionally, some experimental hints will be given. Tables on commercial thermobalances and sorption balances and related apparatus are summarized in the Appendix. In the References the general literature is summarized[1-35].

8.1 Sorption Balances

Stepwise gravimetric investigation of chemical reactions is a very old experimental practice. The first thermogravimetric assembly seems to have been that described by Nernst and Riesenfeld in 1903[36]: a quartz balance with electric oven. In 1915 the first thermobalance (Fig. 8.1) was developed by Honda[37], who also created the name. Further developments were made in particular in France by Guichard[38], Dubois[39], Chevenard[40], and Duval[9]. The first commercial thermogravimetric apparatus was manufactured in 1945 by ADAMEL, and C. and I. Eyraud[41,42] constructed the first commercially avail-

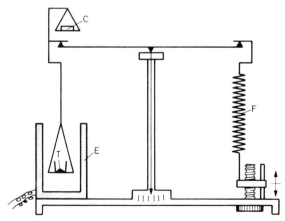

Fig. 8.1 Schematic   representation   of   Honda's thermobalance; T crucible with sample, C counterweight, E electric oven, F adjusting spring

328

Fig. 8.2 Registration of the metabolism of a plant

able compensating vacuum thermo-balance. In 1953 de Keyser[43] developed the differential thermogravimetric method.

Another line of development was started as a consequence of the application of gravimetry to sorption measurements. One very early application is shown in Fig. 8.2. A prerequisite for such measurements was the development of sensitive microbalances, the first one being generally attributed to Warburg and Ihmori[44]. Pettersson[45,46] published the first gravimetric observation of adsorption in 1914. Further important developments were made by Rhodin[47], Gulbransen[48], McBain and Bakr[49], Gregg and Wintle[50], Cahn[51], and Gast[52–55]. One of the most essential steps forward in this development was the introduction of vacuum, which affected the construction of the balance[56]. In general, all balances which feature a high relative sensitivity (ratio of maximum load to smallest detectable value), must be protected from temperature changes, and will not be corroded by the measuring gas or gases evolved from the sample to make them suitable for the work in vacuum and can be used for surface gravimetry. With a view to universal applicability, the balances should be suitable for measurements in ultrahigh vacuum ($< 10^{-5}$ Pa), i.e. they should not contain any gassing components (wire insulations, electronic components) or cavities difficult to evacuate.

Sorption and thermobalances are usually designed for maximum loads between 1 mg and 500 g. The maximum load/sensitivity ratio today amounts to 10^8, the accuracy, however, being limited by the experimental conditions (buoyancy, thermal flow, etc.). Thermogravimetric measurements are carried out in an extended temperature region (4 to 3000 K) and in the pressure region from UHV to 500 bar.

8.1.1 Beam balances

With beam balances the mass difference in the gravitational field between the sample and the counterweight is measured. The relative sensitivity of 10^8 is usually approached, and in special cases a sensitivity of 10^9 is obtained.

Inclination balances

These balances are characterized by a change in beam inclination when the mass of the sample is varied, until equilibrium has been re-established. This type of balance was often used for thermogravimetry but nowadays is mostly replaced by compensating beam balances. For applications in UHV and corrosive atmospheres, bakeable quartz beam balances are sometimes used, with microscopic observation of the inclination (cf. the Rodder balance[57] shown in Fig. 8.3).

The beam inclination can be recorded in various ways: Chevenard[58] used photographic registration (Fig. 8.4); Chevenard-Duval actuated electrical contacts with the beam, the pulses being recorded; Gordon and Campbell[59] used a potentiometer; Petersen a magnetic detector[60], others a differential transformer; Rulfs[61] performed registration with the aid of photocells, using a diaphragm with varying aperture; their equipped Seederer and Feuer[62] balance with a radium pin, the position of which was determined by two ionization chambers.

Compensating beam balances

With compensating beam balances the momentum due to a change in equilibrium is compensated by a counterforce returning the beam to zero. This counterforce serves as a measure for the mass change. The balance can be made very sensitive and independent of positional variations by locating the centre of gravity in the pivot. Stable position of the sample is advantageous because the temperature field of the thermostat often is not homogeneous. Compensating, equal-armed beam balances are most favourable in terms of the measuring procedure. In balances of this type, sample and counterweight can be kept at the same temperature, so that buoyancy and convection are largely compensated. For the measuring system of the balance a temperature compensation between 0 and 40 °C is generally sufficient; for water vapour sorption measurements, it should be between 80 and 120 °C.

Bartlett and Williams[63] describe a balance in which the beam is restored by a counteracting pointer of an electrical instrument arranged in a Wheatstone bridge. Eyraud's balance[41,42] is equipped with a metal plate cutting off a light beam and, via a photocell, controlling a d.c. magnet suspended at the balance (Fig. 8.5). A differential photoelectric detector is described by Mauer[64]. Brockdorff[65] used a coil at the beam to counteract a permanent magnet and thus compensate the deflection after its photoelectric determination. Similar devices have been described by Cahn[51] (Fig. 8.6), Müller[66], Hirone and

Fig. 8.3   UHV quartz beam balance for optical observation after Rodder[57]

Maeda[67], and are manufactured by several companies (Fig. 8.7). Manigau
and Tsai[68] used electromagnetic forces applied to a core of soft iron which wa
attached to the beam; the current required to compensate the deflection wa
operated manually. A coil system with controlled d.c. flow was used by Greg
and Wintle[50], the deflection being observed with a photocell. Similar device
have been developed by many others[69,70]. Czanderna[71] developed a com
mercial UHV quartz-beam compensating balance with a relative sensitivity c

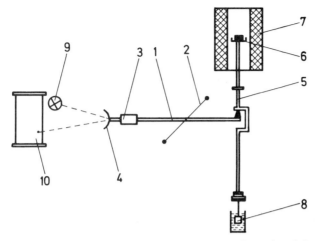

Fig. 8.4   Guichard's thermobalance; 1 beam, 2 taut band, 3 counterweight, 4 mirror, 5 shaft, 6 pan with sample, 7 oven, 8 counterweight and damper, 9 lamp, 10 recorder cylinder with photo-paper

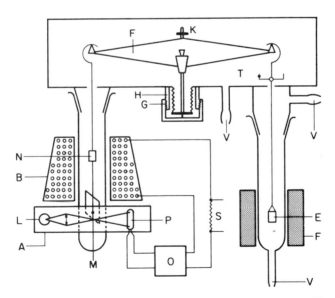

Fig. 8.5   Eyraud's thermobalance; K, G adjusting screws, F beam, H bellows, N soft iron magnet, B d.c. magnet, L. lamp, A case, M diaphragm, T tare pan, V vacuum flanges, E sample pan, F heater, S shunt, P photocell, O amplifier. Manufacturer: SETARAM, Lyon, France

332

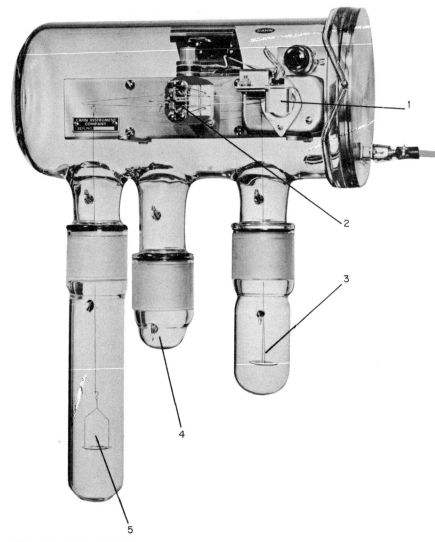

Fig. 8.6 Cahn RG balance; 1 photo cell detector for a beam deflection, 2 magnet/coil compensation system, 3 tare pan, 4 position for 2.5 g samples, sensitivity 0.5 μg, 5 position for 1 g samples, sensitivity 0.1 μg. Manufacturer: Cahn Instruments, Cerritos, CA, USA

$2 \cdot 10^8$. Photocell and lamp are arranged outside the case, the light beam being introduced through borosilicate windows (Figs. 8.38, 8.39).

The sensor of Gast's balances[52,53] (Fig. 8.8) is composed of coils which are crossed in zero position. After deflection a high-frequency signal is transmitted, which is subsequently rectified and fed back to the beam coil, restoring the beam against a permanent magnet. The d.c. serves as a measure for the mass change.

333

Fig. 8.7   CI Electronics balance. Manufacturer: CI Electronics Ltd., Churchfields, Salisbury UK

Fig. 8.8 Electromagnetic microbalance after Gast. Manufacturer: Sartorius, Göttingen, West Germany

Former thermobalances were compensated by chains which could be varied automatically in length[72]. Garn[73] used a servo-motor controlled by a differential transformer for this (Fig. 8.9). Waters[74] described a differential thermobalance, in which the mass change was compensated by electrolytic precipitation of silver from $AgNO_3$. Buoyancy in a liquid is occasionally used

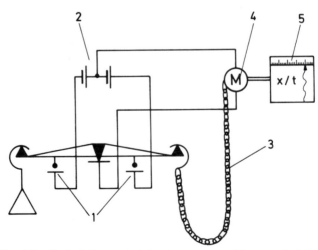

Fig. 8.9 Chain balance; 1 deflection contacts, 2 battery, 3 chain, 4 servo-motor, 5 recorder

to compensate balance deflection. Automatic balances of this kind are described by Papailhau[75] and Somet[76]. Dybwad and Zinnow[77,78] used the force of a light beam as restoring force; the lowest mass change detectable with their balance was 10^{-10} g.

Torsion balances where the torsion wire is turned by a servo-motor have been described; a photocell mostly being used as a position sensor[79]. The micro-balances described above (e.g. Cahn, Gast, Czanderna) can also be regarded as torsion balances because the beam is suspended in taut bands.

8.1.2 Spring balances

With respect to simplicity of design, quartz spiral balances are particularly favourable. In fact, self-manufacturing is possible. These balances consist of only few materials and thus lend themselves to work in UHV and corrosive atmospheres. However, because of their moderate resolution related to the maximum load of about 10^4, they have largely been displaced by commercial electric beam balances.

Spring balances with deflection measurement

The McBain balance[49] consists of a quartz spiral in a glass tube. Deflection is observed using a cathetometer. A modification is described by Rhodin[47]. Despite the small coefficient of expansion, it is recommended to keep the spiral at constant temperature. Ernsberger[80] calculated the error by thermal expansion to be

$$\Delta L = -1.23 \cdot 10^{-4} k \left(M + \frac{m}{2} \right) \Delta T \qquad (8.1)$$

where ΔL is the elongation of the spiral (mm), ΔT the temperature difference (K), M the sample mass, m the spiral mass (mg), and k the sensitivity (mm/mg).

The sensitivity of the balance depends on its geometry. For a maximum load of 1 mg it may be 100 mm/mg, and for 10 g about 0.01 mm/mg. Quartz springs and spring balances are commercially available (see Appendix D).

The deflection of the spring balance can be read using a differential trans-former[81,82]; (Fig. 8.10). In an improved version the coil system is auto-matically guided[83] to expand the range, which results in a sensitivity of 10 μg for 1 g load. Some spring balances are equipped with a light-beam recorder[84,85]

Compensating spring balances

Spring balances can be magnetically equilibrated by attaching a soft-iron magnet to the balance pan, as described by Clark[86]. Using a photoelectric control and a d.c. coil system, the elongation can be compensated to zero. A

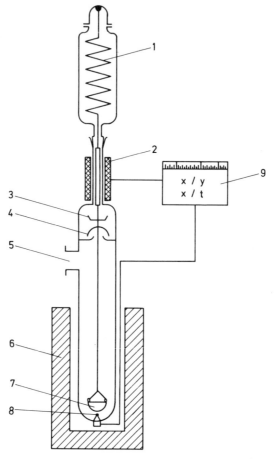

Fig. 8.10 'Aminco Thermo-Grav'; 1 quartz spring,
2 induction coil, 3 tare pan, 4 temperature screen, 5
vacuum flange, 6 heater, 7 sample pan, 8 thermocouple, 9 recorder

similar balance is described by Beams et al.[87]. See also the quartz pressure
gauges described in Section 8.2.

Strain gauge balances

The measuring method using strain gauges or streched resistance wires
exhibits similarities to the operating principle of spring balances. This method
is increasingly being used for weighing heavy loads. The small relative sensitivity of 10^{-5} restricts its use in thermogravimetry to special tasks.

8.1.3 Suspension balances

Suspension balances are defined as instruments where the sample is freely suspended in the atmosphere without mechanical connection to the measuring system. There are two possibilities of realization electrostatic or electromagnetic. Millikan suspended charged particles to determine the ratio of charge e to mass m. If e is known (and constant during the experiment), then m and variations of m, e.g. due to adsorption, can be determined.

Straubel[88] improved the method by using a capacitor with three circular parallel plates, each with a hole in its centre (Fig. 8.11). If an a.c. voltage is applied between the intermediate plate and the ground, small particles carry-

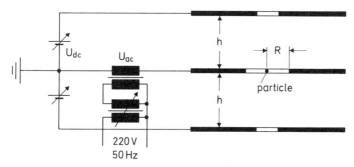

Fig. 8.11   Straubel's three-plate capacitor

Fig. 8.12   Straubel's three-plate capacitor

ing a sufficiently high charge will be trapped in the inhomogeneous field of the hole. These particles will be kept exactly in the centre of the hole but, according to their mass, somewhat below the horizontal plate. To counter-balance the mass a constant field may be applied across the two outer plates (Millikan experiment). Figure 8.12 shows the corresponding experimental set-up. The particles are charged, for example in a corona discharge, and dusted into the capacitor from above. All particles but one will be removed by varying the a.c. voltage (about 10 kV, 50 Hz). The remaining particle is illuminated from below and observed with a stereo microscope.

When slowly increasing the voltage, the particle suddenly starts to oscillate. By determining the onset of oscillation it is possible to calculate the ratio e/m.

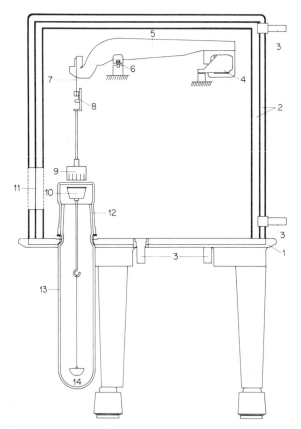

Fig. 8.13 Electromagnetic suspension balance according to Gast; 1 basic plate, 2 thermostatted case, 3 hose connections, 4 magnet and coil system for mass measurement, 5 beam, 6 knife edge, 7, 8 suspension, 9 electromagnet, 10 suspended permanent magnet, 11 window, 12 joint, 13 quartz tube, 14 sample pan. Manufacturer: Sartorius, Göttingen, West Germany

In addition, relative weight changes of the particle are obtained from the relation

$$\frac{\Delta m}{m} = \frac{\Delta U}{U} \tag{8.2}$$

by repeated determination of the a.c. voltage U at the onset of oscillation. Particles up to milligrams may be used; the smallest mass change observed was 0.1 pg (Figs. 7.36, 7.37).

For studying sorption in a corrosive atmosphere or in ultrahigh vacuum, the electromagnetic suspension balance (Fig. 8.13) according to Gast[53] is particularly suitable. This is a single-armed beam balance with electromagnetic compensation in which the sample pan is attached to a permanent magnet which is kept in suspension at a distance of about 10 mm below an electromagnet attached to the hangdown wire, the distance between the two magnets being controlled electromagnetically. The reaction space, a quartz vessel, thus contains only the sample attached to the permanent magnet. The measuring system of the balance is outside the reaction space, thermostatted in air. The sample temperature can be transmitted without wires[54]. Special versions for work in corrosive atmospheres (Fig. 8.48) and at high pressures (up to 150 bar) are available.

8.1.4 Oscillation balances

Crystal balances

A change of the mass of the crystal m_0 results in a change of it eigenfrequency f_0:

$$\frac{\Delta f}{f_0} = \frac{\Delta m}{m_0} \tag{8.3}$$

The smallest mass difference observed so far is about 1 pg. The maximum coverage measurable amounts to about 0.1 mg. It is essential that the sample be firmly connected to the crystal. Otherwise it is not the mass that is measured, but the impedance of a stationary wave within the sample. The application is therefore restricted to the measurement of growing layers (vacuum evaporation, sputtering, etc.[89–92]), and vapours condensed in a porous surface layer. The temperature effect could be compensated so that measurements in the range of 4 to 373 K are possible.

String balances

The eigenfrequency of strained wires and bands is varied by the deposition of material. This principle has been proposed for weighing[55,93]. A balance pan can be attached to a strained string. This method has been implemented in some technical balances[94] for loads in the range of grams to kilograms, but not yet for thermogravimetric applications.

8.1.5 *Multicomponent balances*

Such balances, mostly electromagnetic systems, are used for thermogravimetric applications where additionally to the mass change, the impulse of a molecular beam is to be measured[95–97].

8.2 Instruments for temperature measurement and control

Temperature measurement is most accurate when performed directly at the sample on the balance pan. Deviations of the sample temperature from the temperature preset with the thermostat can be used to determine the heat of reaction. If a second sensor is arranged in a reference sample, it is possible in addition to supplement the gravimetric measurements by differential thermal analysis (DTA).

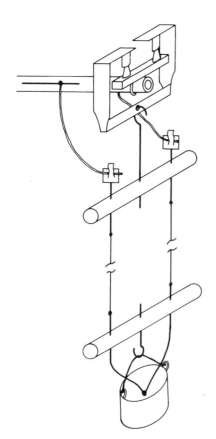

Fig. 8.14 Arrangement of a thermocouple in the pan of a microbalance. The suspension bearings are bridged by two gold bands leading to the taut bands via baked silver enamel lines on the quartz beam

In the case of microbalances, however, direct temperature measurement presents difficulties which are due to the weight of the sensors and the connections to the sample. As shown in Fig. 8.14, a thermocouple placed in the sample can be connected to an instrument outside the balance via two hangdown wires, two baked silver enamel lines on the balance beam, and the taut bands. The suspension bearing has to be bridged by two gold bands leading from the hangdown wires to the balance beam. In the case of DTA arrangements, a third hangdown wire has to be arranged parallel to the other two wires.

In addition, wireless transmission of the measured values is possible[98,99]. The transmitter arranged at the suspension wire, however, results in an additional load on the balance. In the case of the suspension balance, the trans-

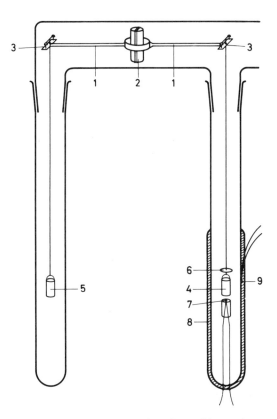

Fig. 8.15 Microbalance after Gast with tape heater and separately arranged thermocouple; 1 balance beam, 2 magnet/coil system, 3 sapphire pans on diamond pins, 4 sample pan, 5 counterweight pan, 6 heat shield (metal disc), 7 thermocouple covered with a void balance pan, 8 tape heater, 9 thermocouple for temperature control

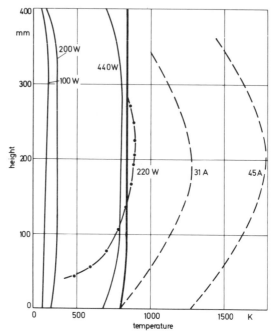

Fig. 8.16 Temperature profile of vertical tube ovens ———— Megapyr on a steel tube, ————— Megapyr on a steel tube with light metal insert, —·—— Megapyr on a ceramic tube, – – – Molybdenum band on a ceramic tube

mitter could be incorporated in the suspension magnets. Contactless measurement by means of pyrometers is suitable only at elevated temperatures and if very high accuracy is not required.

In most cases, the temperature is not measured in the sample, but determined either by means of a sensor arranged close to the balance pan or inside the thermostat. An example is shown in Fig. 8.15. To simulate the conditions in the sample pan, a similar pan has been tilted over; the sample mass, however, has not been considered. In this arrangement a measurement error can occur due to the inhomogeneous temperature field of the oven; typical profiles of perpendicularly arranged tube heaters are depicted in Fig. 8.16. In order to avoid incorrect measurements it is necessary to generate a very constant temperature field around the sample, using thermostats with equalized temperature profile.

A wide variety of heaters permitting the temperature to be kept constant and varied by programmed control within a temperature range between room temperature and about 3300 K is commercially available. To equalize the temperature profile, the windings of the resistant wire should be narrower at

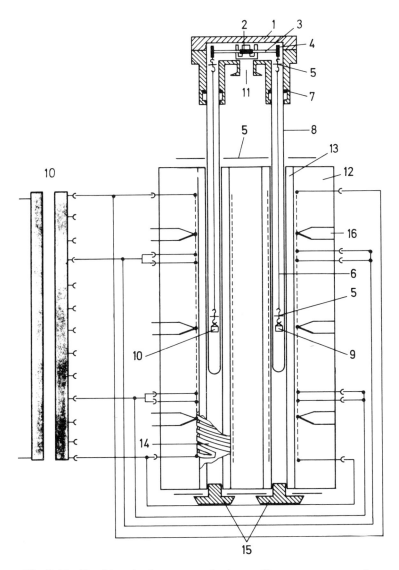

Fig. 8.17   Double tube furnace to obtain a uniform temperature along the axis; 1 balance case, 2 coil and magnet, 3 balance beam, 4 bearings, 5 heat shields, 6 suspension wires, 7 squeeze connection, 8 balance tubes, 9 balance pans, 10 tapped transformer, 11 vacuum flange, 12 insulation, 13 ceramic tube, 14 bifilar molybdenum band, 15 ceramic plug, 16 thermocouples

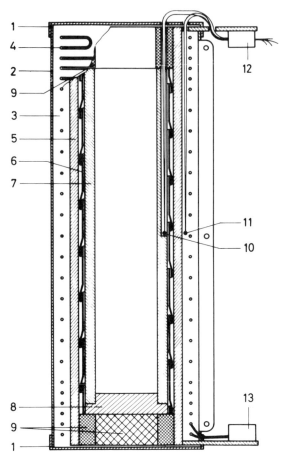

Fig. 8.18 Heater for vacuum microbalance; 1 cover (2 mm St. 0012), 2 sleeve (2 mm St. 0012), 3 Fiberfrax, 4 bifilar winding (Megapyr), 5 outer tube (5 mm St. 4841), 6 fibreglass, 7 inner tube (light metal), 8 plug (light metal), 9 asbestos board, 10 Ni–CrNi thermocouple for measurement, 11 Ni–CrNi thermocouple for control, 12 connection for thermocouples, 13 terminal for heater filament. This heater is designed for temperatures up to 600 °C. Using an inner tube made of temperature resistant steel, a similar construction can be made for temperatures up to 1280 °C. The temperature profile is depicted in Fig. 8.16

the ends of the tubular ovens or, if the windings consist of several sections, the end sections should be provided with higher energy (Fig. 8.17). Up to temperatures of about 1500 K temperature equalizing may be performed by inserting a metal tube in the oven tube which is thermally insulated against the outer tube but has a good thermal conduction in the axial direction (Fig. 8.18).

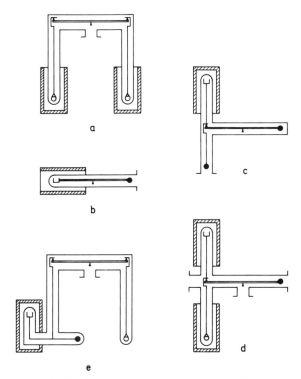

Fig. 8.19   Oven arrangements for thermobalances

To generate a very uniform temperature around the sample it may be surrounded by a metal cup, as shown in Fig. 8.20 for low temperatures[7]. For electricity conducting samples or with platinum pans, inductive heating can be applied[100].

Ovens can be arranged in various ways at the balance[101], as shown in Fig. 8.19, the objective being mainly to prevent convection, as discussed in section 9.4.9. Because of the connection of the sample to the balance it is not possible to surround the sample completely with the thermostat. Even when inserting screens, heat radiation along the suspension wire affects the sample temperature. Only in cases (d) and (e) of Fig. 8.19 is the sample almost surrounded by the oven. In arrangement (e), too, convection is avoided, which has also an effect on thermostatting.

Furthermore, heat capacity considerations influence the choice of furnace. After a run of a thermogravimetric experiment, the furnace and sample must be cooled to room temperature before beginning the next run. Because the cooling-down time limits the number of measurements which can be carried out within a day, the furnace should have a small heat capacity or be provided with a means for cooling, e.g. a water jacket.

For temperatures between 77 and 500 K, controllable liquid thermostats

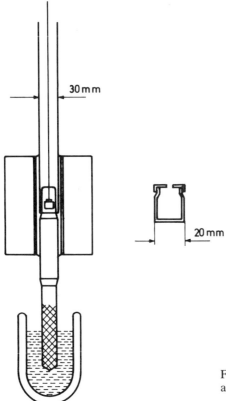

Fig. 8.20 Liquid nitrogen thermostat according to Eyraud. The sample is sur- rounded by a copper cup

and cryostats are available from numerous suppliers. As a constant tempera- ture is usually required for low temperature experiments, Dewar vessels containing liquid gases or freezing mixtures are generally used as thermostats. It must be taken into consideration that the temperature of these baths is dependent on the atmospheric pressure and on the concentration of the indi- vidual constituents. To avoid temperature inhomogeneities the bath has to be slowly moved by stirring or by supplying small amounts of heat at the bottom of the Dewar vessel. To reduce heat radiation from above the sample must be shielded as shown in Figs. 8.15, 8.17, and 8.20, and the Dewar vessel must be covered with a reflecting sheet. The sample should be immersed at least 200 mm in the temperature bath. Because the sample temperature increases with decreasing level of the liquid, the Dewar must be sufficiently long. For a 12-hour experiment, a Dewar vessel 1 m in length is sufficient. Alternatively the level of the liquid can be controlled. To adjust intermediate temperatures the balance tube can be enclosed with a copper tube which is immersed in the liquid bath at a controlled level (Figs. 8.20, 8.21).

Besides the measures to produce a homogeneous temperature field around the sample, the transmission of the thermostat temperature to the sample requires careful consideration (see section 9.4.9).

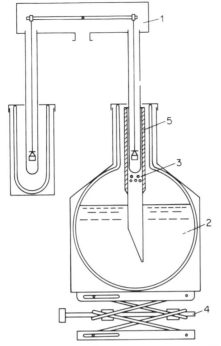

Fig. 8.21 Temperature control with liquid nitrogen; 1 balance, 2 Dewar vessel with liquid nitrogen, 3 copper tube with vent borings, 4 pedestal with height control, 5 heat tape

8.3 Instruments for pressure measurement and control

Instruments are available for three pressure ranges: vacuum, pressure below atmospheric, and overpressure. The limits are at about 10 and 10^5 Pa, respectively. Pressure measurements in the vacuum range are carried out mainly with the commercially available instruments. Criteria for selection are corrosion resistance and the possibility of degassing. Unfavourable are instruments which contain gas-releasing plastic components or liquids. Instruments with large volume or with cavities that are not easily accessible present difficulties in evacuation. Hot-cathode ionization gauges give trouble because they often burn out if they are not switched off before working at higher pressures.

Instruments and controls are also available for pressures above atmospheric. Special solutions may be necessary if a more sensitive measurement or a more exact control is required. Some of the methods discussed for pressures below atmospheric can be applied similarly.

As an important example, the measurement of whole nitrogen isotherms requires the use of manometers covering the range between 10^3 and 10^5 Pa. A control system is required to keep the pressure constant in this range with a tolerance of about 10 Pa. These requirements are met only by a small number of pressure sensors: the mercury gauge, the buoyancy gauge, and special diaphragm and Bourdon gauges[102].

On account of their simplicity, sensitivity (10 Pa), and the wide measuring range ($10-10^5$ Pa and more), mercury manometers have been used extensively. Figure 8.22 shows a recording mercury manometer and Fig. 8.23 a multicontact manometer as used for an automatic sorption measuring instrument[103]. Connecting groups of contacts to solenoid valves with different opening diameters, pressure control up to 10 Pa is possible in the whole range of 10 to 10^5 Pa, using the arrangement depicted in Fig. 8.24, with a fore-pressure of 2 bar and vacuum on the other side produced by a rotary vane pump.

Mercury gauges have to be connected via a cold trap or a sorption trap (thin gold sheets, baked in vacuum) in order to prevent the penetration of mercury vapour into the apparatus[103]. When the manometer is not used it should be shut off, in particular when the apparatus is held under vacuum, because then distribution of the vapour proceeds quickly. Provisions should be made to ensure that in case of a break the mercury cannot overflow into the apparatus or flow out.

Due to the danger of contamination and because mercury is hazardous, mercury manometers today are mostly replaced by diaphragm instruments exhibiting the same range and sensitivity.

A number of commercial diaphragm gauges with capacitive sensing are well suited as sorption measuring instruments if there are not corrosive gases

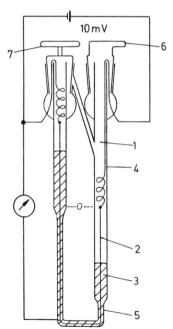

Fig. 8.22 Recording mercury manometer with a sensitivity of 10 Pa and only minor temperature influence; 1 platinum wire, 0.5 mm ⌀, 2 platinum-iridium wire PtIr 30 166 Ω/m, 3 mercury, 4 glass tube, 12 mm inner ⌀, 900 mm in legnth, 5 capillary, 2 mm inner ⌀, 6 to apparatus and pump, 7 evacuation tap

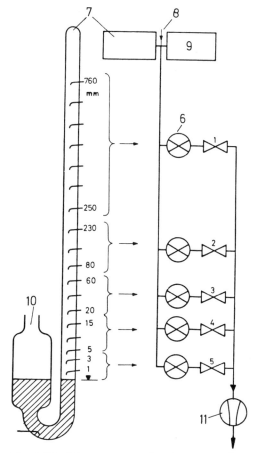

Fig. 8.23 Mercury control manometer 10 to
10^5 Pa; 1–5 needle valves differently adjusted,
6 solenoid valves, 7 contact manometer with
evacuated tube, 8 gas inlet, 2 bar, 9 balance, 10
to apparatus, 11 rotary vane pump

attacking the thin metal diaphragm (usually zirconium alloys). In such cases a
Bourdon or Bodenstein gauge[98,104,105] with glass or quartz spiral may be employed. These gauges are also available as instruments with electric sensing,
which can be used for pressure control; an example of this is shown in
Fig. 8.25.

An electromagnetic microbalance equipped at one side with a glass balloon
can be used as a buoyancy gauge. It is actually a gas densimeter and therefore
has to be calibrated for every measuring gas. However, despite the relatively
sophisiticated equipment required, the buoyancy gauge is of interest for
gravimetric measurements because it can be mounted on the present balance
support and occasionally it may be used as a second balance when pressure

350

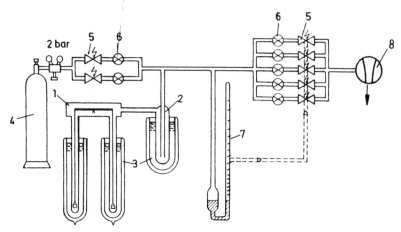

Fig. 8.24 Pressure control with mercury manometer; 1 balance, 2 cold trap, 3 Dewar vessels, 4 nitrogen cylinder, 5 solenoid valves, 6 needle valves, 7 contact manometer, 8 rotary vane pump

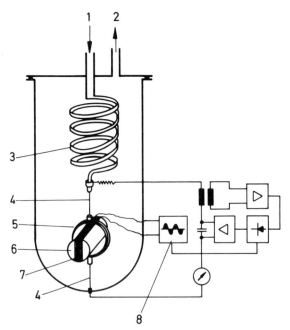

Fig. 8.25 Compensating quartz spiral manometer, after Gast; 1 to apparatus, 2 reference pressure, 3 hollow quartz spiral, 4 taut bands, 5 moving coil, 6 permanent magnet, 7 fixed coil, 8 oscillator

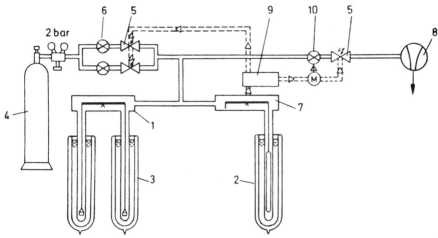

Fig. 8.26 'Gravimat' with buoyancy pressure controller; 1 balance, 2 Dewar vessel filled with water, 3 Dewar vessels as sample thermostat, 4 nitrogen cylinder, 5 solenoid valves, 6 needle valves, 7 buoyancy gauge (balance with glass balloon), 8 rotary vane pump, 9 control, 10 motor valve. Manufacturer: Netzsch, Selb, West Germany

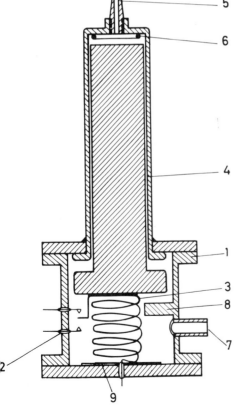

Fig. 8.27 Pressure difference control, after Huser and Kuhn; 1 metal case, 2 contacts, 3 spring, 4 glass syringe, 5 to apparatus, 6 O-ring, 7 to reference pressure, 8 stopper 9 insulation

control is dispensable. A pressure control using a buoyancy gauge has been realized in the 'Thermogravimat' as shown in Fig. 8.26[102,106,107]. It may be mentioned that the range of the buoyancy gauge can be extended into the high vacuum range making use of the longitudinal Knudsen effect[102,108] described in section 9.4.6. A simple sensor to control small pressure differences using a syringe (Fig. 8.27) has been constructed by Huser and Kuhn (cf. ref. 102).

The pressure of adsorptives which are liquid at ambient temperature may be easily controlled by adjusting their temperature by means of a thermostat.

8.4 Instruments for the determination of the saturation vapour pressure

The manometers described in the preceding section can be used to measure the saturation vapour pressure during simultaneous observation of the condensation of the gas. To measure the temperature of the liquid gas bath, semiconductor and resistance thermometers are available. Liquid column thermometers only work down to 83 K. Vapour pressure thermometers like the argon thermometer or the nitrogen thermometer (Fig. 8.28) are more exact. The measurement has to be carried out with a sensitivity of 0.01 K, because of the steep slope of the vapour pressure curve which is used to convert the temperature into saturation pressure.

8.5 Gas circulation pumps

In case a reaction of the gas occurs at the sample surface or when the gas contains several components, circulation of the gas is necessary. At very low pressure, diffusion or Toepler pumps may be used for this purpose. An oscillating magnet in a glass tube in connection with a glass sphere valve may be suitable (Fig. 8.29). Commercially available membrane pumps equipped with PTFE or stainless steel membranes sometimes cover the required pressure range. A special membrane pump for low pressures and low differential pressure, exhibiting an extremely small dead volume, is shown in Fig. 8.30.

8.6 Vacuum techniques

In this section some general remarks are made on the construction of vacuum manifolds and special hints are given with regard to sorption measurements and investigations of surface structure. For more detailed information, the reader is referred to the literature on vacuum techniques[109–119].

In the measurements discussed in this book, vacuum is needed for two different steps:
1. Degassing of the sample and establishment of the zero-point of the measurement.
2. Establishment and control of low pressures.

353

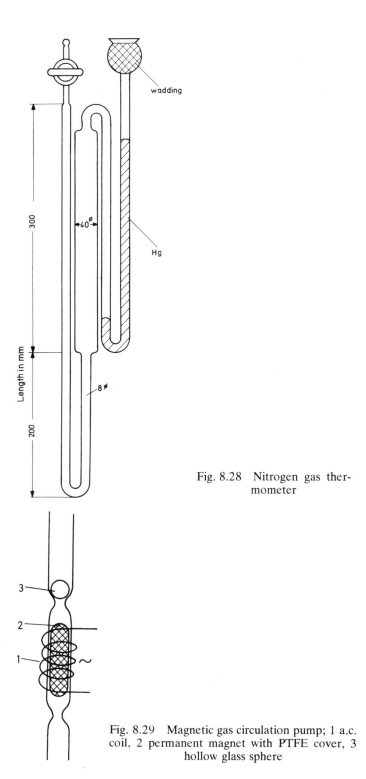

wadding

Hg

Length in mm

300

40 ⌀

200

8 ⌀

Fig. 8.28 Nitrogen gas thermometer

3

2

1

~

Fig. 8.29 Magnetic gas circulation pump; 1 a.c.
coil, 2 permanent magnet with PTFE cover, 3
hollow glass sphere

354

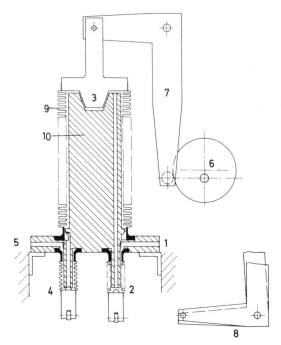

Fig. 8.30 Low-pressure stainless steel gas circulation pump; 1 inlet, 2 inlet valve, 3 plunger, 4 outlet valve, 5 outlet, 6 cam lifter, 7 plunger cam, 8 valve cam, 9 stainless steel bellows, 10 filler block

The second task can mostly be fulfilled by using a roughing pump, whereas the first makes considerable demands on the equipment.

'Vacuum' does not describe a state of absolute emptiness: a vacuum vessel is always filled with many residual gases. To examine the adsorption on a noncontaminated surface, the measurement has to be started in the ultrahigh vacuum (UHV) since at a pressure of 10^{-4} Pa, 10^{15} molecules per second strike $1 \ cm^2$ of the sample. Supposing a sticking probability of 1, this area will be covered by a complete monolayer within one second (Fig. 8.31). In all experiments at pressures below, say, 1 Pa, vapours from the walls of the apparatus, from sealing or insulating materials, or from pump oil may reach the sample within seconds without being impeded by a diffusion barrier. Furthermore, we have to take into account possible poisoning by diffusion from the bulk. Fortunately, in most cases the real surface area is much larger than the geometric surface of the sample due to surface roughness and pores, and contaminating layers have only a small effect on the result of surface area determinations. A remarkable error, however, may occur when investigating micropores.

There exists an important divide line between vacuum and high vacuum as

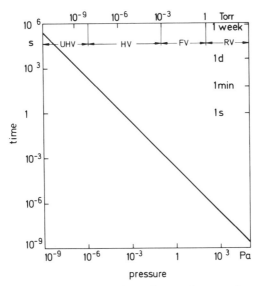

Fig. 8.31 Pressure-dependence of contamination time

characterized by the Knudsen number

$$Kn = \lambda/l, \qquad (8.4)$$

where λ is the mean free path of a gas molecule and l a characteristic length of the apparatus, e.g. tube or vessel diameter. The dependence of the mean free path on pressure is shown in Fig. 8.32 for some gases. Pumping down from atmosphere, what happens in the vacuum region is boiling of liquids and some desorption. As soon as a value of $Kn = 1$ is reached, which with usual apparatus dimensions is at about 1 Pa (compare Fig. 8.33), the mean free path of the gas molecules becomes larger than the vessel diameter and all properties of the gas change dramatically. A gas component evolved from the sample at $Kn \ll 1$ remains concentrated in the vicinity of the sample because it diffuses slowly through the surrounding gas. At $Kn \gg 1$ it is rapidly distributed and sucked off by the pump. At $Kn = 1$ the Knudsen forces (discussed in section 9.4.6), which disturb weighings, are at their maximum.

This means that investigations of the kind discussed here should be started at least in high vacuum (about 10^{-4} Pa) and line pumps which can produce UHV should be used to avoid contamination from the vacuum. To produce such a vacuum, two pumps are necessary: a roughing pump, usually a two-stage rotary vane pump, and a high vacuum pump, usually an oil diffusion pump or a turbo-molecular pump. The diffusion pump must be provided with a cooled, preferably built-in, baffle and should be operated using a low vapour pressure oil. Additionally, a cryogenic trap will be useful.

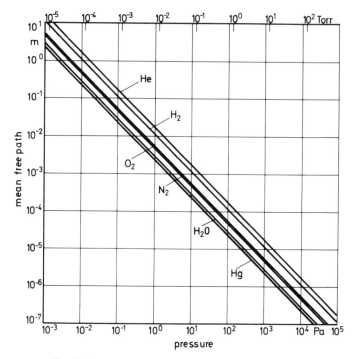

Fig. 8.32   Pressure-dependence of mean free path

High vacuum is often compared to a highly viscous liquid. Therefore, all pipes should be as wide as and as short as possible. In the rough and fine vacuum range (at $Kn \ll 1$) the gas is a continuum and the diameter of the tube is not critical, whereas in the high vacuum range the conductance is inversely proportional to the square of the diameter. This means that the fore-pump can be placed at some distance from the appratus, but the high-vacuum pump should be as close to the vessel as possible (Fig. 8.34).

It does not make sense to use a big high-vacuum pump connected to the vessel by thin pipes. The suction velocity is always determined by the smallest

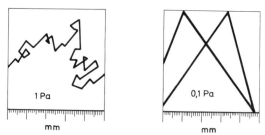

Fig. 8.33   Pressure-dependence of the path of a
gas molecule

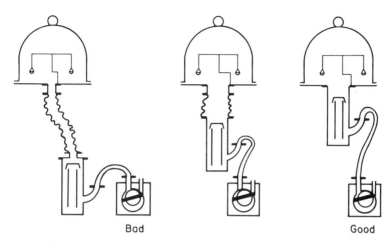

Bad   Good

Fig. 8.34   Arrangement of the vacuum pumps at the vessel

orifice; per square centimetre it is 11 l/s. Bellow pipes should be avoided; they exhibit a large surface area with pockets and are depots for contaminating gases. A bad example is shown in Fig. 8.35. Much better is the arrangement with a turbo-molecular pump shown in Fig. 8.36.

Figure 8.37 shows an apparatus for the investigation of corrosion in the presence of nuclear radiation[120]. The thermostatted stainless steel vessel contains six microbalances, one of which is charged with a dummy to control the effect of the flow of the reacting gas. The vessel has been evacuated by a turbo-molecular pump. It has been demonstrated that the balances were not seriously affected by vibrations from the directly connected pump. The oil diffusion pump shown was used to evacuate the gas supply.

Two diffusion pumps are used in the case of a thermogravimetric apparatus[121] equipped with a large milligram balance. One of the pumps evacuates the balance case, the other the sample vessel (see Fig. 8.49).

To avoid contamination with hydrocarbons, the 'Thermomat' with Gast's magnetic suspension balance[53], shown in Fig. 8.48, is made of quartz[122]. A mercury diffusion pump is used as high-vacuum pump, with a water jet pump as fore-pump. This arrangement is also suitable for work with corrosive gases.

It should be noted that all commercially available vacuum microbalances are not directly suitable for work in UHV. Suitable balances include the suspension balance of Gast[123] (Fig. 8.13), Czanderna's balance[124] (Figs. 8.38, 8.39), and a balance of Rodder shown in Fig. 8.3. Figure 8.40 shows a special version of an electromagnetic balance of Gast as used in the apparatus shown in Fig. 8.37 which is suitable for UHV. As can be seen, hollow spaces which are scarcely accessible have been avoided. Screw holes are tapped so that they can be evacuated, as shown in Fig. 8.41.

In special cases, UHV can be produced only in the vicinity of the sample, whereas the balance is only in a high vacuum. An example is shown in Figs.

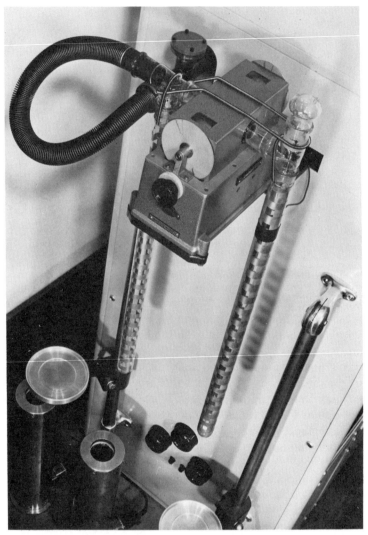

Fig. 8.35 Force-free connection to a vacuum microbalance. Vibrations are excellently shielded off, but the vacuum conductance is poor and the long bellows tube can be a contamination source

8.42 and 8.43, where a helium cryopump is incorporated in the hangdown tube. The outer Dewar vessel is filled with liquid nitrogen, the inner with liquid helium. The helium consumption was 0.5 l/h; the vacuum obtained 10^{-8} Pa[125].

Absolutely leakproof vacuum apparatus do not exist. Since leak detection is time-consuming, frustrating work, all connections (castings, solderings, and

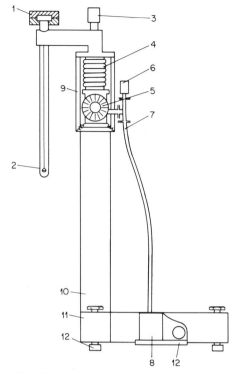

Fig. 8.36 Vacuum microbalance with turbo-molecular pump. All high vacuum tubes have the same diameter as the flange of the pump; 1 microbalance in stainless steel case, 2 balance pan in a quartz tube, 3 Penning gauge, 4 stainless steel bellows, 5 turbo-molecular pump, 6 Pirani gauge, 7 hose, 8 rotary vane pump, 9 console, 10 stand, 11 massive steel T, 12 shock absorber

flange connections) should be carefully constructed and elaborated. Some leaks, however, are in fact caused by dirt. A hollow space, e.g. a blowhole in a weld (Fig. 8.44), which is filled with water may destroy vacuum for a long period. Before starting an extended search for leaks, the pressure curve (Fig. 8.45) should be analysed. After pumping down, the valve to the vacuum line is closed. Thereupon a pressure increase is observed. If the pressure increases roughly linearly without approximating a final constant value, a leak must be suspected. Curve 2 shows the pressure course in the presence of an evaporating material (oil, grease, plastics, dirt). Curve 3 shows a combination of both effects.

Cleaning of the vacuum apparatus is thus very important. Depending on

360

Fig. 8.37 Apparatus for corrosion measurements in the presence of nuclear radiation; 1 vessel, 2 microbalances, 3 reaction tube, 4 diffusion pump for the gas supply part, 5 butterfly valve, 6 lead shield against nuclear radiation, 7 turbomolecular pump, 8 rotary pump

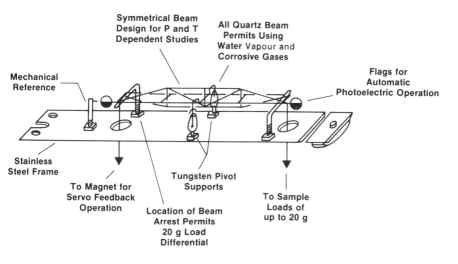

Symmetrical Beam
Design for P and T
Dependent Studies

All Quartz Beam
Permits Using
Water Vapour and
Corrosive Gases

Flags for
Automatic
Photoelectric Operation

Mechanical
Reference

Stainless
Steel Frame

To Magnet for
Servo Feedback
Operation

Tungsten Pivot
Supports

Location of Beam
Arrest Permits
20 g Load
Differential

To Sample
Loads of
up to 20 g

Figs 8.38, 8.39   UHV ultramicrobalance in a bakeable stainless steel vessel according to Czanderna et al.[117]. Manufacturer: Ultramicrobalance Instruments, Denver, Col. USA

362

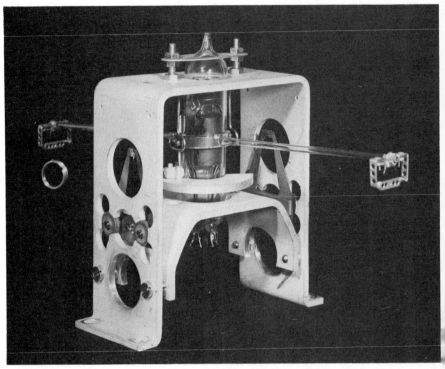

Fig. 8.40 Microbalance after Gast for the measurement in corrosive gases and in UHV. The permanent magnet is enclosed in a glass bulb, the PTFE-insulated balance coil glued with PTFE spray. All screw holes are accessible; washers are slitted

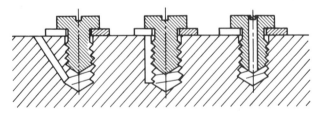

Fig. 8.41 For work in vacuum all screw holes must be accessible for evacuation

the materials built in, this should be done with hot water (to remove salts) and acetone (to remove greases), if possible. After cleaning, the solvents must be immediately and completely removed to avoid corrosion. At the last step the apparatus should be baked, if possible, under high vacuum at the maximum possible temperature for some hours. A typical degassing curve for stainless steel is shown in Fig. 8.46[126].

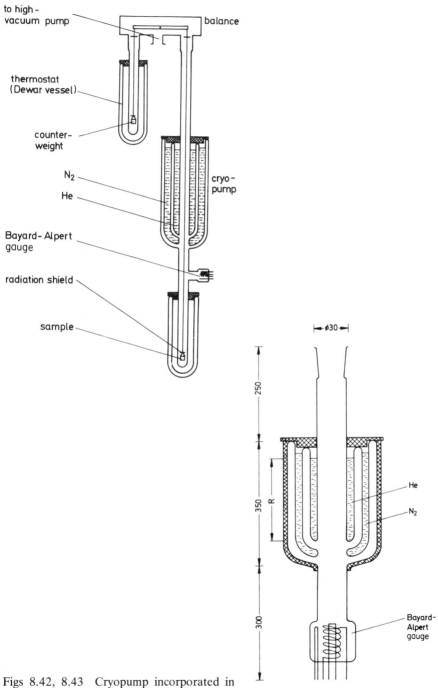

Figs 8.42, 8.43 Cryopump incorporated in the hangdown tube of a vacuum microbalance

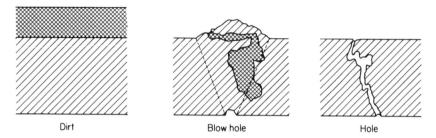

Dirt   Blow hole   Hole

Fig. 8.44   All leaks are not leaks in the strict sense of the word

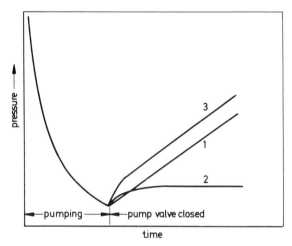

Fig. 8.45   To determine which kind of 'leak' is responsible for insufficient vacuum, the pump valve is closed after evacuation and the pressure increase observed; 1 real leak (hole), 2 dirt: matter with relatively high vapour pressure, 3 both: hole and dirt

8.7 Gravimetric apparatus

Thermogravimetric instruments are characterised by heating equipment with a temperature programme. Gravimetric instruments for investigating physisorption are equipped with pressure and temperature controls and devices for programmable changes of one or both variables. They also include a vacuum apparatus. In addition, simple apparatus for special technical measurements are on the market.

8.7.1 Moisture meters

A very simple application of gravimetric sorption measurement is in moisture balances. Commercially available moisture balances usually are milligram

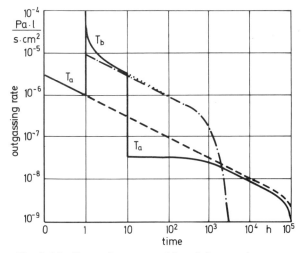

Fig. 8.46 Degassing curve with stainless steel ——————
Starting with temperature T_a in vacuum, the temperature is increased to T_b after 1 h and again decreased to
T_a after 9 h, – – – – – Degassing curve for temperature
T_a, —.—.— Degassing curve for temperature T_b

balances equipped with infrared heaters, where the moisture contained in the sample is vaporized. In the case of fibrous samples (textiles), a change in moisture content can be measured by observing the change in frequency of the fibre excited to oscillations.

When loaded with an adsorbent which exhibits a hysteresis-free isotherm, a balance can be used as a hygrometer for the measurement of air humidity and indirect moisture determinations measuring the equilibrium humidity above a sample. A special design making use of this method is a quartz-covered oscillator with an adsorbent layer.

8.7.2 Thermogravimetric instruments

These consist basically of a balance with a programme controlled heater, usually for linear temperature rise. Whereas earlier apparatus was equipped with special milligram balances, microbalances are now increasingly being used. Even small apparatus is equipped with vacuum aggregates. More sophisticated instruments include provisions for working with different gases at controlled pressure and reduced temperatures. Research apparatus of this kind is provided with connections for auxiliary instruments. Some typical examples are briefly described below.

The 'Derivatograph' (Fig. 8.47) includes a milligram balance with automatic weight switching. It is an inclination balance with light-beam registration on photosensitive paper. The temperature, the mass, and the derivative of the mass change are recorded. DTA is built in. The balance can be used alterna-

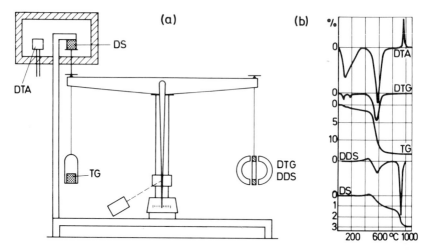

Fig. 8.47 'Derivatograph'; (a) Instrument used either as thermogravimetric instrument or as dilatometer. Besides a DTA instrument is arranged; (b) The corresponding curves. Manufacturer: MOM, Budapest, Hungary

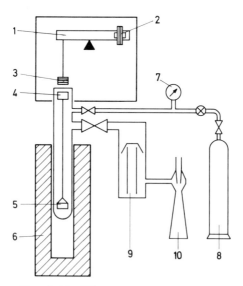

Fig. 8.48 'Thermomat', all-quartz version; 1 balance beam, 2 mass sensor coils, 3 electromagnet, 4 suspended permanent magnet, 5 sample pan, 6 heater, 7 quartz spiral pressure gauge, 8 gas cylinder, 9 mercury diffusion pump, 10 water jet pump. Manufacturer: Netzsch, Selb, West Germany

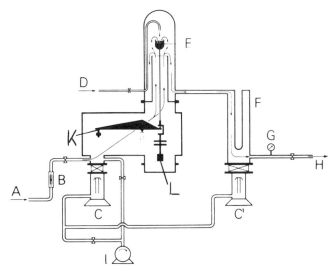

Fig. 8.49 'Thermoanalyser'; A protecting gas supply, B gas
dryer, C oil diffusion pumps, D reaction gas supply, E sample, F
cold trap, G diaphragm pressure gauge, H exhaust, K electromagnetic balance, L balancing weight, I rotary vane pump.
Manufacturer: Mettler, Greifensee, Switzerland

tively as dilatometer, squeezing the sample between a yoke and the balance
beam. The first derivative is also recorded[27,127–131].

The 'Thermomat' (Fig. 8.48) includes an electromagnetic suspension balance according to Gast[53,122]. The whole apparatus is made of quartz. An
automatic Bodenstein quartz spiral manometer serves for pressure measurement from UHV to 1 bar. Valves are equipped with PTFE seals. A mercury
diffusion pump is combined with a water jet pump as forepump. This version
is suitable for work in UHV and in corrosive atmospheres. Another version
can be used at high pressures up to 150 bar.

The 'Thermoanalyser'[121] (Fig. 8.49) is equipped with a milligram balance.
The sample can be arranged either below or above the beam. The vacuum
aggregate includes two diffusion pumps, one for the instrument case, the
other for the sample space. DTA at the balance pan is possible (Fig. 8.50).

The 'microthermoanalyser'[41,42,132] (Fig. 8.51) is equipped either with an
Eyraud balance or a compensating microbalance. The mass and the first
derivation of the mass are recorded. DTA is included. Temperature control is
up to 2700 K. It has a favourable arrangement of the balance on a free stand
accessible from all sides, which facilitates the connection of other instruments.

8.7.3 Sorption meters

The characteristic feature of sorption measuring instruments is the
programme-controlled variation of the gas pressure for the measurement of

368

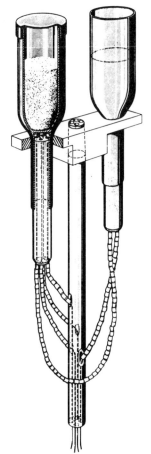

Fig. 8.50 DTA at the Thermoanalyser. Manufacturer: Mettler, Greifensee, Switzerland

isotherms. Preferably, this is performed by stepwise isobaric pressure change, while the temperature is kept constant. Temperature programmes are optional. Another typical characteristic of this type of instrument is that it is equipped with thermostats for low temperatures: baths of liquid gases, freezing mixtures, or cryostats. The 'Gravimat'[102] may serve as an example of an extensively equipped commercial instrument: this apparatus (Fig. 8.52) is equipped with several electromagnetic microbalances according to Gast[52,53]. One of these carries a glass bulb and is used for the pressure measurement and control by buoyancy. Depending on the balance type, the balances carry a maximum load of 2.5 or 25 g. In the range of 1 and 10^5 Pa the pressure is adjusted in 100 stages and maintained for a preselected period of time. The vacuum installation includes a turbo-molecular pump. The normal temperature range extends down to 77 K. The 'Thermogravimat' is equipped in addition with a time-controlled temperature programme up to 2500 K.

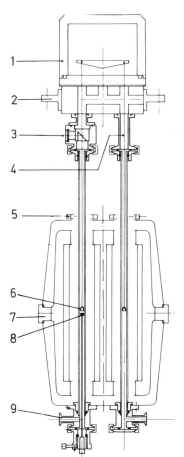

Fig. 8.51 'Microthermoanalyser'; 1 electromagnetic balance in vacuum case, 2 base plate with vacuum manifold, 3 window and mirror for the observation of the sample, 4 counterweight suspension, 5 heat shields, 6 sample pan, weight suspension, 5 heat shields, 6 sample pan, 7 oven, 8 DTA instrument, 9 gas supply. Manufacturer: SETARAM, Lyon, France

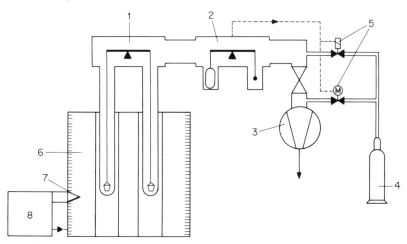

Fig. 8.52 'Gravimat' thermogravimetric and sorption measuring instrument; 1 microbalance, after Gast, 2 buoyancy pressure gauge, 3 turbomolecular pump, 4 gas vessel, 5 pressure control, 6 thermostat or oven, 7, 8 temperature control. Manufacturer: Netzsch, Selb. W. Germany

8.7.4 Composite instruments

The results of sorption measurements can often be interpreted only with the aid of additional measuring methods. Research apparatus therefore includes auxiliary instruments. As mentioned above, a very useful and simple supplement for thermogravimetric investigations is differential thermal analysis (DTA) performed on the sample on the balance pan or on a second sample arranged near the balance pan. Examples are shown in Figs. 8.47, 8.49 and 8.50. An arrangement suitable for microbalances is shown in Fig. 8.53.

In the set-up shown in Fig. 8.47, dilatometry is used as a supplementary method which is of particular interest for ceramic materials. After completion of the thermogravimetric measurement a second, identical sample is placed on the balance. The sample is inserted between a fixed yoke and the balance beam, and the balance measures the variations in sample length.

Frequently it is of interest to identify the gases which have been released. Because of the small quantities that have to be analysed, mass spectrometry or gas chromatography seem to be best suited. When investigating the adsorp-

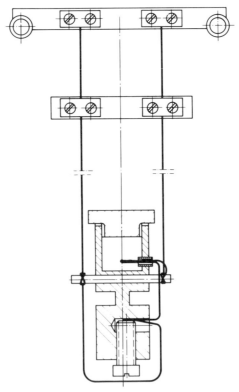

Fig. 8.53 DTA with nickel bloc reference suspended at a double-beam microbalance, after Gast

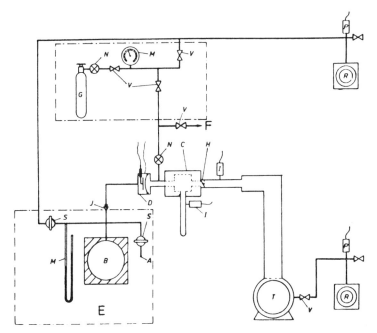

Fig. 8.54 Arrangement for measuring the sorption of gas mixtures using gravimetry and volumetry simultaneously; A gas supply, B gas reservoir (buffer), C microbalance, D diaphragm pressure gauge, E reference pressure, F to mass spectrometer, G gas cylinder, H, S, V valves, I ionization vacuum gauge, J joint, M Bourdon pressure gauge, N leak valve, P Pirani vacuum gauge, R rotary vane pump, T turbo-molecular pump

tion of gas mixtures an additional parameter must be measured. This can be achieved by a simultaneous volumetric determination of the pressure change (Fig. 8.54).

References

1. J. Reimpell and W. Bachmann, *Handbuch des Waagenbaus*; Voigt, Hamburg, 1955–1966
2. A. E. Newkirk, Thermogravimetric measurements; *Anal. Chem.*, **32**, 1558–1563 (1960)
3. S. Gordon and C. Campbell, Automatic and recording balances; *Anal. Chem.*, **32**, 275R (1960)
4. Th. Gast, *Bulletin des Schweizerischen Elektrotechnischen Vereins*, **53**, 1061–1069 (1962)
5. Gravimetrie; *Techniques de l'Ingénieur* K 870
6. Balances et pesées au laboratoire; *Techniques de l'Ingénieur* P 270
7. C. Eyraud, M. Cronenberger, and M. Cogniat, Thermogravimetrie; *Techniques de l'Ingénieur* P 880
8. *Vacuum Microbalance Techniques*, Vols. 1–8; New York: Plenum Press, 1961–1970

372

9. C. Duval, *Inorganic Thermogravimetric Analysis*, 2nd edn, Elsevier, Amsterdam, 1963
10. A. W. Coats and P. Redfern, Thermogravimetric analysis; *Analyst*, **88**, 906–924 (1963)
11. Surveys under the title: Thermal analysis, in: *Cumul. Rev. Anal. Chem.*: C. B. Murphy; **36** (1964) 347 R–354 R; **38** (1966) 443 R; **40** (1968) 380 R
12. W. W. Wendlandt, *Thermal Methods of Analysis*, Interscience, New York, 1974
13. B. Ke (ed.), *Thermal Analysis of High Polymers*, Interscience, New York, 1964
14. J. M. Thomas and B. R. Williams, *Quarterly Review*, **19**, 231–253 (1965)
15. J. P. Redfern (ed.), *Thermal Analysis '65'*, MacMillan, London, 1965
16. P. D. Garn, *Thermoanalytical Methods of Investigation*, Academic Press, New York, 1965
17. R. F. Schwenker, Jr. (ed.), *Thermoanalysis of Fibers and Polymers, 1965*, Interscience, New York, 1966
18. M. Harmelin and C. Duval, *Microchimica Acta*, 17–26 (1967)
19. E. Robens, *Geräte zur Messung der Gassorption*, ATM, Abschnitt V 1285–1/2, 45–50, 69–74 (1968)
20. R. F. Schwenker, Jr. and P. Green, *Thermal Analysis*, 2 vols, Academic Press, New York, 1968
21. C. Keattch, *An Introduction to Thermogravimetry*, Heyden/Sadtler, London, 1969
22. E. Robens and G. Walter, Thermogravimetrische Arbeitsmethoden; *Sprechsaal*, **104**, 426–428, 489–492 (1971)
23. H.-G. Wiedemann (ed.), *Thermal Analysis*, 3 vols, Birkhäuser, Zürich, 1973
24. *Progress in Vacuum Microbalance Techniques*, Vols. 1–3; Heyden, London, 1973–1975
25. Recording differential balances for thermogravimetric analysis; *Coke and Gas*, **20**, (1958) Nr. 229, S. 252; Nr. 230, S. 289
26. C. J. Keattch and D. Dollimore, *An Introduction to Thermogravimetry*, 2nd edn, Heyden, London, 1975
27. L. Erdey, *Theorie und Praxis der gravimetrischen Analyse*. Akademischer Verlag, Budapest, 1963
28. S. P. Wolsky, E. J. Zdanuk (eds.), *Ultra Micro Weight Determination in Controlled Environments*, Wiley, New York, 1969
29. A. W. Czanderna and S. P. Wolsky, *Microweighing in Vacuum and Controlled Environments*, Elsevier, Amsterdam, 1980
30. S. Gál, *Die Methodik der Wasserdampf-Sorptionsmessung*, Springer, Berlin, 1967
31. *Thermal Analysis Review*, Stanton Instrum. Ltd., London
32. *Thermochimica Acta*, Elsevier, Amsterdam
33. *Journal of Thermal Analysis* (E. Buzàgh, J. Simon (eds.)), Heyden & Son, London
34. *Wägen und Dosieren*, Kirchheim, Mainz
35. *Thermal Analysis Abstract* (J. H. Sharp (ed.)), Heyden 9 Son, London
36. W. Nernst and H. Riesenfeld, *Chem. Berichte*, **36**, 2086, (1903)
37. K. Honda, *Science Reports, Tohoku Imperial Univ.*, **4**, 97, 2610 (1915)
38. M. Guichard, *Bull. Soc. Chim. Fr.*, **37**, 62, 251, 381 (1925)
39. P. Dubois, Contribution à l'étude des oxydes de manganèse. Thèse Université de Paris (26 juin 1935) Nr. 2418
40. P. Chevenard, X. Waché, and R. de la Tullaye, *Bull. Soc. Chem. Fr.*, **10**, 31 °5, 41 (1944)
41. C. Eyraud and I. Eyraud, *Laboratoires*, No. 12, 13 (1953)
42. C. Eyraud and I. Eyraud, *Catalogue 50ᵉ expos. Soc. fr. Physique*, p. 163 (1953)
43. W. L. DeKeyser, *Nature*, **172**, 364 (1953)

44. E. Warburg and T. Ihmori, *Ann. d. Physik u. Chemie*, **27**, 481 (1886)
45. H. Pettersson, A new microbalance and its use. Diss. Göteborg, 1914
46. H. Pettersson, *Proc. Phys. Soc. (London)*, **32**, 209 (1920)
47. T. N. Rhodin, in: *Advances in Catalysis*, Vol. 5, Acad. Press, New York, 1953, p. 53
48. E. A. Gulbransen, in: *Advances in Catalysis*, Vol. 5, Academic Press, New York, 1953, pp. 152, 166
49. J. W. McBain and M. M. Bakr, *J. Amer. Chem. Soc.*, **48**, 690 (1926)
50. S. J. Gregg and M. F. Wintle, *J. Sci. Instrum.*, **23**, 259 (1946)
51. K. Cammann, and L. Cahn, *Chemie für Labor und Betrieb*, **18**, 6, 254 (1967)
52. Th. Gast, *Feinwerktechnik*, **53**, 167 (1949)
53. Th. Gast, *Vakuum-Technik*, **14**, 41 (1965)
54. Th. Gast, in: C. Eyraud and M. Escoubes (eds.), *Progress in Vacuum Microbalance Techniques*, Vol. 3; Heyden & Son, London, 1975, p. 108
55. Th. Gast in, C. H. Massen and H. S. van Beckum (eds.) *Vacuum Microbalance Techniques*, Vol. 71, Plenum Press, New York, 1970, p. 105
56. Th. Gast, *J. Physics E*, Scientific Instr., **7**, 865 (1974)
57. J. Rodder, in: A. W. Czanderna (ed.), *Vacuum Microbalance Techniques*, Vol. 8, Plenum Press, New York, 1970
58. P. Chevenard, X. Waché, and R. de la Tullaye, *Bull. Soc. Chim. Fr.*, **10**, 31 ° 5, 41 (1944)
59. S. Gordon, C. Campbell, *Anal. Chem.*, **28**, 124 (1956)
60. A. Peterson, *Instrum. Automation*, **28**, 1104 (1955)
61. C. L. Rulfs, *Anal. Chem.*, **20**, 262 (1948)
62. L. Feuer, *Anal. Chem.*, **20**, 1231 (1948)
63. E. S. Bartlett and D. N. Williams, *Rev. Sci. Instrum.*, **28**, No. 11, 919 (1957)
64. Mauer: Analytical and recording balance. Tech. Report Nr. 1762, U.S. Department of Commerce N.B.S., Washington 1953
65. U. V. Brockdorff and K. Kirsch, *Elektrotechn. Z.*, **71**, 611 (1950)
66. R. H. Müller, *Anal. Chem.*, **29**, 49 A (1957) No. 4
67. T. Hirone and S. Maeda, *Rev. Sci. Instr.*, 516 (1954)
68. P. Manigaut and B. Tsai, *C.R. Acad. Sci.*, **214**, 658 (1942)
69. M. J. Pope, *J. Sci. Instrum.*, **34**, 229 (1957)
70. C. Groot and V. H. Troutner, *Anal. Chem.*, **29**, 835 (1957)
71. A. W. Czanderna, W. Kollen, J. R. Biegen, and J. Rodder, *J. Vac. Sci. Technol.*, **13**, 1, 556 (1976)
72. R. Bauwens and G. Biezunski, *Mesures*, **1**, 71 (1957)
73. P. D. Garn, *Anal. Chem.*, **29**, 839 (1957)
74. P. L. Waters, *J. Sci. Instrum.*, **35**(2), 41 (1958)
75. J. Papailhau: Appareil d'analyses thermiques pondérales et differentielles simultanées. Fr. Patent No. 1 205 513
76. P. W. Lévy-Lebar, *Automatisme*, 102 (1958)
77. K. P. Zinnow and J. P. Dybwad, in: A. W. Czanderna (ed.), *Vacuum Microbalance Techniques*, Vol. 8, Plenum Press, New York, 1971, p. 147
78. K. P. Zinnow and J. P. Dybwad, in: Th. Gast and E. Robens (eds.), *Progress in Vacuum Microbalance Techniques*, Vol. 1, Heyden & Son, London, 1973, p. 355
79. P. L. Waters, *Anal. Chem.*, **32**, 852 (1960)
80. F. M. Ernsberger, *Rev. Sci. Instrum.*, **14**, 998 (1953)
81. J. G. Hooley, *Can. J. Chem.*, **35**, 374 (1957)
82. J. Nixdorf, E. Poeschel, and R. Skoutajan, in: Th. Gast and E. Robens (eds), *Progress in Vacuum Microbalance Techniques*, Vol. 1, Heyden, London, 1972, p. 63
83. J. L. Stephenson, G. W. Smith, and H. V. Trantham, *Rev. Sci. Instr.*, **28**, 381 (1957)

374

84. P. Barret, *Bull. Soc. Chim. Fr.*, **3**, 376 (1958)
85. G. Fouretier, *Usine nouv.*, 1 (1957)
86. J. W. Clark, *Rev. Sci. Instr.* **18**, 915 (1947)
87. J. W. Beams, C. W. Hulburt, W. E. Lotz, and R. M. Montague, *Rev. Sci. Instr.*, **26**, 1181 (1955)
88. G. Böhme, E. Robens, H. Straubel, and G. Walter in: S. C. Bevan, S. J. Gregg, and N. D. Parkyns (eds.), *Progress in Vacuum Microbalance Techniques*, Vol. 2, Heyden & Son, London, 1973, p. 169
89. W. H. King, Jr., in: A. W. Czanderna (ed.) *Vacuum Microbalance Techniques*, Vol. 8, Plenum Press, New York, 1971, p. 183
90. J. Ph. Termeulen, F. S. van Empel, J. J. Hardon, C. H. Massen, and J. A. Poulis, in: Th. Gast and E. Robens (eds.) *Progress in Vacuum Microbalance Techniques*, Vol. 1, Heyden, London, 1972, p. 41
91. M. A. Baker, in: Th. Gast and E. Robens (eds.), *Progress in Vacuum Microbalance Techniques*, Vol. 1, Heyden, London, 1972, p. 49
92. F. Wehking, K. Hartig, and R. Niedermayer in, T. Gast and E. Robens (eds.), *Progress in Vacuum Microbalance Techniques*, Vol. 1, Heyden, London, 1972, p. 25
93. R. N. Caffin, *Rev. Sci. Instrum.*, **46**, 11 (1975)
94. H. S. Sacht, in: H. Mintrop (ed.), *Dosieren, Wägen, Abfüllen; Haus der Technik — Vortragsveröffentlichungen*, No. 229, Vulcan, Essen, 1970, p. 16
95. V. L. Rogallo and H. F. Savage, *Rev. Sci. Instruments*, **34**, 988 (1963)
96. Th. Gast in, A. W. Czanderna and S. P. Wolsky (eds.), *Microweighing in Vacuum and Controlled Environments*, Elsevier, Amsterdam, 1980, Chapter 10
97. Th. Gast in, H. G. Wiedemann (ed.) *Thermal Analysis*, Vol. 1, Birkhäuser, Basel, 1972, p. 235
98. Th. Gast in, C. Eyraud and M. Escoubes, *Progress in Vacuum Microbalance Techniques*, Vol. 3, Heyden, London, 1975, p. 108
99. G. R. Blair in, A. W. Czanderna (ed.), *Vacuum Microbalance Techniques*, Vol. 8, Plenum Press, New York 1971, p. 173
100. E. Steinheil in, Th. Gast and E. Robens (eds.), *Progress in Vacuum Microbalance Techniques*, Vol. 1, Heyden, London, 1972
101. B. Neeb and E. Robens, *Wagen + Dosieren*, 1 (1977)
102. E. Robens and G. Sandstede, *Vakuum-Technik*, **16**, 125 (1967)
103. E. Robens and G. Sandstede, *Z. Instrumentenkunde*, **75**, 167 (1967)
104. Th. Gast, K.-P. Gebauer, and E. Robens, *Technisches Messen*, **47**, 405 (1980)
105. B. Schubart and E. Knothe in, Th. Gast and E. Robens (eds.), *Progress in Vacuum Microbalance Techniques*, Vol. 1, p. 207
106. E. Robens and G. Sandstede, *J. Phys. E.: Sci. Instr. Ser.*, **2**, 365 (1969)
107. H. Fischer, R. Robens, G. Sandstede, R. Sieglen, and G. Walter, *Meßtechnik*, **80**, 73 (1972)
108. C. H. Massen, B. Schubart, E. Knothe, and J. A. Poulis in, H. G. Wiedemann (ed.), *Thermal Analysis*, Vol. 1, Birkhäuser, Basel, 1972, p. 225
109. S. Dushman and J. M. Lafferty (eds.), *Scientific Foundation of Vacuum Technique*, Wiley, Chichester, 1962
110. K. Diels and K. Jaeckel, *Leybold Vacuum Handbook*, Pergamon, Oxford, 1966
111. W. Espe, *Materials of High Vacuum Technology*, Vol. 3, Pergamon, Oxford, 1966–68
112. R. R. La Pelle, *Practical Vacuum Systems*, McGraw-Hill, Maidenhead, 1972
113. W. Pupp, *Vakuumtechnik, 2nd ed*, Thiemig TB 43, Thiemig, München, 1972
114. L. Holland, W. Steckelmacher, and J. Yarwood (eds.), *Vacuum Manual*, Spon., London, 1974
115. L. Holland *et al.*, *Vacuum Manual*, Methuen Inc., London, 1974
116. J. Yarwood, *High Vacuum Technique*, Chapman & Hall, London, 1975

117. A. Roth, *Vacuum Technology*, Elsevier, Amsterdam, 1976
118. J. Yarwood (ed.), *Vacuum and Thin Film Technology*, Pergamon, Oxford, 1978
119. M. v. Ardenne, *Tabellen zur angewandten Physik*, Vol. 1, 4th ed., Deutscher Verl. d. Wiss., Berlin, 1979
120. W. H. Kuhn and G. Walter, *Microgravimetric Investigation into the Mechanisms of Corrosion of Reactor Materials in the Presence of Nuclear Radiation*, Euratom Report 1474. e, Presses Académiques Européennes, Brüssel, 1964
121. H. G. Wiedemann, *Chem.-Ing.-Techn.*, **36**, 1105 (1964)
122. F. B. Hugh-Jones and E. Robens, *Lab. Equipm. Digest*, **11**, 52 (1973)
123. Th. Gast in, A. W. Czanderna (ed.), *Vacuum Micro-balance Techniques*, Vol. 6, Plenum Press, New York, 1967, p. 59
124. A. W. Czanderna, W. Kollen, J. R. Biegen, and J. Rodder, *J. Vac. Sci. Technol.*, **13**, 556 (1976)
125. E. Robens, *J. Vac. Sci. Technol.*, **17**, 277 (1980)
126. B. B. Dayton in A. H. Beck (ed.), *Handbook of Vacuum Physics*, vol. 1; Pergamon Press, Oxford, 1964, p. 21
127. L. Erdey, F. Paulik, and J. Paulik, *Acta Chim. Acad. Sci. Hung.* **7**, 27 (1955)
128. L. Erdey, F. Paulik, and J. Paulik, *Acta. Chim. Hung.*, **10**, 61 (1956)
129. F. Paulik, J. Paulik, and L. Erdey, *Z. f. anal. Chemie*, **160**, 241 (1958)
130. F. Paulik, J. Paulik, and L. Erdey, *Z. f. anal. Chemie*, **160**, 321 (1959)
131. F. Paulik, J. Paulik, and L. Erdey, *Anal. Chim. Acta*, **41**, 170 (1968)
132. J. Mercier in: C. Eyraud and M. Escoubes (eds.), *Progress in Vacuum Microbalance Techniques*, Vol. 3, Heyden, London, 1975

Chapter 9

Gravimetric Measuring Techniques

The following measuring techniques are those which use microbalances in vessels under vacuum, with variations in pressure and temperature along the instrument. The measurements often go down to the detection limits and, therefore, very careful sample preparation and instrument handling are necessary. The following comments cover the temperature range between 77 and 2000 K and the pressure range between 10^{-6} and 10^6 Pa. Measurements at extreme temperatures, in ultrahigh vacuum or at pressures far above atmospheric, in general require special equipment.

9.1 Installation, safety measures

When using a sensitive balance, environmental events like traffic, the beginning and ending of the working time, conversation, intensity of room cleaning, etc., can be easily recorded. If such effects are not to influence the final results of the measurements, many precautions must be observed.

9.1.1 Installation

The apparatus should be placed in a room, thermostatted at about ± 0.5 K. If heat or cold is produced by ovens or liquefied gases, protective shields should be placed above these devices. Influence on the apparatus by direct radiation from the sun can be avoided by use of venetian blinds outside the windows. Draughts from open doors and windows should be prevented. To precondition samples which adsorb water, a humidity control of the room may be useful. The room should be free of vibrations and variations of ground inclination. The apparatus should be placed in such a way that all parts are easily accessible and the balance must be free enough to place thermostats beneath it, and allow for other instruments near the sample.

To damp vibrations from the ground, rotating vacuum pump, valves, etc., the balance must be fixed on a heavy stand insulated from the ground by shock absorbers which are accommodated to the load and inflexible enough that they do not cause changes in the condition of the balance with time, and after shocks, due to manipulations, return to the initial position. A suitable stand is shown in Fig. 9.1. This stand consists of massive steel girders 12 × 12 cm, the connections of which are reinforced with corner plates with adjusting screws. The stand is placed on rubber-metal mountings (compare also Fig. 8.37).

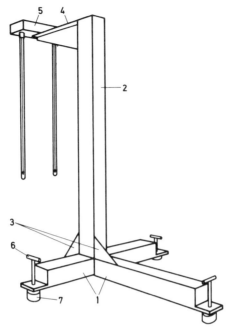

Fig. 9.1 Balance stand; 1 massive steel
girders, 2 hollow stand casted of two
U-bars, 3 connecting sheets, 4 support, 5
balance, 6 adjusting screws, 7 vibration
dampers

9.1.2 Safety measures

Besides the normal laboratory safety measures for working with vacuum
equipment, the use of liquid gases and high temperatures requires some caution. Parts of the apparatus that are made of glass or quartz may implode
when evacuated, especially when temperature gradients are applied or the
temperature is changed quickly. This applies also to working with Dewar
vessels. Metal stockings over the hangdown tubes may serve as splinter protection. The use of safety-goggles is indispensable.

A protection circuit should be installed to prevent the oven from attaining
excessively high temperatures. Otherwise the hangdown tubes might fuse
together under the influence of the vacuum and the whole balance could be
destroyed.

If a major leak occurs, e.g. because of a glass break, air condenses in the
sample space when cooled with liquid nitrogen. In this case the Dewar vessel
should not be removed too quickly, to avoid sudden boiling of the liquid air.
The liquid should then be sucked off using the vacuum pump of the
apparatus.

Because a sudden expansion of condensed gases may occur when measur-

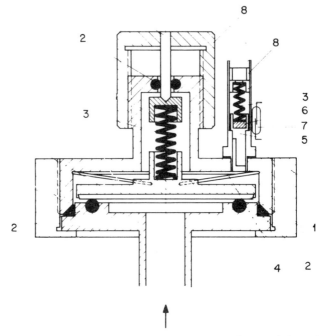

Fig. 9.2 Pressure relief valve; 1 glass fibre reinforced PTFE disk, 60 mm ϕ, 2 O-rings (neoprene), 3 springs, 4 three sickle-shaped springs, 5 PTFE piston, 6 permanent magnet, 7 reed relay, 8 adjusting screws

ing near the condensation pressure, or when determining the saturation pressure (Section 8.5) the apparatus should be protected by a pressure relief valve. A reliable valve[1] is shown in Fig. 9.2. This relief valve is tight for small pressure differences even near atmospheric. It opens at a preset value between 1 and 1.1 bar and it responds on an overpressure 100 to 400 Pa (with a disk diameter of 60 mm). Even when not actuated for a long time, it does not stick because of the combination of neoprene and PTFE as gasket material. The leak rate is better than 10^{-6} Pa m^3 s^{-1}. A small PTFE piston provided with a permanent magnet actuates a reed relay as soon as a small gas volume leaves the valve. The signal can be used to check solenoid valves.

9.2 Pretreatment of materials

9.2.1 Sample preparation

The selection of a very small sample from large material masses should be carefully performed. Mechanical sample dividers are available and some companies offer sample division in the contract. The question of whether 10 g or 1 mg can be considered as a representative sample, when taken from some tons, is of minor importance.

The sample is outgassed in a vacuum at elevated temperature in most cases in order to obtain a sufficiently defined surface. During this treatment, a change in surface geometry may occur either by sintering, by swelling, or recrystallization, so that an optimum temperature has to be evaluated by some preliminary trial experiments (see Fig. 2.15 and Section 9.5.2).

When tolerating an error of about ±10%, vacuum alone or flushing with a nonadsorbing gas (e.g. nitrogen at room temperature) may be used. These procedures are time consuming but are unavoidable in the case of temperature-sensitive samples.

Incompletely removed water or solvents may form a white, frostlike structure with high surface area and mask the real sample surface. Moreover, the ice will dissolve the adsorbed molecules, thus simulating a very high surface area. Such an effect, however, is revealed by a strikingly slow uptake of the adsorbate when measuring the isotherm.

Sufficient desorption of contamination layers is sometimes difficult to observe, for example in the case when the bulk sample consists of a volatile compound, an unstable hydrate or oxide. In this case, residuals of a chemisorbed layer do not seriously affect either the value of the specific surface area or the mesopore distribution curve; the micropore characteristic of course will be disturbed.

To obtain a clean surface, it is necessary to generate this surface under UHV conditions by vapour deposition or sputtering. With cleaving and erasing, vapours included in the solid are set free temporarily so that the virgin surface is covered at once. Some materials may melt in vacuum. Some metal surfaces can be cleaned by outgassing at elevated temperature in a vacuum, followed by treatment with oxygen (e.g. at 10^4 Pa), outgassing in a vacuum,

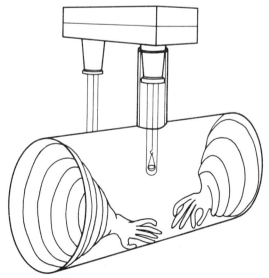

Fig. 9.3   Glove box for a vacuum microbalance

reduction in hydrogen (10^4 Pa), and outgassing. This OAOR cycle[2,3] has been performed to clean silver several times at temperatures of 600–700 K.

To examine the adsorption on a noncontaminated surface, the measurement has to be started in the UHV since at a pressure of 10^{-4} Pa, some 10^{15} molecules per second strike one square centimeter of the sample. If the sticking probability is unity, this area will be covered by a complete monolayer within 1 s (Fig. 8.31). In all experiments at pressures below about 1 Pa, vapours from the walls of the apparatus, from sealing or insulating materials, or from pump oil may reach the sample within seconds if not impeded by a diffusion barrier. Furthermore, poisoning by diffusion from the bulk must also be taken into consideration. Fortunately such adsorbed species have only a small influence on the pore structure and surface area. For handling air-sensitive samples, a glove box attached to the balance as shown in Fig. 9.3 can be used.

9.2.2 Adsorptives

Gaseous adsorptives are in general available in metal cylinders. Even those of high purity can have a high water content. They must be dried, and it is advisable to clean the gas additionally using a catalyst. It should be taken into account that organic vapours may change their chemical nature with time by polymerization or decomposition, and that dangerous pressures can arise.

Liquids can be degassed by alternate boiling and freezing during evacuation. Drying agents like sodium metal or molecular sieves may be placed in the liquid.

9.3 Pretreatment of the instrument

9.3.1 Cleaning of the balance

This has to be done carefully, especially for measurements with water vapour or organic solvents. The movable parts should alternately be boiled in distilled water (or at least wetted) and rinsed with acetone. The last bath should be water. Because fingerprints, due to their salt content, absorb water (see Fig. 9.4), the balance and the sample have to be handled using clean tweezers[4].

9.3.2 Thermostatting

The balance system should be thermostatted at a temperature above the condensation temperature of the measuring gas at the pressure applied. For use with water vapour up to 10^5 Pa, therefore, the balance system should be thermostatted at 110 °C.

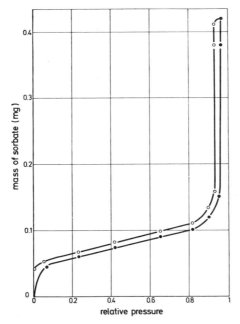

Fig. 9.4 Sorption of water vapour on a
fingerprint at 293 K

9.3.3 Buoyancy compensation

A symmetric design of the balance beam and the suspension system ensures
that the buoyancy of those parts remaining at room temperature is kept
small[5]. The residual buoyancy is determined at two widely separated pressures,
e.g. 10^4 and 10^5 Pa. For this measurement the balance should be loaded on
either side with identical pieces of gold corresponding to the later load,
because the zero point may be somewhat load-dependent. The residual
buoyancy then can be offset by suspending an aluminium wire at one side and
a gold wire of the same mass at the opposite side. The mass of the wires is
calculated as follows:

$$m_{Au} = m_{Al} = \frac{\rho_{Au}\rho_{Al}A \cdot 10^5}{\rho_g(\rho_{Au} - \rho_{Al})} \tag{9.1}$$

with $\rho_{Au} = 19.3 \times 10^3$ kg m^{-3} (density of gold)
  $\rho_{Al} = 2.70 \times 10^3$ kg m^{-3} (density of aluminium)
  $\rho_g = 1.15$ kg m^{-3} (density of nitrogen at 20 °C, 10^5 Pa)
  A = the buoyancy related to unit pressure

9.3.4 Gas supply

If a change of gas is necessary during the investigation, the influence of the gas stream on the balance must be controlled. Typical calibration curves are shown in Fig. 9.5. For accurate determination the influence can be estimated by intermittent measurements with a temporarily stopped gas stream or by a second balance equipped with a dummy (see Fig. 8.37). To avoid convection effects the gas should be brought to the sample temperature by leading the gas inlet tube through the oven before entering the balance tube, as shown in Fig. 9.6.

If corrosive gases are used, the balance measuring system should be protected with helium. Both gas streams may be exhausted via a connection at the upper end of the hangdown tube[6] (Fig. 9.7).

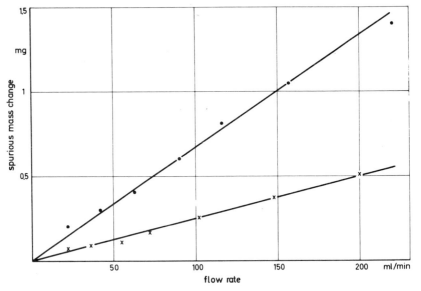

Fig. 9.5 Effect of a gas flow through a microbalance on the readings. Pan ϕ 11 mm; balance tube ϕ 15 mm ·—·—·, 20 mm × × ×

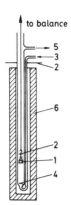

Fig. 9.6 Gas supply for measurements with flowing gas; 1 sample pan, 2 radiation shields (polished stainless steel), 3 gas inlet, 4 wire netting, 5 exhaust, 6 furnace

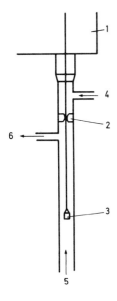

Fig. 9.7 Gravimetric investigation using corrosive gases; 1 balance case, 2 diaphragm, 3 sample pan, 4 protecting gas inlet, 5 corrosive gas inlet, 6 common exhaust

9.4 Errors

This somewhat extended discussion has not been written to discourage the use of microbalance measurements, but to help to avoid and minimize erroneous effects. Erroneous operation and instrument problems have not been mentioned. Here Cahn's rule should be borne in mind: If all else fails, read the instructions.

Sources of measuring errors in physical adsorption studies include mainly:
1. Buoyancy errors proportional to the increase in pressure.
2. Fictitious changes in mass caused by Knudsen forces due to thermal gas flow at pressures below 10^3 Pa.
3. Fluctuations and fictitious changes in mass caused by convection above 10^4 Pa.
4. Electrostatic fields, particularly between powder samples charged by separation of the particles and charges on the hangdown tube.
5. Electromagnetic fields produced by the heater.

9.4.1 Brownian motion

The irregular temperature-dependent movement of gas molecules (compare Fig. 8.33) striking the movable parts of the balance causes spurious mass changes and gives a fundamental limit to the sensitivity. According to the law of equipartition of energy, each body participates in the thermal motion in such a way that the mean energy in each degree of freedom is $kT/2$. The influence on the balance depends on the type, mass, and temperature.

Massen and Poulis[7] calculated the spurious forces for typical devices: for an undamped spring balance with 25 g load at 300 K and an eigenfrequency of 1 Hz, they found a force of about 6 ng. With a critically damped balance with 400 g load and a damping time of 5 s, a spurious force of about 1 ng can be expected. In the case of an automated balance with feedback of the beam to zero position, for 100 g load the force calculated is 0.4 ng.

9.4.2 Temperature effects

Balances show more or less periodic temperature-dependent fluctuations in the mass indication. With commercially available electronic instruments the amplitude may amount up to several micrograms per day. As the control device and the measuring system react independently to variations in temperature and because in addition they are mostly installed at a distance from each other, and thus may be exposed to different temperatures, the resultant fluctuations of the readings may be quite intricate. Characteristic periods are between several minutes and one day.

To suppress these disturbances, the room where the balance is installed should be thermostatted at ± 0.5 K. This requirement cannot, of course, be satisfied when using big ovens for thermogravimetry. In such a case the removal of waste heat by water cooling is recommended. Differences in the temperature of the individual parts of the apparatus should be avoided by uniform air circulation with closed doors and windows. Effects of solar radiation can be prevented by venetian blinds.

Temperature inhomogeneities along the balance beam produce armlength differences[7,8]. This should be avoided by enclosing the measuring instrument with a thick-walled metal case and shielding the ends of the beam with metal disks against radiation from the sample thermostat or heater.

9.4.3 Fluctuation of readings

Occasionally fluctuations of readings are observed which may have various origins. At pressures above 10^4 Pa convection occurs if the temperature of the sample differs from that of its environment. Convection causes pressure-dependent mass changes and in addition irregular fluctuations of the readings at a frequency of about 0.1 Hz. The amplitude of the fluctuations depends on the pressure and the temperature differences; their typical profile is shown in Fig. 9.8(d). The fluctuations and the apparent mass change are particularly large if the sample is at a higher temperature than the measuring system. They are, however, also observed in the inverse case, i.e. if the sample is at lower temperature than the measuring system (for details see Section 9.4.6).

The reading shown in Fig. 9.8(e) is due to contact of a balance pan to the surrounding tube or other disturbances influencing the flexibility of suspension. Fig. 9.8(c) shows the result of shifting the support point of suspension caused by damaged or contaminated knife edges. The typical response to

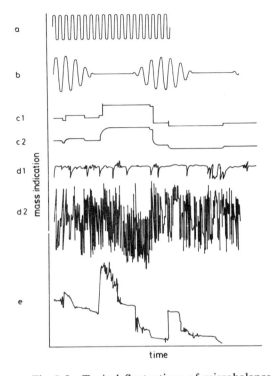

Fig. 9.8 Typical fluctuations of microbalance readings (balance with suspended pans); a vibration of balance beam due to resonant oscillations of the control unit, b pendular motion of balance pans, scarcely damped in vacuum, c1 shifting of the point of support caused by damaged or contaminated knife edges (diamonds), c2 the above signal electrically attenuated, d convection in nitrogen sample 77 K, balance 300 K, d1 $2 \cdot 10^4$ Pa, d2 $5 \cdot 10^4$ Pa, e contact between pans and tube or other mechanical disturbances

pendular motion of balance pans is shown in Fig. 9.8(b). Fig. 9.8(a) shows vibration of balance beam due to resonant oscillations of the control circuit.

9.4.4 Buoyancy

The most typical error in all weight measurements is Archimedes buoyancy, which must be either compensated for or corrected[2,9-13]. With low surface areas the effect of buoyancy exceeds the mass adsorbed, as shown in Fig. 9.9.

If sorption isotherms are measured by means of a beam balance adjusted to zero in vacuum, the buoyancy is super-imposed on the weighing result $m(p)$

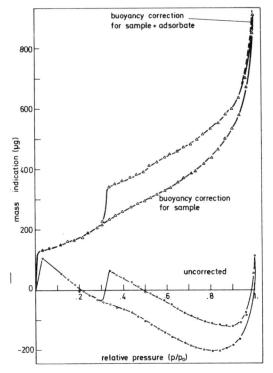

Fig. 9.9 Result of an adsorption isotherm measurement of nitrogen at graphite at 77 K. The density of the sample was $1.7 \cdot 10^3$ kg m^{-3}; that of the quartz counterweight $2.21 \cdot 10^3$ kg m^{-3}

according to the following equation:

$$m(p) = m_a(p) - A \frac{p T_0 M_a}{T M_0} \qquad (9.2)$$

where $m_a(p)$ is the adsorbed mass, A is the specific buoyancy given by $\Delta m / \Delta p$ measured at room temperature in a gas with the molecular weight M_0; p is the pressure to which the balance is set for the specific measurement; T is the temperature of the body causing the buoyancy; and M_a is the molecular weight of the gas used for the measurement.

However, as the different parts of the balance (compare Fig. 9.10) are at different temperatures, the buoyancy error has to be considered in a more differentiated manner. The following sum equation can be derived for a preset pressure:

$$m = m_a - V_a \rho_g(T) - V_s \rho_g(T) - V_{ps} \rho_g(T)$$
$$+ V_c \rho_g(T) + V_{pc} \rho_g(T) - A_b \qquad (9.3)$$

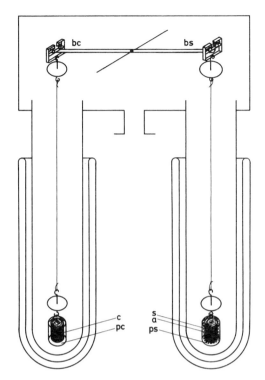

Fig. 9.10 Buoyancy in an equal-armed sorption balance; bc beam + parts of suspension at
the counterweight side, bs beam + parts of
suspension at the sample side, c counterweight, pc pan for counterweight + parts of
suspension; s sample, a adsorbate, ps pan for
sample + parts of suspension

The adsorbed mass m_a appears to be reduced by the buoyancy of the
adsorbed volume V_a in the measuring gas of density ρ_g, by the buoyancy of the
sample volume V_s, and by the buoyancy of the balance pan and the suspension
parts V_{ps} being at the measuring temperature, and it appears to be increased
by the buoyancy of counterweight V_c and the buoyancy of balance pan and
suspension parts V_{pc} at the temperature of the counterweight. It is further
necessary to deduct the buoyancy A_b of the balance beam and of suspension
parts at room temperature, which, therefore, should be compensated for
following the procedure described in section 9.3.3.

Moreover, if sample and counterweight are kept at the same temperature,
Eqn. (9.3) takes the simplified form of

$$m = m_a - V_a \rho_{g0} \frac{T_0}{T} - (V_s - V_c)\rho_{g0} \frac{T_0}{T} - (V_{ps} - V_{pc})\rho_{g0} \frac{T_0}{T} \qquad (9.4)$$

The third correction term is reduced to zero if suspension parts and balance pan on the sample side and on the counterweight side consist of the same material and the same mass, or if the quartz pans are counterbalanced with pieces of quartz.

The buoyancy of the sample can be eliminated by using a counterweight of the same density if this is kept at the same temperature. Pieces of quartz and gold give counterweights with densities between 2.2 and 19.3×10^3 kg m^{-3}. The masses of the counterweight components are calculated as follows:

$$m_Q = m_s \frac{\rho_Q(\rho_{Au} - \rho_s)}{\rho_s(\rho_{Au} - \rho_Q)}; \qquad m_{Au} = m_g - m_Q \qquad (9.5)$$

with m_s mass, ρ_s density of the sample
$\quad m_{Au}$ mass, ρ_{Au} density of gold
$\quad m_Q$ mass, ρ_Q density of quartz

Counterweights with densities below 2.2×10^3 kg m^{-3} may be realized by using hollow glass or quartz beads. Changes in buoyancy difference as a result of differences in the coefficients of thermal expansion of sample and counterweight can normally be neglected as second-order effects.

Frequently, however, the density of the degassed material is not known with sufficient accuracy, so that the use of a counterweight calculated according to Eqn. (9.5) does not exclude the occurrence of a residual buoyancy. The buoyancy determined with nitrogen at room temperature (possibly also with helium at 77 K) by measuring the weight difference at, say, 10^4 and 10^5 Pa,

$$A = \frac{\Delta m}{\Delta p} \qquad (9.6)$$

can be used to calculate the density of the sample:

$$\rho_s = \frac{m_s}{(m_c/\rho_c) - (A \cdot 10^5)/\rho_g} \qquad (9.7)$$

The counterweight can then be corrected.

Density determinations by buoyancy measurements occasionally fail because some samples adsorb a surprisingly large amount of nitrogen at room temperature. Adsorption at low temperatures then is normally so intense that the buoyancy error is of no importance. In some cases, however, at room temperature a gas may have access to micropores which are blocked at low temperatures.

Accurate measurements also have to take account of the buoyancy of the adsorbate. Taking the pressure dependence into consideration, Eqn. (9.4) yields

$$m(p) = m_a(p) - \frac{m_a \rho_g}{\rho_a p_0} p + \cdots \qquad (9.8)$$

For nitrogen at 77 K and 100 kPa, using the density of liquid nitrogen as the mean density ρ_a, the mass reduction is estimated to be of the order of 1 per mil.

For the adsorbate, however, the density of the compact phase can be assumed only for multilayers. In a monolayer the adsorbed molecules may have a mean distance from the sample surface of up to three molecular diameters, which can be calculated from the potential function for the specific gas–solid system. The potential function in turn is dependent on temperature. Pierotti[14] has shown that the resulting buoyancy correction can be calculated with the aid of the virial coefficients for the specific system, a significant contribution being made only by the second virial coefficient:

$$m(p) = m_a(p) - \left\{ \frac{m_a \rho_g}{\rho_a} + m_a \sum_{i=1}^{n} B_{i+1} \left(\frac{p}{kT} \right)^i \right\} p \qquad (9.9)$$

where ρ_a is the density of the compact adsorbed phase and B_i denotes the virial coefficients of the gas–solid system.

The resulting buoyancy may be less than, equal to, or greater than Archimedes buoyancy. A higher density and hence a lower buoyancy and an apparently larger adsorbed mass are obtained at low temperatures, while at high temperatures the opposite effect may occur. For the system helium/carbon, Pierotti[14] calculated a correction of $+100 \, \mu g$ at 78 K, of $0 \, \mu g$ at 300 K, and of $-3 \, \mu g$ at 1000 K for a surface area of $100 \, m^2$ at a pressure of 1 bar. For a more accurate calculation of this correction it is necessary to take account of Coulomb forces and inhomogeneities of the surface structure (micropores), which generally increase the binding forces and hence lead to a greater positive correction.

9.4.5 Adsorption on the counterweight

Whereas most of the adsorption effects can be cancelled out using a symmetrical balance design, there is still adsorption at the counterweight[15]. Typical materials used as counterweights include quartz, glass, and metals. Polytetrafluorethylene (PTFE) is also of interest as a material for counterweights because it is hardly wettable by any condensate.

Adsorption on quartz and laboratory glass

A newly generated quartz or glass surface, e.g. created by breaking, exhibits active free radicals. In air the surface anneals very quickly forming a gel-like surface which is covered in about half an hour by a water film in equilibrium. Degassing experiments (Fig. 9.11) show that in practice at 400 K, about 35% of the water film evaporates independent of the type of glass used, and the

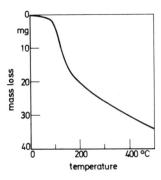

Fig. 9.11 Water desorption from glass according to Korányi[16]

chemisorbed remnant steadily evaporates up to temperatures of 800 K[16,17]. Figures 9.12–9.14 show reversible water isotherms on quartz glass[18], and nitrogen, water and methanol isotherms on glass powder or glass wool[19]. All isotherms are S-shaped with a monolayer cover at a relative pressure of about 0.1 and four layers at about 0.8 (Fig. 9.15). With methanol a certain proportion remains chemisorbed and can be removed only by heating.

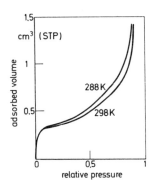

Fig. 9.12 Water adsorption on glass according to Hackerman and Hall[18]

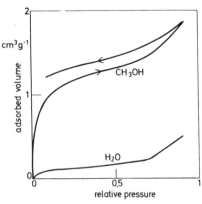

Fig. 9.13 Adsorption of water and methanol at 303 K on glass wool according to Razouk and Salem[19]

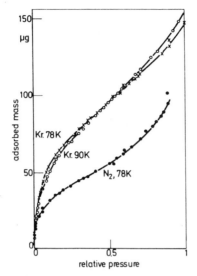

Fig. 9.14 Adsorption of nitrogen at 78 K and krypton at 78 and 90 K on 1.83 g glass spheres

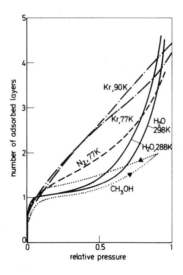

Fig. 9.15 Synopsis of adsorption on glass and quartz

Adsorption on gold

Although in the bulk of gold no oxide is stable, oxygen can be chemisorbed at the surface. Stable surfaces with stoichiometric compositions include Au,

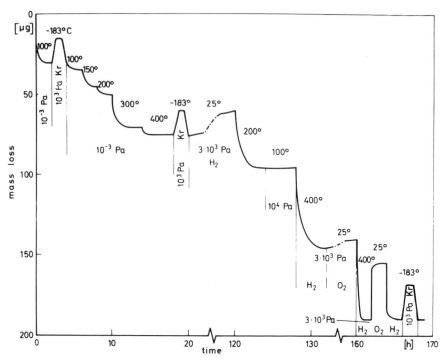

Fig. 9.16 Degassing, oxidation, reduction, and surface area determination using krypton on 1.5 g gold spheres 10 to 60 μm in diameter

AuO, and AuO_2. Small amounts of impurities and lattice defects may explain the contradictory literature reports[20-33]. Above 200 °C gold functions as a catalyst in oxidation/reduction processes. Figure 9.16 shows oxidation/reduction experiments with high-purity gold spheres prepared by melting in hydrogen[24]. After baking in a vacuum and surface area determination with krypton at 90 K, several oxidation/reduction experiments were performed which resulted in a final loss of about seven layers. Oxygen chemisorption was observed even at room temperature. In spite of the relatively clean conditions during handling, the surface was obviously contaminated. Most astonishing, however, is that the specific surface area did not change as a result of this treatment.

Figures 9.17–9.19 show the adsorption of nitrogen, water, ethanol, and neopentene on gold foils[34-40]. All of these reactions are strongly reversible (Fig. 9.20), as is also the case with krypton and xenon. Irreversible adsorption as reported by other authors may be due to impurities.

Adsorption of acetic acid on a pure gold surface[29] is reversible, whereas in the case of an oxygen-covered surface one chemisorbed layer remains at the surface (Fig. 9.21). For subsequent adsorption of acetic acid, this chemisorption layer acts as a stable surface on which reversible isotherms have been observed. The specific surface area is practically the same as that of the pure gold surface. Gold can amalgamate with mercury vapour.

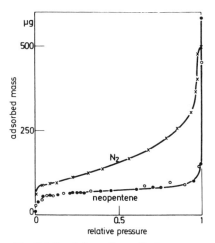

Fig. 9.17 Adsorption of nitrogen at 77 K X–Y– and 2,2-dimethylpropene (neopentene) at 273 K on gold foils; ●–●– adsorption, ○–○– desorption

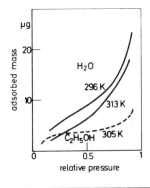

Fig. 9.18 Adsorption of water and ethanol on gold foils

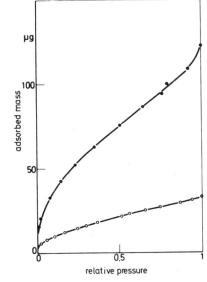

Fig. 9.19 Adsorption of nitrogen at 77 K on beaten ●–●– and rolled ○–○– gold foils

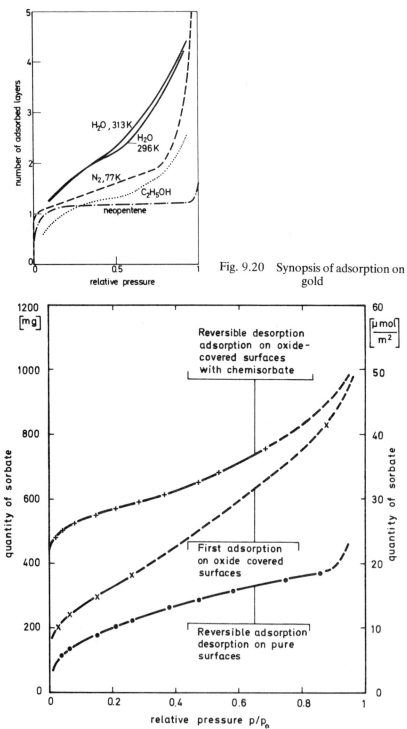

Fig. 9.20 Synopsis of adsorption on gold

Fig. 9.21 Sorption of acetic acid on pure and oxide-covered gold surface[21]

Adsorption on aluminium

Aluminium is always covered with an oxide layer which sometimes exhibits a highly porous structure and consequently a large surface area[41]. Figure 9.22 shows nitrogen isotherms on aluminium foils, on aluminium powder and on pure aluminium oxide. In contrast to the aluminium powder, the isotherm on alumina exhibits a hysteresis loop. Furthermore, two krypton isotherms on a foil and on powder are shown. Because krypton at 90 K condenses in solid form there is no sharp increase near the saturation pressure. With all isotherms, at a relative pressure of 0.1 about one layer is adsorbed and at the saturation point not more than eight layers.

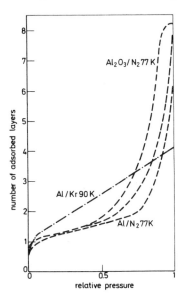

Fig. 9.22 Adsorption on aluminium and alumina

Adsorption on various metals

Pure metals exhibit a hydrophilic surface; small impurities, however, may give an impression that the metal is hydrophobic. They differ in their activity on the gases to be investigated and their catalytic features. The sorption of water from humid air on various metals has been investigated with regard to their suitability as mass standards[41–43]. All isotherms have been found to be revers- ible (Fig. 9.23). Irreversible isotherms (Fig. 9.13) may be due to impurities. Kochsiek[42] observed type III isotherms according to the BDDT classification (Fig. 2.17), whereas type II isotherms should be expected because of the hydrophilic surface.

Adsorption on polytetrafluorethylene

The nitrogen isotherm shown in Fig. 9.24 was measured with PTFE powder (Hostaflon TF 14, Hoechst AG). Similar results with organic vapours are also

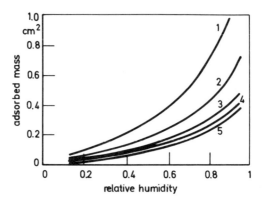

Fig. 9.23 Water adsorption on various metals in dependence of the relative humidity according to Kochsiek[35]; 1 aluminium (99), 2 brass (63), 3 German silver, 4 Pt/Ir (90/10), 5 steel (X 5, Cr, Ni 18, 9); polished surfaces with 0.2 roughness

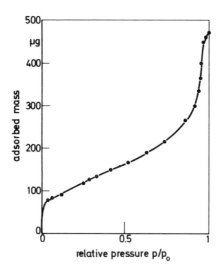

Fig. 9.24 Nitrogen isotherm at 77 K on PTFE powder

reported in the literature[44-47] with nitrogen and with argon. An S-shaped physisorption isotherm was also obtained with propane, whereas a small percentage of the neopentane was absorbed into the bulk.

Condensation in capillaries and on contaminations

Oil and grease vapours from the pump and from sealing materials, as well as grease and salts from fingerprints, form solutions with organic vapours and water vapour, respectively. Figure 9.4 shows the water isotherm on a fingerprint on an otherwise clean stainless steel foil.[4]

Because smooth surfaces reveal a rough and often porous structure under the microscope, condensation takes place below the saturation pressure, which tends to result in a sharp increase in the isotherm near saturation pressure[48–50]. If the saturation pressure has been exceeded for a short time only, an additional amount will condense. When reducing the pressure these layers remain on the surface.

Conclusions

With nitrogen, krypton, xenon, water, alcohol, and neopentane on quartz, glass, gold, and aluminium, S-shaped and mostly reversible physisorption isotherms of type II of the BDDT classification were observed. At a relative pressure of about 0.1 a monolayer, and at saturation pressure four to eight layers are adsorbed. Thus, in most cases the error can be neglected.

In an equal-armed balance the indicated mass m_i must be corrected by adding the mass adsorbed at the counterweight m_c, which depends on the relative pressure p/p_0 (or relative humidity), the surface area of the counterweight s, and the roughness factor R:

$$m_a = m_i + m_c(p/p_0)sR \qquad (9.10)$$

In surface area determinations, the error is the geometric area of the counterweight multiplied by the roughness factor of the material (about 1.05 for quartz and glass, and at least 1.3 for gold and aluminium if the latter surface is proved to be nonporous).

For asymmetrical balances, Czanderna[51,55] estimated the possible error due to adsorption for the Gulbransen torsion balance, the geometric surface area being 0.6 cm^3. Even with an unrealisticly large surface roughness the real surface area will not exceed 3 cm^2. One monolayer of water (molecular area 0.106 nm^2) results in a mass gain of 0.09 μg. Near the saturation point with eight monolayers, the correction is still below 1 μg.

Since PTFE shows the same sorption behaviour but dissolves some vapours, there seems to be no advantage in the use of this material. With gold, the effects of oxidation, reduction, chemisorption, or amalgamation have to be borne in mind. Chemisorption with some vapours can also occur on quartz and glass. Because of the simple composition of quartz, this material should be used rather than glass. Due to its possibly porous surface, aluminium should not be used as counterweight material.

If the saturation pressure is exceeded, additional condensation will occur. At the counterweight this can be reduced by keeping it at a somewhat higher temperature than the sample. When cooling with liquid nitrogen, this may be achieved by the addition of a few mls. of oxygen, without significantly influencing the buoyancy.

Grease, oil, and salts from fingerprints, etc., can be removed by careful cleaning with acetone and hot water.

9.4.6 Knudsen forces

If the sample temperature deviates from the temperature of the balance, thermal gas flow is produced, exerting forces and resulting in spurious mass changes[7,52]. One must distinguish between convection as a result of thermal density changes of the gas (discussed in Section 9.4.9) and the so-called Knudsen forces from direct impulse exchange of striking gas molecules of different temperatures. Whereas convection is observed at pressures above about 10^4 Pa for typical vacuum microbalance dimensions, Knudsen forces have an effect mainly at pressures below 10^3 Pa with a maximum at about 1 Pa, dependent on the type of gas and the geometry of the arrangement.

The prerequisite for Knudsen forces is that a gas molecule can fly from walls of different temperature or along walls with a temperature gradient without coming into collision with other gas molecules. The critical pressure is characterized by the Knudsen number $Kn = 1$, where $Kn = \lambda/l$ is defined as the ratio of the mean free path λ of a gas molecule before striking another molecule and a typical distance l of the apparatus (see Figs. 8.32, 8.33). This distance in a typical vacuum balance is of the order of centimetres and thus the critical pressure for $Kn = 1$ is about 1 Pa, where the maximum of Knudsen forces is observed.

At $Kn \geqslant 1$ the gas molecules exchange momentum almost exclusively with the walls of the equipment rather than with one another. The gas molecules leaving the warmer parts of the walls move faster than those coming from the cooler parts. The number of molecules, however, leaving either part of the wall is identical under steady-state conditions. Thus, a force corresponding to the difference in momentum of the molecules coming from various directions is exerted on any obstacle.

If a horizontal plate is suspended from a balance beam between two parallel horizontal walls, kept at different temperatures, the plate is subject to a force in the direction of the colder wall (transverse Knudsen force; Fig. 9.25(a)). The plate may be positioned between any configuration of walls. Of particular interest for microgravimetry is a plate suspended in a tube (Fig. 9.25(b)).

Temperature differences along the tube result in a pressure difference whose maximum in most cases[53] is defined by the Knudsen formula

$$p_1/p_2 = \sqrt{T_1/T_2}$$

where p is the pressure and T is the absolute temperature. This pressure difference exerts a force on the plate of the same magnitude as in case depicted in Fig. 9.25(a).

A force is also encountered when the walls are of a uniform temperature,

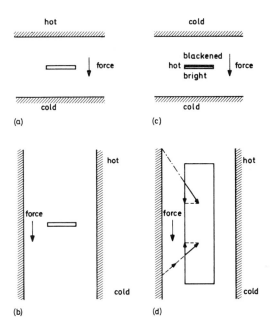

Fig. 9.25 Knudsen forces at various geometries; (a) horizontal plate between parallel walls, (b) horizontal plate in a perpendicular tube, (c) plate with different accommodation coefficient at either side, (d) vertical suspended body between parallel walls

but the temperature of the plate is different from that of the wall and accommodation coefficients of the two sides of the plate are different, for example, because one side is highly reflective and the other side is blackened (Fig. 9.25(c)) as in the Crookes radiometer. The direction of the force is from the higher to the lower accommodation coefficient, i.e. from the blackened to the bright side.

The longitudinal Knudsen forces which can act on the supporting wire and also on the pans (Fig. 9.25(d)) are of great importance to microbalance measurements. The existence of these forces is illustrated by a model (Fig. 9.26) described by Massen and Poulis[7], considering a two-dimensional vessel with a cold bottom and a hot cover. A gas molecule leaving the bottom with a velocity corresponding to the temperature T_1 of the bottom becomes accelerated when striking the wall, whose temperature is somewhat higher. At the hot cover this molecule will be accelerated at once, and decelerated at the wall when returning to the bottom. These changes of impulse are connected with reaction forces to the walls. If the walls are movable and the bottom and cover are fixed, a resulting force along the walls acts from hot to cold.

The dependence of Knudsen forces on the type of gas can be seen in Fig.

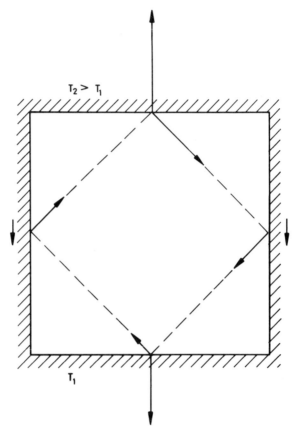

Fig. 9.26 Knudsen forces in a closed vessel with cold bottom and hot cover, according to Massen and Poulis[7]

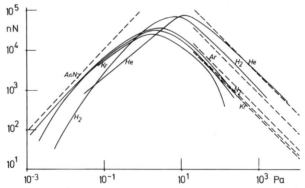

Fig. 9.27 Dependence of longitudinal Knudsen forces on the type of gas. Diameter of the balance tube 27 mm. Sample: aluminium tube 100 mm length, 10 mm ϕ; $T_1 = 90$ K, $T_2 = 295$ K

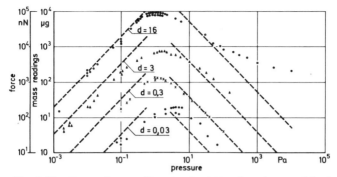

Fig. 9.28 Dependence of longitudinal Knudsen forces with nitrogen on sample diameter; $T_1 = 90$ K, $T_2 = 295$ K, balance tube diameter 27 mm

9.27. For a hollow cylinder 10 mm in diameter, the mass defect amounts to several milligrams. With a 30 μm suspension wire, apparent mass changes of up to 10 μg have been observed (Fig. 9.28). The forces were found to be practically independent of the magnitude of the temperature gradient and also independent of the material used[42].

For pressures where $Kn = 0.1$, the mean free path λ can be calculated from a relation developed from the kinetic theory:

$$\lambda \leqslant kT/\sqrt{2\pi pd^2} \qquad (9.11)$$

where k is the Boltzmann constant, T is the absolute temperature, p is the pressure, and d is the diameter of the molecule. In this range, slip flow occurs along a surface in which temperature differences exist and in a layer thickness corresponding approximately to that of the mean free path (Figs. 9.29 and 9.30). The reaction force is directed from warm to cold as in the case of the Knudsen forces. Indeed, the effect may be regarded like a Knudsen force when the gas continuum at a distance of λ is regarded as a solid wall. Slip flow velocity, and therefore the reaction forces, are proportional to the mean free path. Hence, the Knudsen force decreases with increasing pressure, and at higher pressures it becomes submerged in the growing noise level of convection. The flow velocity was determined to be about 30 mm/s for air at 100 Pa, 290 K, and a temperature gradient of 1 K/mm[54].

Surprisingly, for $Kn \leqslant 0.1$, a plate suspended normal to a temperature gradient in a gas is also subject to a force (Fig. 9.31). This happens because a

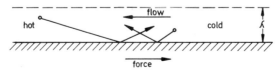

Fig. 9.29 Thermal slip flow

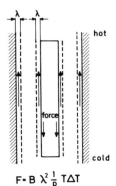

$$F = B \, \lambda^2 \frac{1}{p} \, T \Delta T$$

Fig. 9.30 Slip flow on a sample suspended on a balance

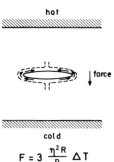

$$F = 3 \frac{\eta^2 R}{p} \Delta T$$

Fig. 9.31 Slip flow on a plate between walls of different temperatures

temperature gradient always arises from the centre to the periphery of the plate. For example, if the plate is suspended between two parallel walls of different temperatures, the centre of the side facing the warmer wall has a higher temperature than the edges, and the lowest temperature is measured at the centre facing the colder wall. The force acts from warm to cold.

The gas set in motion by the processes described will either lead to pressure differences or will flow back another way. While the gas flows considered before are localized exactly by the geometry of the surfaces, counterflow occurs in the free space and may exert forces on obstacles. The flow pattern is less regular and leads to stochastic fluctuations in readings rather than to constant deflections of the balance. These disturbances are small compared with those caused by the actual Knudsen forces.

A theoretical treatment of the Knudsen forces has been established by Massen and Poulis[7]. They developed the following equations for the forces exerted for a cylindrical geometry:

$$F_1 = - R_i R_0 \frac{p}{T} (T_{top} - T_{bottom}) \qquad (9.12)$$

for the longitudinal effect at low pressures, and

$$F_1 = \frac{\pi}{2} \frac{\lambda^2}{1 - \ln(R_0/R_i)} \frac{T}{p} (T_{top} - T_{bottom}) \qquad (9.13)$$

for the slip flow region, where R_0 is the radius of the hangdown tube, R_i the radius of the hangdown wire, F_1 the longitudinal force, p the pressure, T the absolute temperature, and λ the mean free path.

The transverse Knudsen force F_t can be calculated for the low pressure region using

$$F_t = Sp(1 - \sqrt{T_{top}/T_{bottom}}) \qquad (9.14)$$

For the slip flow region

$$F_t = S(p_{top} - p_{bottom}) \qquad (9.15)$$

is valid. S equals the area of the horizontal cross-section of the sample. Surprisingly, the forces resulting from the longitudinal effect are, in general, larger.

Disturbances from thermal gas flow can be kept small by localizing the temperature jump at the thin part of the hangdown wire and using hangdown wires which are as thin as possible. Parts with large surfaces like pans, beam, and bearings should be shielded by use of reflecting metal foils, as shown in Fig. 9.10, so that they assume the temperature of the near environment. Installation of metal screens in the hangdown tube around the suspension wire is useful but produces difficulties in handling.

Measurements in the pressure region where the Knudsen forces exhibit their maximum (about 1 Pa) must be avoided. If necessary the pressure should be increased with a nonreacting gas (e.g. helium when measuring nitrogen adsorption at 77 K).

9.4.7 Zero-point determination

After degassing, the sample is cooled down to 77 K and the zero point of the isotherm is determined in the cooled state. In vacuum, thermal equilibrium is established by radiation alone and therefore takes a very long time. Knudsen forces of a few micrograms, which disappear after 5 h, have been observed at 10^{-5} Pa[5].

To avoid contamination by readsorption after baking, it is necessary to maintain a good vacuum ($\leqslant 10^{-5}$ Pa) and to cool down very quickly after baking. The balance tubes act as baffles for all condensable gases like oxygen, water vapour, or organics, and to some extent for nitrogen as well. Removal of the Dewar vessel during the measurement for control of the sample, therefore, presents difficulties. In this case adsorbed molecules will be desorbed

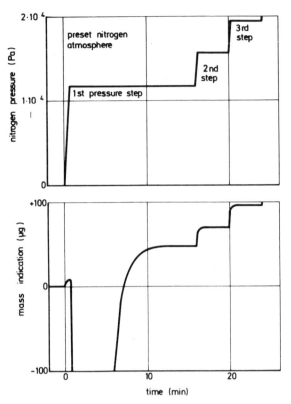

Fig. 9.32 Stepwise isobaric measurement of nitrogen sorption at 77 K. During gas inflow for the first
step the sample had a temperature higher than 77 K

from the hangdown tubes and taken up by the sample, which is cooler. There-
after another complete baking process has to follow.

Adjustment of the balance to the first pressure value (about 10^4 Pa) reveals
whether an adequate thermal equilibrium has been achieved at the time of
zero-point determination. The shape of the mass curve in the case of the
sample not being cooled down to the temperature of liquid nitrogen is as
shown in Fig. 9.32: first a drastic decrease in mass is observed. After about 15
min, a constant equilibrium value is reached. This shape of the mass curve can
be explained by the effect of convection and by the temperature dependence
of adsorption. If the sample was already at the temperature of liquid nitrogen,
the mass curve will not go down.

In order to speed up the measurement, one might consider not determining
the zero point at the beginning of the adsorption isotherm but to use only that
at the end of the desorption isotherm. In the case of microporous material this
would not save much time because the gas release may extend over several
days. Furthermore, it is frequently observed that some percentage of the

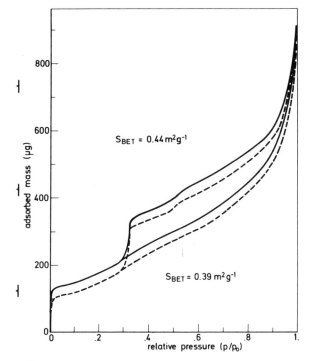

Fig. 9.33 Effect of a zero-point error on adsorption
isotherm and specific surface area

monolayer can be removed only by the addition of heat. This is due to the fact
that desorption involves activated processes (cf. Chapter 3). A better method
would be to accelerate the heat exchange by admitting helium into the balance at a pressure of about 10^3 Pa and pumping it off again after thermal
equilibrium has been established, which takes about 10 min.

The effect of a zero-point error on the isotherm is shown in Figs. 9.33 and
9.34. Not only will the specific BET surface area be falsified, but in addition,
the presence of micropores may be simulated.

9.4.8 Cavity forces

Closely related to Knudsen forces, a spurious mass defect may be observed
when a temperature gradient exists perpendicular to the surface of a porous
sample. A gas molecule entering a pore (Fig. 9.35) has a velocity corresponding to the gas temperature, but leaves the pore after some collisions with the
pore walls with a velocity corresponding to the internal sample temperature.
The velocity change is accompanied with a reactive force onto the sample.
This effect was predicted theoretically by Massen and Poulis but is difficult to
observe because it competes with the Knudsen forces which in general are
predominant.

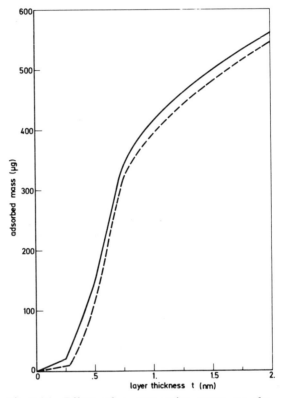

Fig. 9.34 Effect of a zero-point error on the
t-diagram

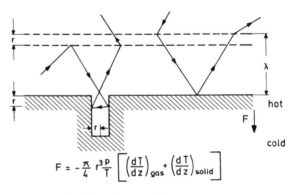

$$F = -\frac{\pi}{4} r^3 \frac{P}{T} \left[\left(\frac{dT}{dz}\right)_{gas} + \left(\frac{dT}{dz}\right)_{solid} \right]$$

Fig. 9.35 Cavity forces

The maximum of the cavity forces will occur not far from that pressure at which the mean free path equals the pore radius. Assuming an area of the porous sample of 10 mm², a temperature gradient perpendicular to that area, parallel to the pore axis of 500 K/m, at its maximum the force is $-4 \cdot 10^{-8}$ N, corresponding to a spurious mass effect of -4 μg. Cavity forces may be avoided by careful thermostatting of the sample, shielding against temperature radiation from the balance with a metal disk some millimetres above the sample fastened at the suspension wire.

9.4.9 Convection

Convection is the gas flow which equalizes density inhomogeneities in the gravitational field caused by temperature differences. Therefore convection is only observed in a gas continuum, which means at Knudsen numbers $Kn \leqslant 1$. In the microgravimetric praxis disturbances due to convection are observed at pressures above about 10^4 Pa, and mainly when the sample suspended below the balance is at higher temperature than the balance which is usually at room temperature[7,52,55].

Convection can manifest itself in the form of a spurious weight change and in the form of irregular fluctuations in readings (Fig. 9.36). The mean frequency of the fluctuations increases with increasing pressure, reaches a value of about 0.1 Hz at about $5 \cdot 10^4$ Pa (for nitrogen), and then remains constant.

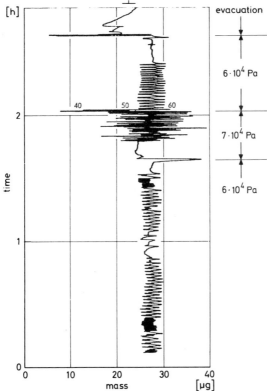

Fig. 9.36 Fluctuation of balance reading due to convection

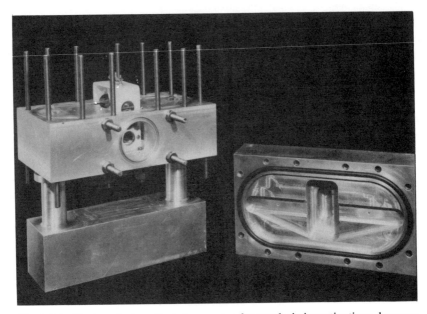

Fig. 9.37   Useless design of a balance case for catalytic investigations, because
of the occurrence of a thermosyphon flow

The mean amplitude of fluctuation increases linearly with the pressure and affects the sensitivity of the balance as a 'noise level'.

When the two balance tubes are connected by a tube at the level of the balance pans (Fig. 9.37), a thermosyphon flow occurs impeding any weighings. Pronounced fluctuations in readings (Fig. 9.38) have been observed while investigating the influence of corrosion on nuclear radiation (Fig. 8.37). These measurements were made in flowing gas (O_2, N_2, H_2O) with six microbalances arranged in one common vessel. No fluctuations were observed when hydrogen and helium were used.

For systematic investigations of the effects of convection on microbalances, a brass disk 10 mm in diameter has been used (Fig. 9.39). At temperature differences of 300 K, effective forces were found in the $1 \cdot 10^4$ to $4 \cdot 10^4$ Pa range which led to apparent mass alterations of 10 μg. Above $4 \cdot 10^4$ Pa, irregular fluctuations in readings were observed which increased monotonically with the pressure (Fig. 9.40). Particularly pronounced fluctuations were observed when the heater was lowered until its edge was at the same height as the brass disk, i.e., when the disk was subject to large temperature inhomogeneities. With argon, the fluctuations began at a pressure as low as $2 \cdot 10^4$ Pa. With hydrogen and helium, no fluctuations have been observed up to atmospheric pressure.

It is not so obvious and may be overlooked by users of microbalances that convection may occur in the supposedly stable situation in which the bottom of the container is colder than its top[56]. This is because temperature differ-

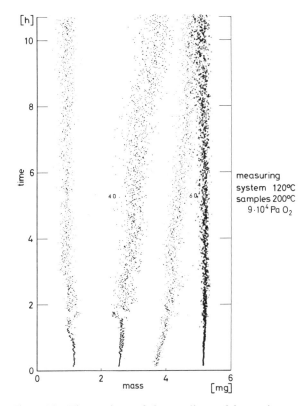

Fig. 9.38   Fluctuations of the readings of four microbalances because of convection

ences exist in an insufficiently thermostatted balance pan producing local gas
flow. It results in irregular fluctuations in readings, as shown in Fig. 9.41. The
temperature differences are caused by heat radiation from the upper part of
the balance. The temperature of an unshielded sample in a liquid nitrogen
bath was measured to be 30 K higher, and at pressures above 1 Pa to be 2 K
higher than the bath.

Any attempts to prevent such disturbances have to ensure above all that
temperature inhomogeneities are localized where the moving parts of the
balance expose the smallest surface area to the gas flow. The temperature
variation should therefore be restricted to a short section of the suspension
wire, which should be as thin as possible.

The other parts of the measuring system and sample have to be well thermostatted to prevent local temperature inhomogeneities. The heaters used
must have a long zone of constant temperature in the vicinity of the sample.
At low pressures and in particular at low temperatures, where heat is transferred primarily by radiation, the samples must be shielded along the hangdown
tube from radiation of heat from the room. This is conveniently accomplished

410

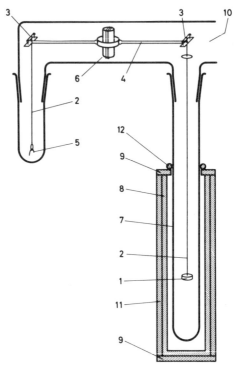

Fig. 9.39 Arrangement with Gast micro-balance; 1 brass disk, dia. 10 mm, 2 suspension wire, dia. 30 μm, 3 sapphire pans on diamond pins, 4 balance beam, 5 counterweight, 6 coil system and magnet, 7 balance tube wrapped in wire gauge for group, 8 aluminium tube wrapped in fibreglass, 9 asbestos cover, 10 nozzle to vacuum pump, gas supply and pressure control, 11 heater, 12 asbestos cord

by mounting a polished metal disk on to the wire directly above the sample (Fig. 9.10). Shielding of the pan in this way reduces the temperature deviation to less than 0.1 K and the disturbances to some micrograms at atmospheric pressure.

A satisfactory method of reducing convective disturbances is to ensure that the higher temperature zone is in the upper part of the vessel (Fig. 8.19). If the sample is at a higher temperature than the measuring system, it is therefore advisable to use a balance with the pans above the measuring system. However, this balance requires a relatively thick supporting bar, on which the gas flow can exert large forces. A particularly favourable arrangement, similar to that shown in Fig. 8.19(e), was suggested by Poulis[57]. One obvious disadvantage of this arrangement is that the capacity of the balance is reduced by

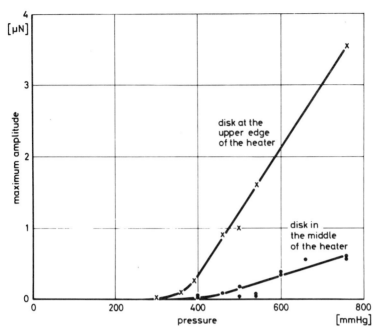

Fig. 9.40 The dependence of the amplitude of fluctuations on pressure and position of heater $T_1 = 298$ K, $T_2 = 573$ K, in N_2, using a brass disk 100 mm in diameter

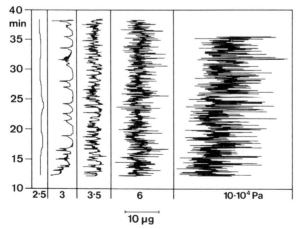

Fig. 9.41 Variations in a recorder tracing of the weight with balance pan at 77 K and beam at 300 K, at various pressures of N_2

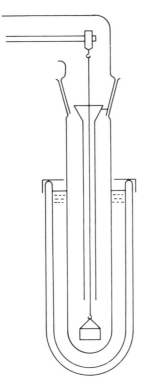

Fig. 9.42 To reduce convection, according to Sappok and Boehm[58], the suspension wire is surrounded with a glass tube

the counterweight. Thin balance tubes and installing a metal beaker enclosing the balance pan are recommended by several authors[6,55]. Sappok and Boehm[58] reduced disturbances by using a thin glass tube suspended in the balance tube (Fig. 9.42). Kuhn and Walter[59] used a system of shields (Fig. 9.43). In addition they filled the balance case with helium and restricted the reacting gases to the sample space.

9.4.10 Condensation value determination

An incorrectly measured condensation pressure mainly affects the scale of the abscissa of the mesopore distribution. Besides, supercooling of the adsorptive may lead to difficulties in the determination of the maximum adsorbed amount and therefore of the overall pore volume. To avoid condensation within the counterweight pan, it is advisable to mix one to two per cent of liquid oxygen into the liquid nitrogen bath on the counterweight side. To ensure complete pore filling, which is indispensable to the measurement of the desorption isotherm, the condensation pressure has to be maintained for at least half an hour after the maximum adsorption value has been attained.

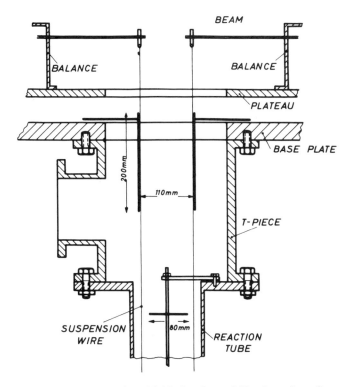

Fig. 9.43   Convection shields for the stabilization of gas flow.
The upper part is filled with helium

9.4.11 Electrostatic charge

An electrostatic charge may be produced when a powder sample is placed in
the pan. The pan can be discharged by touching it with a grounded lead. A
considerable charge is observed at the outer side of the hangdown tube when
the liquid nitrogen bath is removed. This can be avoided by covering the
hangdown tube with metal stockings (copper spun), with a grid of metal paint,
or with a sputtered metal layer. For experiments with radioactive samples or
with irradiation of the sample, the pan must be grounded via the hangdown
wires in a similar way to that shown in Fig. 8.14.

9.4.12 Magnetic fields

Electromagnetic disturbances should be avoided by bifilar winding of the
heater coils (Figs. 8.17, 8.18). The sample and the measuring system should
be carefully shielded from residual fields. Under the influence of electric or
magnetic fields, extremely complicated gas flow can be generated. Effects of
this nature have to be taken into account, for example when measuring the
magnetic susceptibility of oxygen.

It has to be taken into account that the heater control may disturb the network. In addition, the network voltage may break down if high-power ovens are used. Also, the various electronic measuring instruments used for a complex apparatus may disturb each other, for example via the earth circuit.

9.5 Data processing

Computerized methods can be used to speed up degassing experiments and the determination of parameters characterizing drying processes[60]. The search for optimum degassing conditions for samples whose surface structure are to be analysed can be considerably shortened. The extended evaluation of the results is now made exclusively using electronic data processing. Because the measurements proceed slowly, the results of the calculation should be used to control the measurements. In this way not only the tedious observation but also erroneous operation can be avoided.

9.5.1 Drying, evaporation

From the mass loss curve at constant temperature a formal diffusion coefficient D for the characterization of drying, or evaporation of volatile species from the bulk sample can be derived[61]. For spherical particles with the radius r, the equation

$$D = \frac{r^2}{\pi^2 \tau} \qquad (9.16)$$

applies, where τ is a period during which the content of the volatile species decreases to $6/\pi^2 e \approx 0.22$. τ is derived from the decrease in weight Δm_1 and Δm_2 and from the slopes $\dot{m}_1$ and $\dot{m}_2$, at two points of the degassing curves (Fig. 9.44):

$$\tau = \frac{\Delta m_1 - \Delta m_2}{\dot{m}_1 - \dot{m}_2} \qquad (9.17)$$

Thus, complete registration of the degassing curve is avoided.

9.5.2 Degassing

Adsorption measurements always start with the degassing of the sample in vacuum at elevated temperatures (see Section 9.2.1). To ensure reliable pore size analysis, adsorbed foreign molecules have to be completely removed, in particular with microporous samples, which may take several hours and even days. Thus, the highest baking temperature which can be applied without damaging the sample has to be identified experimentally (see Fig. 2.16).

This search can be considerably shortened by analysing the mass loss curve at the very beginning, i.e. by determining whether it approximates a constant

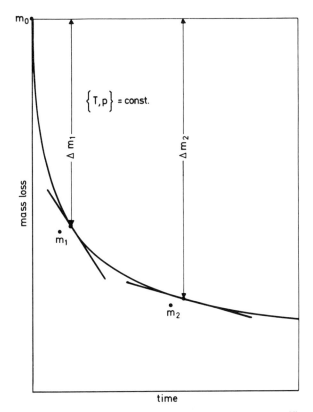

Fig. 9.44   Calculation of the formal diffusion coefficient

value within a reasonable period of time, or whether the differential curve tends to zero. Starting with a relatively low degassing temperature, the mass loss curve is analysed in this way after about 15 minutes, and then three more times at intervals of, say, 5 minutes (Fig. 9.45). If it is confirmed that no decomposition occurs, the temperature is (automatically) increased and after another 15 minutes a new analysis run is started, etc. Of course, this is a first estimate, and the degassing conditions determined have to be proved whether no change of the surface structure, e.g. by sintering without mass loss, has occurred.

9.5.3 Extrapolation of the adsorbed amount

When measuring the isotherm stepwise, it is of interest to extrapolate the equilibrium value in advance and, when a confident value has been calculated, to proceed to the next step. Jäntti et al.[62-64] evaluated some equations based on physical models for this purpose.

An expression for the increase in sample weight, corresponding to the

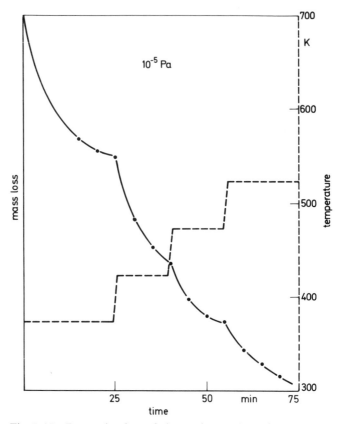

Fig. 9.45 Determination of the optimum degassing temperature

weight of adsorbed nitrogen m after change of pressure can be derived if one
assumes that an increase in pressure creates a certain number of free centres
where adsorption is energetically possible. Denoting the portion of filled
centres by $\theta = m/m_\infty$, where m_∞ = the equilibrium value of weight increment,
and introducing β as rate constant, we find

$$\frac{d\theta}{dt}(1) = \beta(1 - \theta)^2 \qquad (9.18)$$

if adsorption is possible when two adjacent centres are free. When each
adsorbed molecule occupies only one free centre,

$$\frac{d\theta}{dt}(2) = \beta(1 - \theta) \qquad (9.19)$$

In addition to Eqns. (9.18) and (9.19), another equation was used:

$$\frac{d\theta}{dt}(3) = \beta(1 - \theta^2) \qquad (9.20)$$

This is an attempt to take into consideration the possibility of adsorption in multilayers so that, when θ is small, the number of free centres diminishes at a rate slower than proportional to θ.

Integrating Eqns. (9.18) to (9.20), and taking β to be independent of θ, we obtain the following equations for m.

$$m(1) = m_\infty \frac{\beta t}{1 + \beta t} \qquad (9.21)$$

$$m(2) = m_\infty(1 - e^{-\beta t}) \qquad (9.22)$$

and
$$m(3) = m_\infty \tanh \beta t \qquad (9.23)$$

It is seen that in all cases m goes from 0 to m_∞ when t increases from zero to infinity.

By measuring three consecutive values m_1 to m_3 of a with equal time intervals, we may calculate the estimates m_∞ from the following simple formulae that result from Eqns. (9.21) to (9.23), respectively:

$$m_\infty(1) = \frac{m_1 m_2 + m_2 m_3 - 2m_1 m_3}{2m_2 - m_1 - m_3} \qquad (9.24)$$

$$m_\infty(2) = \frac{m_2^2 - m_1 m_3}{2m_2 - m_1 - m_3} \qquad (9.25)$$

$$m_\infty(3) = \sqrt{m_2 m_\infty(1)} \qquad (9.26)$$

The method has been applied to the structural analysis of microporous active carbons where the equilibrium at low pressures settled after 2–3 hours. It was found that Eqn. (9.22) best fitted the weight curve. Figure 9.46 shows schematically a recorder diagram with the conventional and the curtailed measurement of a part of the isotherm. Each extrapolation was made from three values of the mass taken at 5 minute intervals and changing the nitrogen pressure after 15 minutes. The total times of measurement were 720 and 200 minutes, respectively, which means that the time saving was 70%. No significant deviations of the isotherms were observed, and the BET surfaces were found to be equal within 1%, and the pore size distributions agreed quite well.

In the region of low relative pressures, covered by the Dubinin–Radushkevich equation, another method is recommended[53]. After transformation of

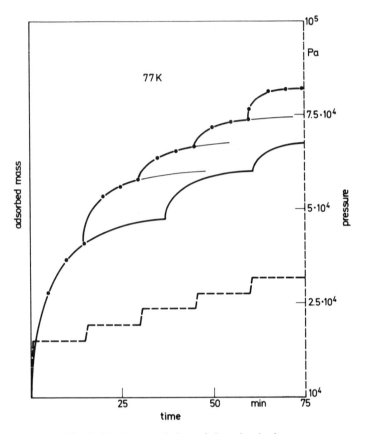

Fig. 9.46   Extrapolation of the adsorbed mass

the adsorption plot (Figs. 9.47, 9.48), using $1/t$ as abscissa, the equation

$$m = A + B/t \qquad (9.27)$$

fits best. The equilibrium mass is given by the ordinate intercept.

Both extrapolation methods have been tested using various types of microporous activated carbons. For other materials the validity should be tested by controlling the squares of correlation and making use of the linear regression programs available.

9.5.4 Calculation of the isotherm

Programs for the evaluation of the adsorption isotherm are shown in section 4.3.4. In the following some additional comments are made. Since generally valid isotherm equations do not exist, interpolation methods for the whole measuring range fail. A much better way to improve the results seems to be to

419

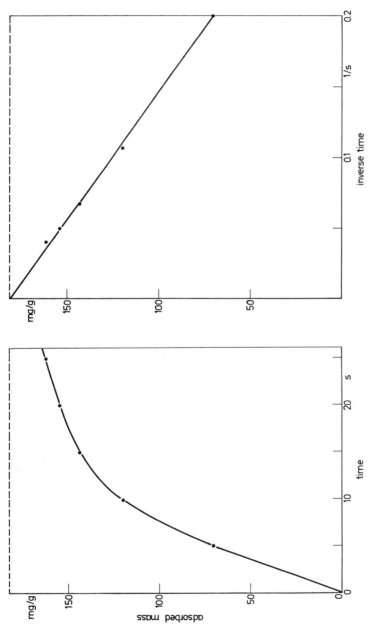

Figs 9.47, 9.48   Extrapolation of the equilibrium adsorbed mass by linear regression

measure many points, and if necessary, reduce the measuring time by extrapolating each point as described above. The lack of an isotherm equation valid for porous materials very early led to the use of numerical methods for the computation of pore size distributions. Making use of the Runge–Kutta formalism, the mass adsorbed is calculated at equal distances of relative pressure. The adsorbed mass, transformed into volume, can then be used to add the core volume distribution or, with correction of the layer adsorbed at the pore walls, of the pore volume distribution[65].

The linear interpolation carried out to obtain the equal distance values masks the fine structure. It is better to carry the calculation out directly with the actual experimental values. In the case of gravimetric measurements the spread of the experimental values to decreasing readings with increasing pressure must be corrected to avoid faulty peaks in the curve of pore radius frequency. This can be done by searching for single erroneously measured points with either too high or too low a level, and by eliminating those values. If there are too many points influenced by experimental uncertainty, all the measured points should be used for the calculation, but after the values in question have been adjusted to their neighbours. This means that a piecewise smoothing or interpolation technique is applied. There are criteria in the computer program which control the various ways of calculation proposed to reach the results that best fit the experimental data.

References

1. E. Robens and R. Sieglen, *Vacuum*, **21**, 484 (1971)
2. A. W. Czanderna, in: S. P. Wolsky and E. J. Zdanuk (eds.), *Ultra Micro Weight Determination in Controlled Environments*, Interscience Publishers, New York, 1969
3. E. Robens, in: A. W. Czanderna and S. P. Wolsky (eds.), *Microweighing in Vacuum and Controlled Environments*, Elsevier, Amsterdam, 1980, p. 127
4. E. Robens, G. Robens, and G. Sandstede; *Vacuum*, **13**, 303 (1963)
5. E. Robens and Th. Gast, *J. Vacuum Sci. Technol.*, **15**, 805 (1978)
6. C. Eyraud, M. Cronenberger, and M. Cogniat, *Technique de l'Ingeénieur*, p. 880
7. C. H. Massen and J. A. Poulis, in: A. W. Czanderna and S. P. Wolsky (eds.), *Microweighing in Vacuum and Controlled Environments*, Elsevier, Amsterdam, 1980, p. 95
8. W. Kuhn, E. Robens, G. Sandstede, and G. Walter, in: C. H. Massen and H. J. van Beckum (eds.), *Vacuum Microbalance Techniques*, Vol. 7, Plenum Press, New York, 1970, p. 161
9. E. Robens and G. Sandstede, *Z. Instrum.*, **75**, 167–178 (1967)
10. H. Förster and V. Meyn, in: S. C. Bevan, S. J. Gregg, and N. D. Parkyns (eds.), *Progress in Vacuum Microbalance Techniques*, Vol. 2, Heyden, London, 1973, pp. 139–146
11. Th. Gast, *Feinwerktechnik*, **53**, 167–172 (1949)
12. K. M. Laing, in: A. W. Czanderna (ed.), *Vacuum Microbalance Techniques*, Vol. 6, Plenum Press, New York, 1967, pp. 149–155
13. E. Robens and G. Sandstede, *Vak.-Techn.*, **16**, 125–130 (1967)
14. R. A. Pierotti, in: A. W. Czanderna (ed.), *Vacuum Microbalance Techniques*, Vol. 6, Plenum Press, New York, 1967, p. 1

15. E. Robens, *Wägen & Dosieren* (1981)
16. G. Korányi, *Surface Properties of Silicate Glasses*, Akadémiai Kiado, Budapest, 1963, pp. 29 ff.
17. S. Gal, *Die Methodik der Wasserdampf-Sorptionsmessungen*, Springer-Verl., Berlin, 1967
18. N. Hackerman and A. C. Hall, *J. Phys. Chem.*, **62**, 1212–1216 (1958)
19. R. I. Razouk and A. S. Salem, *J. Phys. Chem.*, **52**, 1208–1227 (1948)
20. M. F. Schrader, *J. Colloid Interface Sci.*, **59**, 456–460 (1977)
21. A. F. Benton and J. L. Elgin, *J. Amer. Chem. Soc.*, **49**, 2426 (1927)
22. N. N. Dobrovol'skii, V. E. Ostrovskii, A. M. Rabshov, and M. I. Temkin, *Dokl. Akad. Nauk. SSSR*, **183**, 1120 (1968)
23. N. P. Kulkova and L. P. Leveschenko, *Kinet. Catal.*, **6**, 688 (1965)
24. E. Robens, in: *Haus der Technik–Vortragsveröffentlichungen*, Nr. 158: *Kontinuierliche, physikalische Meßverfahren in der chemischen Technik*, Vulkan-Verl., Essen, 1968, pp. 89–103
25. N. Endow, B. I. Wood, and H. Wise, *J. Catalysis*, **15**, 316 (1969)
26. P. C. Richardson and D. R. Rossington, *J. Catalysis*, **20**, 420 (1971)
27. W. R. McDonald and K. E. Hayes, *J. Catalysis*, **18**, 115 (1970)
28. B. M. W. Trapnell, *Proc. Roy. Soc. A*, **218**, 566 (1953)
29. G. Sandstede, E. Robens, and G. Walter, *3rd Int. Kongress für Grenzflächenaktive Stoffe*, Vol. II, Section B, Verl. der Univ.-Druckerei Mainz, 1960, pp. 409–414
30. O. D. Gonzalez and G. Parravano, *J. Amer. Chem. Soc.*, **78**, 4533 (1956)
31. D. Y. Cha and C. Parravano, *J. Catalysis*, **18**, 200 (1970)
32. S. Galvagno and G. Parravano, *J. Catalysis*, **55**, 178 (1978)
33. T. Fukushima, S. Galvagno, and G. Parravano, *J. Catalysis*, **57**, 177–182 (1979)
34. F. P. Bowden, F. R. S. Throssell, and W. R. Throssell, *Proc. Roy. Soc. London*, **209** (A), 297–308 (1951)
35. D. Wischlitzki, R. Ahrends-Botzong, P. Hess, and K. Schäfer, *Ber. Bunsenges. f. Phys. Chem.*, **79**, 348–352 (1975)
36. S. J. Gregg and K. S. Sing, *Adsorption, Surface Area and Porosity*, Acad. Press, London, 1967, p. 6ff.
37. D. H. Everett and R. H. Ottewill, *Surface Area Determination*, Butterworth, London, 1970
38. E. Robens and G. Walter in: F. Korte (ed.), *Methodicum Chimicum*, Vol. 1, Part 2: *Analytik*, Thieme-Verl., Stuttgart, 1973, pp. 704–716
39. E. Robens, G. Robens, and G. Sandstede, in: G. Güntherschulze (ed.), *Vacuum Technique*, Pergamon Press, Oxford, 1965, pp. 76–81
40. T. Smith, *J. Colloid Interface Sci.*, **75**, 51–54 (1980)
41. G. Bochmann, *Metalloberfläche*, **15**, 145–147 (1961)
42. M. Kochsiek, *PTB-Mitteilungen*, **87**, 478–485 (1977)
43. R. Strömberg, *Kungl. Svenska Akademiens Handlinger*, **6**, Nr. 2 (1928)
44. R. P. N. Lee and J. W. Whalen, *J. Colloid Interface Sci.*, **73**, 45–49 (1980)
45. J. W. Whalen, *J. Colloid Interface Sci.*, **28**, 443–448 (1968)
46. J. W. Whalen, W. H. Wade, and J. J. Porter, *J. Colloid Interface Sci.*, **24**, 379–383 (1967)
47. R. B. Perry and K. H. Svatek, *J. Colloid Interface Sci.*, **68**, 393–395 (1979)
48. P. J. Møller, *Thermochimica Acta*, **29**, 339–344 (1979)
49. E. L. Fuller, J. A. Poulis, A W. Czanderna, and E. Robens, *Thermochimica Acta*, **29**, 315–318 (1979)
50. E. Robens, in: H. G. Wiedemann (ed.), *Thermal Analysis*, Vol. 1, Birkhaeuser, Basel, 1980, pp. 213–218
51. A. W. Czanderna in: S. P. Wolsky and A. W. Czanderna (eds.), *Microweighing in Vacuum and Controlled Environments*, Elsevier, Amsterdam, 1980

52. E. Robens, in: A. W. Czanderna (ed.), *Vacuum Microbalance Techniques*, Vol. 8, Plenum Press, New York, 1971, p. 73
53. S. Weber and G. Schmidt, *Communications from the Kamerlingh Onnes Laboratory of the University of Leyden*, **22**, No. 246c (1936/37)
54. J. D. Swift, in: A. H. Beck (ed.), *Handbook of Vacuum Physics*, Vol. 1, Pergamon, Oxford, 1966, p. 297.
55. L. Cahn and H. Schultz, *Analytical Chem.*, **35**, 1729 (1963)
56. E. Robens, G. Sandstede, G. Walter, and G. Wurzbacher, in: C. H. Massen and H. J. van Beckum (eds.), *Vacuum Microbalance Techniques*, Vol. 7, Plenum Press, New York, 1970
57. J. A. Poulis, *Appl. Sci. Res.*, **14**(A), 98 (1965)
58. R. Sappok and P. Boehm, *Chem.-Ing. Techn.*, **41**, 829 (1969)
59. W. H. Kuhn and G. Walter, *Microgravimetric investigation into the mechanisms of corrosion of reactor materials in the presence of nuclear radiation*, Euratom Report EUR 1474.e; Presses Académiques Européennes, Brussels, 1964
60. J. Ochs and E. Robens, Keram. Z., **35**, (1983)
61. H. Czabon, E. Robens, G. Walter, M.-L. Welling, and G. Hild, *I & EC Product Research and Development*, **9**(3), 27–30 (1970)
62. O. Jäntti, J. Junttila, and E. Yrjänheikki, in: T. Gast and E. Robens (eds.), *Progress in Vacuum Microbalance Techniques*, Vol. 1, Heyden, London, 1972, p. 345
63. O. Jäntti and E. Robens, *Thermochimica Acta*, **51**, No. 1 (1982)
64. O. Jäntti, *Kemia-Kemi*, **7**, 539 (1980)
65. M. Büchner, E. Robens, and R. Sh. Mikhail, in: C. Eyraud and M. Escoubes (eds), *Progress in Vacuum Microbalance Techniques*, Vol. 3, Heyden, London, 1975, p. 324

Part 4

Appendixes

Introduction to Part 4

There follow some tables which have been compiled and are useful for the experimental work in this area. Of course, these tables cannot be complete, and they reflect the situation of the publishing year. It is planned to supplement and renew the tables at a later date. The authors therefore will be indebted for comments.

In the first table a survey is a given on parameters in question for surface investigations and the possibilities of measurement.

Appendix A

Surface Effects and Measuring Methods

Effect	Parameter	Measuring method/ measured parameter
adhesion	strength	force
glueing	modulus of elasticity	adhesion
friction	micro hardness	roughness
wear	surface tension	mechanical resistance
hardness	crystal structure	wear
precipitation	chemical composition	
epitactic growth	surface structure	
physiosorption	chemical composition	adsorption
chemisorption	free valences	X-ray diffraction
chemical reaction	specific surface area	electron diffraction
catalysis	pore size distribution	ion diffraction
surface diffusion	particle size distribution	ellipsometry
electro-catalysis	accommodation coefficient	electron microscopy
electro-osmosis	heat of adsorption	flow experiments
	heat of reaction	surface titration
	contact angle	Auger spectroscopy
		calorimetry
		Mössbauer spectroscopy
		mass spectroscopy
		gas chromatography
		electron spin resonance
		nuclear magnetic resonance
		magnetic susceptibility
		molecular beam experiments
		infrared absorption
		Raleigh sound-wave absorption
		X-ray fluorescence
		field ion and electron spectroscopy
		wetting experiments
		electrochemical experiments
electron entrance	work function	charge
vaporization	surface resistance	conductivity
electron disipation	electron mobility	field emission
electrostatic charge	number of free electrons	photo effect
rectification		recombination
tunnel effect		
photo effect		
light absorption	roughness	microscopy
light reflection	colour	refraction
refraction	extinction coefficient	absorption
	refraction index	reflection
	absorption coefficient	

Appendix B

Standardization

B.1 Reference materials and standardized measuring methods

Two routes have been taken to make industrial products more easily comparable and to facilitate the exchange of measuring results[1]. (a) standardizing of measuring methods and instruments, and (b) certification of reference materials. As regards powders and porous materials, remarkable work is currently underway in this field.

B.1.1 Reference materials

Many manufacturers of powders, adsorbents, catalysts, etc., used to produce reference materials and model substances for their own need. This had the advantage that the materials could be adapted to the relevant tasks. However, a serious drawback was that a comparison with results published elsewhere was hardly possible. Therefore, some industrial companies and public authorities are now producing, certifying, and storing referenced materials for public use.

Research in this field is being carried out at the National Physical Laboratory in Teddington, UK[2,3], using α-alumina, soot, and silca gel. AFNOR in France has investigated alumina as a specific surface reference material, and is now distributing two reference materials[4]. The American ASTM is working on alumina and silica gel. This list obviously is not complete.

We would like to draw attention to a relatively new initiative of the Community Bureau of Reference in Brussels (BCR)[5,6]. This European authority has founded several working groups which are now engaged in selecting suitable reference materials from standard industrial products. One of the sub-groups is that on Particulate Materials headed by Prof. D. H. Everett of Bristol University. The objective of the work of this group is the preparation of particle size reference materials in the range of 0.1 μm to 1000 μm, surface area reference materials in the range of 0.1 to 1500 m^2 g^{-1}, and pore size reference materials for the mesopore range (2 nm to 100 nm). These materials are designed for the calibration of measuring instruments for particle size distribution, surface area determination, and the investigation of pore size distribution. Another group is investigating the preparation of reference materials for various dusts as model substances for environmental research.

As regards the achievements of the Particulate Materials Group, the first certified reference materials are now available from BCR. There are five reference materials for certified particle size distribution, i.e. quartz powders with mean particle sizes about 1 μm, 3 μm, 10 μm, 30 μm, and 300 μm respectively[7]. Two additional quartz powders with mean particle sizes of 100 μm and 2000 μm are under investigation.

426

Another team is currently studying powders (titanium, quartz, alumina, tungsten, bronze) with a view to establishing certification reference materials for specific surface (determined by permeametry, low temperature adsorption, and other methods). A group of laboratories is also investigating several spherical polymer lattices in aqueous suspension in the range 1 μm to 12 μm. These substances are to be certified as small particle size reference material, intended for calibration and verification of various instruments for size measurements. Finally, as regards pore size reference materials, several laboratories are examining the suitably of silica gels, porous glass, and molecular sieves.

B.1.2 Standardized measuring methods

In standardizing test methods, measuring procedures, and measuring instruments, two approaches can be observed. First, to comply with the requirements of various industries, rather practical methods have been standardized in different countries. Nowadays technical committees at both national and international levels are trying to harmonize those methods, and in certain cases to standardize physically based absolute methods from which convertible parameters can be derived. Investigations into particle size and surface area determinations are curently being carried out in some European countries, especially in France[4], Germany[8] and the United Kingdom[9]. On the international level, the ISO and IUPAC[10] programmes and in particular that of the Technical Committee of Powder Metallurgy should be mentioned. The standardization of particule size measurements includes sedimentation methods, optical and electrical counters, microscopic methods, and flow methods like the well-known Blaine test (see Fig. 3.33).

The BET method used for surface area determination which involves the stepwise measurement of at least five points of the nitrogen adsorption isotherm at 77 K in the relative pressure region from 0.05 to 0.35 and evaluating using the two-parameter BET equation (Eqns. (3.10), (3.13), and (3.36) has been standardized in some countries. In the United Kingdom a (noncommercial) volumetric apparatus is standardized (Figs. 2.6–2.8); in Germany the Haul–Dümbgen apparatus (Fig. 2.12); and in several countries powder analysers.

Specific standards for pore size distribution measurements have not been issued so far, with the exception of that for the volumetric BET apparatus which may also be used for the measurement of the whole isotherm. An IUPAC committee is currently engaged in calculating and evaluating methods for this purpose. We presume that the evaluation will be based on the adsorption isotherm and, as suggested by Harvard and Wilson[11], that the Kelvin equation without the factor of 2 (Cohen equation):

$$\ln(p/p_0) = \frac{\gamma V_{\mathrm{m}}}{r_{\mathrm{K}} RT} \cos \theta \qquad (\text{B.1})$$

with a value of the surface tension of $8.72 \cdot 10^{-3}\,\mathrm{N\,m^{-1}}$ and the condensed molar volume $V_m = 34.68\,\mathrm{cm^3\,mole^{-1}}$ as used by de Boer[12] and a contact angle θ of zero will be proposed. The correction for the multilayer thickness t could be made using the Halsey equation[13]:

$$t = \sigma\sqrt{\frac{-5}{\ln(p/p_0)}} \qquad \text{(B.2)}$$

with the cross-sectional area $\sigma = 0.162\,\mathrm{nm^2}$.

B.2 Institutions and societies involved in standardization work

Most work in this area is done with regard to the characterization of small particles and its industrial use, and with hazards involved with working with dusts. Only a little standardization work until now has been completed in the area of surface and pore structure analysis.

Many more institutions, not covered by the following list, are also working in this field; not mentioned are the numerous university institutes engaged in this work. The preponderance of German addresses is due to the fact that these are best known to one of the authors.

Belgium

Commission of the European Community, Community Bureau of Reference (BCR), 200 rue de la Loi, B-1049 Brussels

France

AFNOR, Tour Europe, F-92 Courbevoie-Paris, Association Francaise de Normalisation

Germany

Battelle-Institut e.V., Am Römerhof 35, D-6000 Frankfurt am Main 90

Deutsche Keramische Gesellschaft, Arbeitskreis Kohlenstoff; Prof. Dr. E. Fitzer, Universität Karlsruhe, Institut für Chemische Technik, Kaiserstr. 12, D-7500 Karlsruhe

Fachausschuß 'Keramische Werkstoffe in der Technik'; Dr. F. J. Esper, Robert Bosch GmbH, Postfach 50, D-7000 Stuttgart 1

Materialprüfungsausschuß; Prof. P. Fischer, Fachhochschule, Fachrichtung Keramik, Rheinstr. 56, D-5410 Höhr-Grenzhausen

Rohstoffausschuß; Prof. Dr. K. H. Schüller, Rosenthal AG, Institut für Werkstofftechnik, Wittelsbacherstr. 49, D-8672 Selb

Deutscher Normenausschuß (DIN), Fachnormenausschuß Siebböden und Kornmessung (NASK), Reichpietschufer 72–76, D-1000 Berlin 30

Gesellschaft für Aerosolforschung, Rossertstr. 11, D-6232 Bad Soden

Gesellschaft für Strahlen- u. Umweltforschung mbH, Abt. Biophysikalische Strahlenforschung, Aerosol-Gruppe; Paul-Ehrlich-Str. 20, D-6000 Frankfurt am Main

Silikose-Forschungsinstitut, Hunscherdstr. 12, D-4630 Bochum

Staubforschungsinstitut des Hauptverbandes der gewerblichen Berufsgenossenschaften e.V., Langwartweg 103 D-5300 Bonn 1

Steinkohlenbergbauverein, Hauptstelle für Staub- und Silikosebekämpfung, Frillendorfer Str. 351, D-4300 Essen-Kray

Verein Deutscher Ingenieure, Graf Recke-Str. 84, D-4000 Düsseldorf 1
VDI-Fachausschuß Partikelmeßtechnik
VDI-Kommission Reinhaltung der Luft

Wäschereiforschung Krefeld e.V., Adlerstr. 44, D-4150 Krefeld

Wirtschaftsverband Asbestzement e.V., Arbeits- und Umweltschutz; Kölner Str. 102–104, D-4040 Neuss

United Kingdom

International Union of Pure and Applied Chemistry (IUPAC), c/o Hoffman-La Roche & Co., Grenzacherstr. 124, CH Basel 2. Secr.: Bank, 2, Pound Way, Oxford, UK

Society of Chemical Industry (SCI), 14 Belgrave Square, London SW1

National Physical Laboratory (NPL), Teddington, Middlesex TW11 0LW

British Standards Institution (BSI), BS House, 2 Park Street, London W1Y 4AA

United States of America

American Society for Testing and Materials (ASTM), Philadelphia 3, Pa. 1916 Race Street

American Water Work Association (AWWA), 2 Park Avenue, New York, NY, 10016 USA

B.3 Measuring standards for surface area and pore size analysis

— AFNOR X 11-601 (1974): Determination of the specific surface per mass or volume of powders by flowmethods. Method of lea and Nurse[14].

— AFNOR X 11-621: Determination of the specific surface per mass of a powder by use of gas adsorption measurement.
BET method: Volumetric measurement of nitrogen adsorption at low temperature[14].
— ASTM Standard C 204-68 (1968): Standard for the determination of the fineness of Portland cement by air flow. Blaine-method[15].
— BS 4359: Method for the determination of the specific surface of powders[14].
Part I (1969): Nitrogen adsorption (BET method)
Part II (1971): Air permeability
Part III (1970): Determination from the particle size distribution
— DIN 66 131 (1973): Determination of the specific surface area of solids by gas adsorption according to the method of Brunauer, Emmett, and Teller (BET). Fundamentals[16].
— DIN 66 132 (1975): Determination of the specific surface area of solids by nitrogen adsorption. One-point differential method after Haul and Dümbgen[16].
— DIN 11 64 (1970) Portland-, rotary tubular kiln- and puzzolan cement. Fineness, Blaine method[16]
— DIN 66 127 (1976): Determination of the specific surface area of powder materials; method and instrument according to Blaine[16].
— VDI 2031 (1962): Determination of the fineness of dusts[17].
— VDI 2269 (1972): Microscopic investigation of fine particles. Survey[17].
— VDI 3491 (1975): Measurement of particles. Criteria and test methods for methods and instruments designed for the determination of particles in gases. Terms and definitions[17].
— IUPAC (1972): Manual of Symbols and Terminology, Appendix 2, Part I: Colloid and Surface Chemistry[10].

There are also a variety of standards for testing the porosity of building materials[18], leather, laquer, foils, insulators, paper, etc., which, in general, are concerned with the measurement or detection of macropores.

B.4 Manufacturers of reference materials

An inquiry made by the European Community Bureau of Reference (BCR)[19] revealed that in many industries many factories use and produce their own reference material. For the calibration of measuring instruments most manufacturers will provide reference samples for their clients. Also a variety of reference materials are commercially available; many of them certified by recognized authorities.

— BCR is just preparing a variety of surface area and pore size reference materials, covering the whole range of the instruments described in this book. (BCR, 200 rue de la Loi, B-1049 Brussels)

— Duke Standards offers about 90 inorganic, organic, and biological reference materials. The particle size range is between 0.01 to 18 μm, the specific surface area between 0.6 and 1000 $m^2 g^{-1}$. (Duke-Standards Co., 445 Sherman Avenue, Palo Alto, CA 94306, USA)
— Particle Information Service offers about 180 materials, among those with surface areas between 0.7 and 1000 $m^2 g^{-1}$. (Particle Information Service, Inc., P.O. Box 702, 222 Granite Hill Road, Grands Pass, Oreg. 97526, USA)
— SCI/IUPAC/NPL offers various reference materials. For surface area and pore size analysis some carbons, silica gels, and molecular sieves are certified. The materials are sold by the National Physical Laboratory, Division of Chemical Standard, Teddington, Middlesex TW11 0LW
— Service des Materiaux de Référence offers various powdered materials (organic, inorganic, and biological)[20]. (SMR-LNE; 1, rue Gaston Boissier, F-75015 Paris)
— Test dust: Alumina, quartz, feldspar, street dust (Loughborough University, Loughborough, UK; Carborundum Co., UK; A.C. Delco, UK; Spark Plug Co., USA; Quarzwerke GmbH, Postfach 1780, D-5020 Frechen 1, Germany; Wäschereiforschung e.V., Adlerstr. 44, D-4150 Krefeld, Germany)
— Textile fibres (US Department of Agriculture, Washington, DC)
— Slate according to DIN 70 (IKO Industriekohle GmbH, Schmielenfeldstr. 82, D-4370 Marl, Germany)

Appendix C

Data on Materials

C.1 Cross-sectional area of adsorbed molecules

The table is mostly based on the work of McClellan and Harnsberger[21]. It has been confirmed that until 1982 no similar compilation of such data has been made. For practical use some of the data have been condensed; for more details compare the original paper. Doubtful data are set in parentheses. Temperatures specified are connected either to area values calculated from liquid densities or to values derived from adsorption measurements. Average values are derived from all reliable adsorption results in the McClellan/Harnsberger table.

Table C.1   Cross-sectional area of adsorbed molecules

Adsorbate compound name (formula)	Area per molecule (nm²)			Adsorbent compound name (formula)	T (K)	Area per molecule from sorption measurement (nm²)	average value	recommended value
	from van der Waals' constant	from liquid density at boiling point	from model					
argon (Ar)	.136	.114	.138	aluminium foil (Al)	78		.147	.138 (.142)
				aluminium oxide (Al₂O₃)	77–90	.179		
					77	(.248)		
					87	.154–.166		
				boron nitride (BN)	78	.143		
				cadmium oxide (CdO)	63–76	.140		
				diamond (C)	78–90	.128		
				graphite graphitized carbon (C)	78	.111–.138		
					90	.128		
				coal (C)	89	.133		
				graphon (C)	88	.144		
				caesium iodide (CsI)	77	.133		
				iron oxide (Fe₂O₃)	78	.166		
				magnesium oxide (MgO)	78	.166–.178		
					90	.178		
				molybdenum (Mo)	78–90	.143		
				nickel oxide (NiO)	78	.154		
				nickel hydroxide (NiOH₂)	78	.136		
				potassium chloride (KCl)	88	.139		
				silicon dioxide (SiO₂)	78	.147–.176		
					90	.143		

435

Adsorbate				Adsorbent	Temp		
				silver iodide (AgI)	78	.100	
				titanium dioxide (TiO₂)	78	.166	
				anatase (TiO₂)	90	.143	
				rutile (TiO₂)	77	.138	
				anatase (TiO₂-HI)	77	.166–.169	
					90	.182	
				zirconium (Zr)	77–90	.182	
				cement paste	78	.193	
					90	.160	
				glass	78	.137	
				polypropylene	83	.138	
				polytetrafluorethylene	84	.138	
arsine (AsH₃)				arsenic (As)	94.5	.11	
dichlorodifluoromethane (Freon-12) (CCl₂F₂)	.29		.167–.181	coal (C)	240	.40	
trichlorofluoromethane (CCl₃F)				graphitized carbon (C)	195–286	.276	
carbon tetrachloride (CCl₄)	.344	.323	.234	graphitized carbon (C)	233–323	.289	.392
				graphitized carbon (C)	293	.37–.44	
				graphite charcoal (C)	273	.407	
				magnesium oxide (MgO)	298	.421	
				nickel oxide (NiO)	298	.445	
				silicon dioxide (SiO₂)	299	(.636)	
carbon tetrachloride (CF₄)	.220		.139	faujasite	466.1	.227	
				polypropylene	142	.214	
				polytetrafluorethylene	150	.217	.219
dichlorofluoromethane (CHCl₂F)	.272	.257	.154–192	silver, tungsten, zinc oxide, glass, monel (Ag, W, ZnO)	{195, 273}	.375, .401	
chloroform (CHCl₃)	.295	.285	.183–197	graphitized carbon (C)	223–323	.279	
formic acid (CH₂O₂)	.165	.199	.106–158	silicon dioxide (SiO₂)	299	(.547)	
methane (CH₄)		.158	.106	silicon dioxide (SiO₂)	311	.1338	.178
		.159			77		
		.161			89		
		.164			109		
					113–143		

Table C.1 (*continued*)

Adsorbate compound name (formula)	Area per molecule (nm²) from van der Waals' constant	from liquid density at boiling point	from model	Adsorbent compound name (formula)	T (K)	Area per molecule from sorption measurement (nm²)	average value	recommended value
methanol (CH_4O)	.222	.18	.122–.140	ammoniumphosphomolybdate ((NH_4)$PO_4 \cdot$12MoO_3)	90	.150	.219	
				carbon (C)	70–82	.173–.18		
				graphitized carbon (C)	113–143	.166		
				graphitized carbon (C)	128	.181		
				activated charcoal (C)		.194		
				sodium bromide (NaBr)	65–75	.168		
				silicium dioxide (SiO_2)	70–82	.173		
				Linde 5A	70–82	.173		
				aluminium oxide (Al_2O_3)	293–298	.187–.272		
				aluminium oxide (Al_2O_3)	298	.241		
				aluminium oxide (Al_2O_3-ZnO)	298	.198–.264		
				carbon (C)	293	.185		
				graphite (C)	273–302	.141–.16		
				graphitized carbon (C)	293	.160		
				charcoal (C)	298	.248		
				magnesium dioxide (MgO)	273	.221		
				silicium dioxide (SiO_2)	298	.157–.310		
				SiO_2-Al_2O_3		.25		
				attapulgite	308–338	.167		

26-30 Ampules *(handwritten margin note)*

Substance				Adsorbent	T	Value	
...(continued)		.131		graphitized carbon (C)		.377	
methylamine (C...)				faujasite	616	.377	
1,2-dichloro-1,1,2,2-tetra-fluoroethane (C₂Cl₂F₄)	.35		.148–.260	faujasite	576	.402	
perfluorethane (C₂F₆)			.137–.211	faujasite	496	.304	
				faujasite	526	.330	−.220
acetylene (C₂H₂)	.185	.187	.062–.147	carbon (C)	195	.197	
				activated charcoal (C)	198	.198	
				glass	195	.222	
				magnesium oxide (MgO)	193	.2650	
1,2-dichlorethylene (C₂H₂Cl₂)		.278	.124–.286	homoionic kaolinite (Al₂O₃·2SiO₂)	301	.422	
chloroethylene (C₂H₂Cl)		.249	.117–.203	homoionic kaolinite (Al₂O₃·2SiO₂)	273	.368	
				(Al₂O₃·2SiO₂)	133		
ethylene (C₂H₄)	.201 (X-ray: .176)	.206	.092–.170	activated charcoal (C)	183	.231	
				aluminium oxide (Al₂O₃)	298	.312–.396	.354
				Al₂O₃–ZnO	275	.319–.379	
				SiO₂	311	.1958	
				graphitized carbon (C)	293	.26–.30	—
1,2-dichloroethane (C₂H₄Cl₂)	.306	.281	.223–.271	aluminium oxide (Al₂O₃)	308	(.63)	
acetic acid (C₂H₄O₃)	.305	.229	.155–.207	graphite (C)	195	.232	
					273	.261–.297	
				charcoal (C)	195	.232	
					273	.30	
chloroethane (C₂H₅Cl)	.272	.260	.141–.166	graphitized carbon (C)	195	.232–.326	.301
					278	.316	
					273	.333	
					298	.372	
iodoethane (C₂H₅I)	.282		.170–.173	iron (Fe)	348	.266	
				glass spheres	342	.29	
				porous glass	348	.20	

Table C.1 (*continued*)

Adsorbate: compound name (formula)	Area per molecule (nm^2): from van der Waals' constant	Area per molecule (nm^2): from liquid density at boiling point	Area per molecule (nm^2): from model	Adsorbent: compound name (formula)	T (K)	Area per molecule from sorption measurement (nm^2)	average value	recommended value
ethane (C_2H_6)	.217	.227	.104–153		185			
					87		.230	.213 (.205)
				ammoniumphosphomolybdate ($(NH_4)_3PO_4 \cdot 12MoO_3$)	173	.246		
				carbon (C)	195	.259		
				graphitized carbon (C)	148–213	.227		
				sodium chloride (X-ray: .317) (KCl)	90	.23		
				anatase (TiO_2-HI)	90	.24		
				sodium chloride (X-ray: .295) (NaCl)	90	.23		
				quartz beds (SiO_2)	255	.205		
				uranium oxide (UO_2)	87	.213		
					90	.205		
				glass beds	90	.205		
				glass tubes	87	.205		
				soils	195	.255		
				Fuller's earth	187	(.268)		

Compound				Adsorbent	Temp		
ethanol (C₂H₆O)	.257	.231	.128–.188				
				aluminium oxide (Al₂O₃)	298	.202–.360	.283
				Al₂O₃-ZnO	298	.286–.349	
				graphite (C)	293	.22	
				silicium dioxide (SiO₂)	298	.220–.378	
				attapulgite	283–343	.246	
				glass	273	.20	
1,2-diaminoethane (C₂H₈N₂)			.156–.219				
				Al₂O₃	298	.255–.290	
				Al₂O₃-ZnO	298	.255–.290	
perfluoropropane (F₆)			.202–.281				
				faujasite	616	.465	
				faujasite	676	.485	
propene (C₃H₆)							
				graphitized carbon (C)	218–238	.30	
				silicium dioxide (SiO₂)	218–238	.39	
acetone (C₃H₆O)							
				carbon (C)	293	.167	
				graphitized carbon (C)	293	.34	
propionic acid (C₃H₆O₂)	.314	.275	.202–.235				
				SiO₂	311	.2501	
chloropropane (C₃H₇Cl)	.324	.274	.158–.267				
				NiO, MgO	298	.425	
propane (C₃H₈)	.316	.31	.173–.252		231		
	.27	.273	.157–.208				
				ammoniumphosphomolybdate ((NH₄)₃PO₄·12MoO₃)	209	.355	.364
				aluminium oxide (Al₂O₃)	273	.39	
				carbon (C)		.40	
				graphitized carbon (C)	218–238	.32	
				cativated charcoal (C)	234	.360	
				Fuller's earth	228	.358	
2-propanol (C₃H₈O)	.308	.272	.194–.253				
				aluminium oxide (Al₂O₃)	298	.250–.402	.328
				Al₂O₃-ZnO	298	.372–.443	
				germanium (Ge)	298	(.27–.36)	
				iron oxide (Fe₂O₃)	298	(.31–.37)	
				titanium oxide (TiO₂)	293	.210	
				titanium dioxide (TiO₂)	298	(.37)	
				rutile (TiO₂)	298	.266	
				silicium dioxide (SiO₂)	293	.210	
				silicium dioxide (SiO₂)	299	.340	

Table C.1 (continued)

Adsorbate compound name (formula)	Area per molecule (nm²) from van der Waals' constant	Area per molecule (nm²) from liquid density at boiling point	Area per molecule (nm²) from model	Adsorbent compound name (formula)	T (K)	Area per molecule from sorption measurement (nm²)	average value	recommended value
2-propanol (C_3H_8O)	.299	.277	.201–.242	aluminium oxide (Al_2O_3)	298	.306–.432	.388	
				Al_2O_3-ZnO	298	.367–.442		
perflourobetan	.415		.204–.321	faujasite	716	.518		
				faujasite	576	.553	.403	
furan (C_4H_4O)		.266	.144–.270	aluminium oxide (Al_2O_3)	293	.352–.40		
				carbon (C)	296	.40		
				silicium dioxide (SiO_2)	296	.43–.438		
thiophene (C_4H_4S)	.298	.282	.181–.307	nickel (Ni)	298	.33		
butadiene (C_4H_6)				carbon (C)	273	.329		
1-butene (C_4H_8)	.307	.305	.154–.251		267		.385	
				aluminium oxide (Al_2O_3)	273	.427		
				carbon (C)	273	.378–.406		
				graphitized carbon (C)	273	.378		
				SiO_2-Al_2O_3	195	.315		
cis-2-butene (C_4H_8)				carbon (C)	273	.385		
trans-2-butene (C_4H_8)	.305	.313	.176–.278	carbon (C)	273	.334		
butyric acid ($C_4H_8O_2$)	.335	.316	.200–.327	kaolinite ($Al_4Si_4O_{10}(OH)_8$)	273	.374		
				graphitized carbon (C) (SiO_2)	311	.3135		
1-chlorobutane (C_4H_9Cl)			.197–.226	rutile (TiO_2)	293	.43		
					298	.462		

Adsorbate				Adsorbent	Temperature	Value
butane (C$_4$H$_{10}$)	.320	.323	.245–.303		261	.448
					273	.444 (.469)
				ammonium phosphomolybdate (NH$_4$)$_3$PO$_4$·12MoO$_3$)	250	.441
				aluminium oxide (Al$_2$O$_3$)	273	.371–.494
				barium sulfate (BaSO$_4$)	273	.51
						.47
				carbon (C)	273	.32–.451
				carbon (C)	273	.397
				graphitized carbon (C)	303–315	.42
				graphitized carbon (C)	273	.415
				graphite (C)	273	.421–.534
				activated charcoal (C)	273	.420
				nickel oxide (NiO)	273	.376–.534
				silicium dioxide (SiO$_2$)	273	.376
				titanium dioxide (TiO$_2$)	273	(.57)
				uranium dioxide (UO$_2$)	156	.425
				zinc (Zn)	273	.41–.52
				zinc oxide (ZnO)	273	.372
				Fuller's earth	273	.470
				glass	273	.469
						(.558)
				porous glass	195	.434
				metal	273	.49
				metal	195	.434
					273	.469
2-methylpropane (C$_4$H$_{10}$)	.320	.323	.245–.303		261	.507
				aluminium oxide (Al$_2$O$_3$)	273	.485–.57
				carbon (C)		.51
				charcoal (C)	255	.474
				charcoal (C)	273	.504
				silicium dioxide (SiO$_2$)	273	.485–.57

Table C.1 (continued)

Adsorbate compound name (formula)	Area per molecule (nm²)			Adsorbent compound name (formula)	T (K)	Area per molecule from sorption measurement (nm²)	average value	recommended value
	from van der Waals' constant	from liquid density at boiling point	from model					
1-butanol (C₄H₁₀O)	.321	.312	.17–.33	aluminium oxide (Al₂O₃)	298	.365–.407	.354	
				graphite (C)	298	.353		
				zinc oxide (ZnO)	293	.410		
2-butanol (C₄H₁₀O)	.20	.313	.176–.30	aluminium oxide (Al₂O₃)	298	.317–.476	.394	
				(Al₂O₃-ZnO)	298	.488		
2-methyl-1-propanol (C₄H₁₀O)	.319		.222–.273	aluminium oxide (Al₂O₃)	298	.306–.468	.401	
				(Al₂O₃-ZnO)	298	.440–.518		
2-methyl-2-propanol (C₄H₁₀O)	.337		.226–.307	aluminium oxide (Al₂O₃)	298	.362–.392	.395	
				(Al₂O₃-ZnO)	298	.488		
ethyl ether (C₄H₁₀O)	.353	.338	.19–.315	carbon (C)	293	.42		
diethylamine (C₄H₁₁N)	.361	.342	.268–.31	(SiO₂)	298	.432		
n-butylamine (C₄H₁₁N)		.309	.20–.32					
pyridine (C₅H₅N)			.39–.44	graphite (C)	293	.39		
				graphitized carbon (C)	293	.382		
				carbon (C)	273	.47		
cyclopentane (C₅H₁₀)	.321	.495	.245–.262	graphitized carbon (SiO₂)	293	.385		
					293	.42		

443

Compound		Value	Value	Range
1-methyl-2-butene	(C$_5$H$_{10}$)	.365		.22–.31
2-methyl-2-butene	(C$_5$H$_{10}$)			
1-pentane	(C$_5$H$_{10}$)		.349	.184–.34
2-pentane	(C$_5$H$_{10}$)		.370	.286–.34
methyl isobutyrate	(C$_5$H$_{10}$O$_2$)	.40	.362	.225–.34
pentane	(C$_5$H$_{12}$)	.37		
2,2-dimethylpropane (neopentane)	(C$_5$H$_{12}$)	.365		.28–.29
2-methylbutane	(C$_5$H$_{12}$)	.37	.351	.26–.34
1-pentanol	(C$_5$H$_{12}$O)			.19–.36
benzene	(C$_6$H$_6$)	.325	.32	.16–.34

Adsorbent	Temp	Value	Value
(Al$_2$O$_3$)	293–423	.46–.49	
(Al$_2$O$_3$-Cr$_2$O$_3$) carbon (C)	273	.57	
carbon (C)	293	.467	
(Al$_2$O$_3$-Cr$_2$O$_3$-K$_2$O)	293	.57	
anatase (TiO$_2$)	293	.493	
carbon (C)	273	.478	
carbon (C)	293	.377	
	293		.492
ammoniumphosphomolybdate ((NH$_4$)$_3$PO$_4$·12MoO$_3$)	273	.533	
aluminium oxide (Al$_2$O$_3$)	298	.332	
aluminium oxide (Al$_2$O$_3$)	293	.45–.636	
aluminium oxide (δ-Al$_2$O$_3$)	293	.45	
(Al$_2$O$_3$-ZnO)	298	.515–.693	
carbon (C)	273	.53	
carbon (C)	283	.371	
graphitized carbon (C)	293	.450	
graphite (C)		.46	
silver (Ag)	293	.46–.54	
anatase (TiO$_2$)	293	.523	
glass spheres	293	.64	
porous glass	293	.56	
carbon (C)	273	.62	
carbon (C)	227–293	.57	
graphitized carbon (C)	261	.41	
(Al$_2$O$_3$-Cr$_2$O$_3$-K$_2$O)	293–423	.56	
(Al$_2$O$_3$)	298	.276–.460	.388
(Al$_2$O$_3$-ZnO)	298	.378–.456	
	353		
aluminium oxide (Al$_2$O$_3$)	293	(.314)	.436
boehmite (Al$_2$O$_3$)	293	.391	.430

Table C.1 (*continued*)

Adsorbate compound name (formula)	Area per molecule (nm^2) from van der Waals' constant	Area per molecule (nm^2) from liquid density at boiling point	Area per molecule (nm^2) from model	Adsorbent compound name (formula)	T (K)	Area per molecule from sorption measurement (nm^2)	average value	recommended value
benzene (*continued*)				barium sulphate ($BaSO_4$)	323	(.61–.69)		
				carbon (C)	273	.465		
				carbon (C)	293	.440		
				carbon (C)		.39–.59		
				graphitized carbon (C)	293	.40–.483		
				graphite (C)	279	.41		
				(Cr_2O_3-Al_2O_3-K_2O)	293	.50		
				gold (Au)	296	.45		
				iron (Fe)	348	.46		
				magnesium oxide (MgO)		.36		
				silicium dioxide (SiO_2)		.41		
				silicium dioxide (SiO_2)	293	.36–.527		
				silicium dioxide (SiO_2)	299	.518		
				silicium dioxide (SiO_2)	311	(.291)		
				silicium dioxide (SiO_2)	339	(.222)		
				glass spheres	348	.38		
				porous glass	348	(.57)		
cyclohexane (C_6H_{12})	.367	.363	.294–.35		298		.417	
				aluminium oxide (Al_2O_3)	298	.31–.434		
				carbon (C)	293	.48		
				graphite (C)	279	.38		

445

Substance				Adsorbent	T (K)	value
				$(Cr_2O_3\text{-}Al_2O_3\text{-}K_2O)$	293	.53
				silicium dioxide (SiO_2)	293	(.111–.136)
				silicium dioxide (SiO_2)	298	.45
						.433–.465
						(.768)
methylcyclopentane (C_6H_{12})	.42	.413	.19–.38	silicium dioxide (SiO_2)	293	.483
n-hexane (C_6H_{14})				graphitized carbon (C)	293	.46
					298	.562
					298	.606
				ammoniumphosphomolybdate $((NH_4)_3PO_4\cdot12MoO_3)$	293	.352–.412
				aluminium oxide (Al_2O_3)	293	.72–.81
				barium sulphate $(BaSO_4)$		.515
				carbon (C)	273	.577
				carbon (C)	293	.51–.515
				graphitized carbon (C)		.51
				magnesium oxide (MgO)	298	.474–.740
				silicium dioxide (SiO_2)		.72
				quartz (SiO_2)		
2,2-dimethylbutane (C_6H_{14})	.432	.402		metals oxides } sulphides	273	.589
		.417	.402	aluminium oxide $(\gamma\text{-}Al_2O_3)$	293	.46
2-methylpentane (C_6H_{14})			.33–.43	graphitized carbon (C)	293	.460
propyl ether $(C_6H_{14}O)$				$(\gamma\text{-}Al_2O_3)$	293	.485
triethylamin $(C_6H_{15}N)$				(MgO)	298	.624
				(SiO_2)	593	.43
perflourmethyl cyclohexan (C_2F_{11})	.48		.37–.48	jaujasite	616	.636
				jaujasite	576	.659
toluene (C_4H_8)	.385	.344	.18–.39	graphitized carbon (C)	298	.552
				iron (Fe)	293	.46
					348	.59–.62
				magnesium oxide (MgO)	298	.486
				molybdenum disulfide (MoS_2)	296	.672

Table C.1 (continued)

Adsorbate compound name (formula)	Area per molecule (nm²) from van der Waals' constant	from liquid density at boiling point	from model	Adsorbent compound name (formula)	T (K)	Area per molecule from sorption measurement (nm²)	average value	recommended value
toluene (continued)				nickel oxide (NiO)	298	.486		
				silicon dioxide (SiO₂)	293	.494		
				silicon dioxide (SiO₂)	299	.582		
				zinc oxide (ZnO)	298	.474		
				glass spheres	348	.46		
				porous glass	348	.61–.62		
n-heptane (C₇H₁₆)	.47	.427	.21–.44	ammoniumphosphomolybdate ((NH₄)₃PO₄·12MoO₃)	298	.678	.631	
				aluminium oxide (Al₂O₃)	298	.54–.66		
				barium sulphate (BaSO₄)	298	.72		
				graphitized carbon (C)	293	.573		
				iron oxide (Fe₂O₃)	290	.632		
				iron oxide (Fe₂O₃)	296	.657		
				iron oxide (Fe₂O₃)	303	.692		
				magnesium oxide (MgO)	298	.356		
				molybdenum disulphite (MoS₂)	299	.652		
				nickel oxide (NiO)	298	.690		
				silicon dioxide (SiO₂)	298	.54–.836		
				silicon dioxide (SiO₂)	311	(.292)		
				titanium dioxide (TiO₂)	298	.578–.64		

Compound				Adsorbent	T	value	
2,2-dimethylpentane (C_7H_{16})	.452	.431	.33-.44	zinc oxide (ZnO)	298	.598	
2-methylhexane (C_7H_{16})				oxides sulphides }	298	.64	
				(SiO_2)	298	.36	
perflouromethylcyclohexane (C_8F_{26})			.36-.54	graphitized carbon (C)	338.6	.540	
				jaujasite	616	.700	
ethylbenzene (C_8H_{10})				jaujasite	676	.676	
m-xylene				(SiO_2)	293	.547	
p-xylene				(SiO_2)	293	.558	
n-octane (C_8H_{18})	.508	.466	.15-.51	(SiO_2)	293	.538	
2,2,4-trimethylpentane (C_8H_{18})				ammonium phosphomolybdate ((NH_4)$_3PO_4 \cdot 12MoO_3$)	302	.750	
				graphitized carbon (C)	293	.610	
				magnesium oxide (MgO)		.58	
				silicium dioxide (SiO_2)	293	.644	
				graphitized carbon (C)	293	.545	
di-n-butylamine ($C_8H_{19}N$)	.478	.472	.30-.53	silicium dioxide (SiO_2)	293	.580	
propylbenzene (C_9H_{12})		.41	.19-.51	(SiO_2)	298	.544	
isopropylbenzene (C_9H_{12})	.478	.412	.19-.51	(SiO_2)	293	.612	
1,3,5-trimethylbenzene (C_9H_{12})				(SiO_2)	293	.623	
				graphitized carbon (C)	293	.78	
n-nonane (C_9H_{20})	.509	.488	.22-.55	silicium dioxide (SiO_2)	293	.612	
				ammonium phosphomolybdate ((NH_4)$_3PO_4 \cdot 12MoO_3$)	299.3	.844	
2,6-dimethyl-2,6-octadiene ($C_{10}H_{18}$)		.484	.34-.56	carbon (C)	373	.80-.84	
n-decane ($C_{10}H_{22}$)	.610	.535	.17-.61	carbon (C)	373	.86-.96	.150
carbon monoxide (CO)	.156	.168	.7-.10				
cadmium oxide (CdO)				cadmium oxide (CdO)	78	.147	

448

Table C.1 (continued)

Adsorbate compound name (formula)	Area per molecule (nm²) from van der Waals' constant	from liquid density at boiling point	from model	Adsorbent compound name (formula)	T (K)	Area per molecule from sorption measurement (nm²)	average value	recommended value
carbon monoxide (continued)				cadmium oxide (CdO)	90	.160		
				graphite (C)	195	.20		
				cesium iodide (CsI)	93–79	.160		
				germanium (Ge)	77	.10		
				nickel oxide (NiO)	78	.125		
				nickel hydroxide (Ni(OH)$_2$)	78	.129		
				anatase (TiO$_2$)	78	.147		
				anatase (TiO$_2$)	90	.162		
carbon dioxide (CO$_2$)	.164	.170	.05–.11	carbon (C)	195	.205–.244	.218	.218
				graphitized carbon (C)	195	(.142)		
				magnesium oxide (MgO)	193	.221		
				silicon dioxide (SiO$_2$)	196	.216		
				sodium dioxide (NaCl)	195	(.144)		
					308	.19–.209		
				titanium dioxide (TiO$_2$)	195	.216		
				anatas (TiO$_2$)	195	.254		
				attapulgite		.205–.268		
				cellulose	195	.19		
				polyvinylidenechloride	195	.19		

Substance				Adsorbent	T	value	
carbon disulphide (CS₂)	.235	.224	.17–.17	glass	195	.201	
				many solids (Zn)	195	(.141)	
				glass spheres	273	.23	
chlorine triflouride (ClF₃)			.13–.19	porous glass	293	.59	
				(NiF₂)	293	.72	
hydrogen (H₂)				graphitized carbon (C)	282	.22	
				platinum (Pl)	90–130	.123	.125 .125
water (H₂O)	.13	.105	.06–.08			.184	.125
				ammonium phosphomolybdate ((NH₄)₃PO₄·12MoO₃)	298	.086	
				calcium carbonate (CaCO₃)	298	.139	
				graphitized carbon (C)	288–298	.105	
				graphitized carbon (C)	292	.106	
				charcoal (C)	303	.079	
				germanium (Ge)	298	.118	
				gold (Au)	298	.17	
				iron oxide (Fe₂O₃)	291	.108	
				silicium dioxide (SiO₂)	298	.105–.198	
				silicium dioxide (SiO₂)	298	(.246)	→ 10.6 ℓ²/mole
				silicium dioxide (SiO₂)	293	(.24–.31)	
				silicium dioxide (SiO₂)	285	.130–.187	
				silicium dioxide annealed (SiO₂)	288–298	.133	
				silicium dioxide annealed (SiO₂)	288–298	.144	
				silver iodide (AgI)	253	.10	
				rutile (TiO)	298	.151	
				attapulgite	323	.108	
				glass	300	.195	
				kalinites	293	.126	
				montmorillonites	298	.098–.148	
hydrogen sulphide (H₂S)	.165		.08–.10	glass spheres	194	.21	
iodine (I₂)			.10–.17	barium chloride (BaCl₂)		.221	
				carbon (C)	298	.40	
				graphitized carbon (C)	293	.237	

450

Table C.1 (continued)

Adsorbate compound name (formula)	Area per molecule (nm²) from van der Waals' constant	Area per molecule (nm²) from liquid density at boiling point	Area per molecule (nm²) from model	Adsorbent compound name (formula)	T (K)	Area per molecule from sorption measurement (nm²)	average value	recommended value
krypton (Kr)	.156		.112		77		.202	.202 (.195)
				aluminium oxide (Al_2O_3)	78	.208		
				calcium carbonate $(CaCO_3)$	89	.215		
				carbon, charcoal (C)	195	.210		
				graphitized carbon (C)	90	(.145)		
				oxidized germanium (Ge)	78	.204		
				nickel oxide $(NiO_4,16H_2O)$	78	.161		
				nickel hydroxide $(Ni(OH)_2)$	78	.201		
				silicon dioxide (SiO_2)	78	.185–.236		
				silicon dioxide (SiO_2)	89	.213		
				tridymite (SiO_2)	77	.195		
				quartz (SiO_2)	77	.195		
				sodium bromide $(NaBr)$	66–83	.171		
				anatase (TiO_2)	78	.195–.218		
				anatase (TiO_2)	90	.218		
				uranium dioxide (UO_2)	78	.21		
				uranium dioxide – partly fluorided (UO_2)	78	.21		
				zinc oxide (ZnO)	78	.208		
				zirconium (Zr)	77–90	.215		

Adsorbate				Adsorbent	T		
ammonia (NH_3)	.150	.129	.07-.10	glass	68	.208-.215	
				glass	78	.216	
				polyethylene	77	.195	
				nylon	77	.195	
				many solids			.140
nitrogen (N_2)	.153	.162	.07-.10	graphitized carbon (C)	195	.114-.160	
				charcoal (C)	195	.148	
				charcoal (C)	235	.149	
				silicon dioxide (SiO_2)	239	.095-.165	
				attapulgite	373	.132	
				aluminium oxide (Al_2O_3)	77	.125-.133	
				silicon dioxide (SiO_2)	78	.129	
				sodium chloride (NaCl)	77	.163	
				anatase (TiO_2)	78	.163-.177	
				titanium dioxide (TiO_2)	77	.129	.162
nitrous oxide (N_2O)	.169	.168	.07-.13	silicon dioxide (SiO_2)	194,5	.193	
				silicon dioxide (SiO_2)	119	.204	
nitric oxide dimer (N_2O_2)				carbon (C)	258-323	.314	
nitrogen tetroxide (N_2O_4)				titanium dioxide (TiO_2)	17	.237	
neon (Ne)				carbon (C)	78	.100	.136 .136
oxygen (O_2)	.135	.141	.06-.09	aluminium foil (Al)	77	.203	
				cadmium oxide (CdO)	78	.137	
				cadmium oxide (CdO)	90	.134	
				carbon (C)	90	.135	
				charcoal (C)	88	.159	
				caesium iodide (CsI)	73	.134	
				molybdenum (Mo)	78-90	.153	
				potassium chloride (KCl)	88	.140	
				silicon dioxide (SiO_2)	90	.135	
				titanium dioxide (TiO_2)	90	.135	
				anatase (TiO_2)	78	.175	

Table C.1 (continued)

Adsorbate compound name (formula)	Area per molecule (nm²)			Adsorbent compound name (formula)	T (K)	Area per molecule from sorption measurement (nm²)	average value	recommended value
	from van der Waals' constant	from liquid density at boiling point	from model					
oxygen (continued)				rutile (TiO₂)	78	.138		
				attapulgite	79	.143		
				cement paste	90	.176		
sulphur hexaflouride (SF₆)	.267		.208	graphitized carbon (C)	197–355	.23		
				jaujasite	496	.273		
				jaujasite	526	.290		
sulphur dioxide (SO₂)	.200		.13–.16	graphitized carbon (C)	273	.138–.194		
				charcoal (C)	273	.271		
xenon (Xe)	.185	.186	.137	carbon (C)	164	(.324)		
				graphitized carbon (C)	78–90	.199		
				charcoal (C)	273	(.282)		
				copper (Cu)	149	.25		
				nickel film (Ni)	273	.186–.268		
				nickel film (Ni)	90	.195–.210		
				silver iodide (AgI)	78	.181		
				titanium dioxide (TiO₂)	90	.273		
				tungsten film (W)	148	.230		
				glass	148	.244–.268	232	.232 (.250)
				inactive glass	90	.249		
				active glass	78	.295		

452

Table C.2 Data on cryogenic gases and liquids

Substance		Boiling point at 1 bar (K)	Melting point (K)	Gas density at 1 bar, 273 K (kg · m^{-3})	Liquid density at 1 bar (kg · m^{-3})	Volume ratio gas/liquid	Heat of vaporization (J)
helium	He	4.2	0.9	0.1785	125	700	20.5
hydrogen	H$_2$	20.3	14.1	0.0899	71	790	452.1
neon	Ne	27.1	24.4	0.8999	1207	1341	85.8
nitrogen	N$_2$	77.3	63.2	1.251	808	646	199.3
carbon monoxide	CO	81.6	74.1	1.250	793	634	
fluorine	F$_2$	85.0	53.6	1.696	1510	890	172.5
argon	Ar	87.2	83.9	1.784	1400	784	163.3
oxygen	O$_2$	90.1	54.7	1.429	1142	799	213.1
methane	CH$_4$	109.1	90.6	0.7168	415	578	510.3
krypton	Kr	119.7	116.5				
ozone	O$_3$	161.3	80.4				
xenon	Xe	165.0	161.2				
ethylene (ethene)	C$_2$H$_4$	169.4	104.0				
ethane	C$_2$H$_6$	184.5	89.8				
nitrous oxide	N$_2$O	184.6	182.3				
acetylene (ethyne)	C$_2$H$_2$	189.1	subl. 192.3				
carbon dioxide	CO$_2$	194.6	subl. 216.5				
ketene	C$_2$H$_2$O	217.1	122.1				
propylene (propene)	C$_3$H$_6$	225.7	87.8				
propane	C$_3$H$_8$	231.0	83.4				
ammonia	NH$_3$	239.7	195.4				
freon$_{12}$	CCl$_2$F$_2$	243.3	115.1				
isobutane	(CH$_3$)$_2$C$_2$H$_4$	261.4	113.7				
sulphur dioxide	SO$_2$	263.1	200.4				
butane	C$_4$H$_{10}$	272.6	134.7				
carbon disulphide	CS$_2$	319.4	162.3				
carbon tetrachloride	CCl$_4$	349.8	250				
benzene		353.2	278.6				

Table C.3   Conversion of units

Quantity	Old unit	SI and related units
length	1 Å	$0.1 \text{ nm} = 10^{-10} \text{ m}$
temperature	5/9 (°F − 32)	°C
		K .°C + 273.15
area	1 sq. inch	$6.4516 \text{ cm}^2 = 0.0006451 \text{ m}^2$
	1 sq. foot	0.0929 m^2
	1 Å²	$0.01 \text{ nm}^2 = 10^{-20} \text{ m}^2$
force	1 dyne	10^{-5} N
pressure	1 Torr = 1 mm Hg	$133 \text{ Pa} = 133 \text{ N m}^{-2} = 1.333 \text{ mbar}$
		$= 1.333 \cdot 10^{-3} \text{ bar}$
	1 μ	0.1333 Pa
	1 atm (phys.) = 760 Torr	$1.013 \cdot 10^5 \text{ Pa} = 1.013 \text{ bar}$
	1 psi (lb/sq. inch)	$6.89 \cdot 10^3 \text{ Pa} = 0.0689 \text{ bar}$
	1 lb/sq. foot	$4.79 \cdot 10^{-3} \text{ bar}$
	1 inch of Hg	$3.386 \cdot 10^3 \text{ Pa} = 0.03386 \text{ bar}$
	1 inch of H_2O	0.00254 bar
	1 m H_2O	0.1 bar
energy	1 cal	$4.1868 \text{ J} = 4.1868 \text{ N m} = 4.1868 \text{ W s}$
	1 cal$_{15°}$	4.1855 J
		1 kW h = 3.6 MJ
	1 erg	10^{-7} J

Appendix D

Commercially Available Instruments

The tables include all instruments available in 1982. The code numbers refer to the manufacturer's addresses compiled in Section D.5.

D.1 Thermobalances

Thermobalances are sensitive balances which can be used in wide temperature and pressure ranges.

D.2 Thermogravimetric instruments

Thermogravimetric instruments consist basically of a thermobalance and a program-controlled oven. Most of the models can be used under vacuum and in a wide pressure range using various gases.

D.3 Sorption meters, surface area and pore size measuring instruments

Table D.3 shows commercially available volumetric, gravimetric, and chromatographic instruments designed for surface area and pore size determination. They all make use of the measurement of the nitrogen isotherm at 77 K (or of one point of it), the argon isotherm at 77 K, or the krypton isotherm at 77 K or 90 K. Some may also be used for investigations with other gases. Thermogravimetric apparatus which exhibit the option for working under vacuum as listed in Table D.2 are also suitable for manual measurements of sorption isotherms. As well as these, simple testing equipment is available for the determination of the capacity of certain adsorbents, and there is a large variety of humidity measuring instruments.

D.4 Porosimeters

Table D.4 shows commercially available porosimeters with which pore size distributions can be measured: those are mercury porosimeters and the Zagar air/water porosimeter. Not included are the various simple instruments using water or air for testing the tightness or the porosity of building materials, etc. The name 'porosimeter' is also used for capacitance measuring instruments for the detection of failures in lacquer, insulating foils, etc.

Table D.1 Thermobalances

Manufacturer	Code no.	Model	Method of operation	Deflection sensor	Balance pans top	Balance pans lat.	Balance pans susp.	Max. load g	Smallest scale value g	Vacuum
Ainsworth	A1		electron. beam balance				2	200	10^{-7}	HV
Beckman	B1	LM 600	compensating beam balance	electromagn.			2	2.5	10^{-7}	HV
		LM 500					2	5	10^{-7}	HV
Berkeley	B2		quartz crystal	piezoelectric	1	—	—	10^{-4}	$5 \cdot 10^{-9}$	UHV
Cahn	C1	RG		photoelectr.			3	2.5	10^{-7}	HV
		RM 2		photoelectr.			1	5	$5 \cdot 10^{-6}$	HV
		1000		photoelectr.			2	100	$5 \cdot 10^{-7}$	HV
Chyo	C2	200 H	inclination balance	visual			1	200	10^{-4}	
		SL 5	quartz spring balance	visual			1	5	10^{-3}	HV
		SL 1	quartz spring balance	different. transformer			1	1	$5 \cdot 10^{-4}$	HV
CI Electronics	C3	Mk. 1	compensating beam balance	photoelectr.			2	0.5	$5 \cdot 10^{-6}$	HV
		Mk. 2					2	5	10^{-5}	HV
Linseis	L1	L 84	substituting beam balance	inductive	1		(1)	20	10^{-4}	
Netzsch	N1	409 E	substituting beam balance	inductive	1		1	20	10^{-5}	HV

Perkin-Elmer	P1	Ar-2	compensating beam balance	photoelectr.		2	5	10^{-7}	HV
Sartorius	S1	4401	compensating beam balance	electromagn.	(2)	2	25	10^{-6}	HV
		4431*	compensating beam balance	electromagn.	(2)	2	3	10^{-7}	HV
		4201	magnetic suspension at compensating beam balance	electromagn.		1	16	10^{-6}	UHV
SETARAM	S2	B 70	compensating beam balance	photoelectr.		1	100	10^{-5}	HV
		MTB10-8	compensating beam balance	electromagn.		2	10/100	$4 \cdot 10^{-7}$	HV
Ultramicro-balance	U1		compensating beam balance	photoelectr.		1	20	10^{-7}	UHV
Voland	V1	1100-11	compensating beam balance	electromagn.		2	1	$5 \cdot 10^{-7}$	HV
Worden	W1	4401	quartz spring balance	visual photo-electr.		1	100	10^{-5}	UHV

*Pressure (bar) = 150.

Table D.2 Thermogravimetric instruments

Manufacturer	Code no.	Model	Balance	Special features	Balance pans top	lat.	susp.	Max. load (g)	Smallest scale value (g)	Temp. min (K)	max (K)	Vacuum
Cahn	C1	Little Gen Gravim. Adsorpt.	compensat. beam bal.				2	2.5– 100	10^{-6}– 10^{-7}	77	900 900	HV HV
Chyo	C2	$TRDA_3$-H	compensat. beam balance	DTA	1			1	10^{-4}		1900	HV
		TR_1-160	inclinat. balance				1	160	10^{-4}		1800	HV
DuPont	D1	950	compensat. beam bal.		1			0.3	$2 \cdot 10^{-3}$		1500	HV
Fisher	F1	100 TGA	compensat. beam bal. (Cahn RG)				1	2.5	10^{-6}		1500	HV
Harrop	H1		(Cahn RG) (Cahn R100) compensat. beam bal.				3 2	2.5	10^{-7}	77	1900	HV
Heraeus	H2		compensat. beam bal. (CI Electronics)				2	1	10^{-6}		1300	—
Linseis	L1	L 83	compensat. beam bal. (Sartorius)	DTA at the balance pan	1		(2)	16	$5 \cdot 10^{-5}$		1800	HV
		L 81	compensat. beam bal.			1		15	10^{-5}	120	1800	HV

Manufacturer	Code	Instrument	Balance type	Description							
Messtec	M3	Kryo-Heiz-system	compensat. beam bal. (Cahn)	continuously adjust. cooling and heating system	1	1			83	900	HV
Mettler	M1	Therm-analyzer	compensat. substitut. beam balance	DTA at the balance pan	1	1	16/42	$3 \cdot 10^{-5}$	123	1900	HV
		TA 2000C	compensat. substitut. beam balance		1		6	10^{-5}		1500	HV
MOM	M2	Derivatograph	beam balance	balance also used as dilatometer	1	1	10	$5 \cdot 10^{-4}$	293	1800	HV
		Derivatograph Q	beam balance	balance also used as dialtometer quasi-isothermal TG	1	1	1	$2 \cdot 10^{-4}$		1800	
Netzsch	N1	STA 429	compensat. beam bal.	DTA at the balance pan	1	1	20	10^{-5}	113		HV
		STA 409	inductive subst.	DTA at the balance pan					293	1900	HV
		Thermo-gravimat	compensat. beam bal. (Sartorius)	program-controlled pressure control for the measurement of adsorption isotherms	(2)	2	3/25	10^{-8}	77	2500	HV
		Thermomat S	magnetic suspens. balance (Sartorius)	corrison-resist. quartz-PTFE version		1	16	10^{-5}	77	2000	HV
Perkin-Elmer	P1	TGS-2	compensat. beam balance	furnace in vacuum		2	5	10^{-7}	77	1300	HV
Rigaku	R1	Thermoflex	beam balance	dilatometric and viscosity measurem. by balance	1	1	450	$2 \cdot 10^{-7}$	293	1800	

Table D.2 (continued)

Manufacturer	Code no.	Model	Balance	Special features	Balance pans top	Balance pans lat.	Balance pans susp.	Max. load (g)	Smallest scale value (g)	Temp. min (K)	Temp. max (K)	Vacuum
SADAMEL	S5	17 AV	substitut. balance	radiation furnace; dilatometer	1			7	10^{-4}	293	1900	HV
SETARAM	S2	microthermo-analyseur	compensat. beam balance B70	combined cryostat/heater			1	100	10^{-5}	77	2700	HV
			compensat. beam balance MTB 10-8				2	10/100	$4 \cdot 10^{-7}$	77	2000	HV
Shimadzu	S3	TGA-20B	beam bal.	dilatometer	1			0.2	10^{-6}	293	1800	HV
Stanton Redcroft	S4	TG 750	comp. beam bal. (C.I. Electron.)	DTA			2	1	10^{-5}	293	1300	HV
		Mass-flow	analys. bal. with autom. balance of weight	DTA	1			20	10^{-4}	293	1800	HV
Stone/Columbia	C4	TGA-5B	comp. beam balance (Cahn – RG)				2	2.5	$2 \cdot 10^{-6}$	293	1900	HV
Theta	T1	Gravitronic	comp. beam bal. (Cahn)				2	100	$5 \cdot 10^{-7}$	120	2000	HV
Voland	V1	1100-11	comp. beam balance				2	1	$5 \cdot 10^{-7}$	293	1300	HV

*Pressure (bar) = 1 †Pressure (bar) = 190

Table D.3 Sorption meters, surface area and pore size measuring instruments

Manufacturer	Code no.	Instrument name	Model	Measuring gas	Measuring method	Relative pressure range	Pressure range (bar)	Temperature range (K)	Sample degassing
Carlo Erba	C5	Sorpty	1700	N_2	volumetric 1 point	0.3	0–0.3	77	vacuum, 1 Pa 320–570 K
		Sorptomatic			volumetric automatic	0–1	0–1	77	separate vacuum apparatus, 1 Pa 320–570 K
CEN	C6	Isothermegraph		N_2, non-corrosive gases	volumetric	0–1	0–1	77–298	vacuum, elevated temperature
Micromeritics	M4	High Speed Surface Area Analyzer	2200	N_2	volumetric 1 point	0.3	0.3	77	flushing gas 300–570 K
			2205	Ar	volumetric 1 point	0.3	0.3	77	flushing gas 300–570 K
		Orr Analyzer	2100	N_2, non-corrosive gases	volumetric	0–1	0–1.3	77–670	vacuum, 10^{-2} Pa, 300–670 K
		Digisorb	2500	N_2, Kr, non-corrosive gases	volumetric automatic	0–1	0–1.3	77–670	vacuum, 10^{-2} Pa, 300–670 K

462

Table D.3 *(continued)*

Manufacturer	Code no.	Instrument name	Model	Measuring gas	Measuring method	Relative pressure range	Pressure range (bar)	Temperature range (K)	Sample degassing
Netzsch	N1	Gravimat		N_2, Kr, non-corrosive gases	gravimetric automatic	0–1	0–1.2	77–800	vacuum 10^{-5} Pa, 300–800 K
		Thermo-Gravimat			gravimetric automatic	0–1	0–1.2	77–2500	vacuum 10^{-5} Pa, temperature program up to 2500 K
Quantachrome	Q1	Monosorb		N_2/He, non-corrosive gases	carrier gas, 1 point	0.3	1	77–298	separate flushing gas apparatus
		Quantasorb		N_2/He, Kr/He non-corrosive gases	carrier gas	0–0.3	1	77–298	separate flushing gas apparatus
Ströhlein	S6	Area-meter		N_2	volumetric-difference 1 point	0.3	0.3	77	separate flushing N_2 apparatus 300–600 K

Table D.4   Intrusion porosimeters

Manufacturer	Code no.	Maximum pressure (bar)	Pore width range (μm)	Sample volume (cm³)	Sensor	Liquid
Aminco	A2	345	0.04–300	6	contact	mercury
		1034	0.01–300	6	contact	mercury
		2068	0.006–300	6	contact	mercury
		4137	0.003–300	6	contact	mercury
Carlo Erba	C5	2000	0.004–7.5	15/20	contact	mercury
Micromeritics	M4	3445	0.004–354	15/20	contact	mercury
Netzsch	N1	1	1–300	20	flowmeter	water/air
Porous Materials	P2	345	0.04–500	15	contact	mercury
		690	0.02–500	15	contact	mercury
		1034	0.01–500	15	contact	mercury
		2068	0.006–500	15	contact	mercury
		4137	0.003–500	15	contact	mercury
Quantachrome	Q1	4137	0.002–108	15	capacitance	mercury

D.5 Manufacturers' addresses

A1   Ainsworth Division of Denver Instrument Co., 2050 South Pecos Street, Denver, Colorado 80223, USA
A2   Aminco, American Instrument Company, Silver Spring, Maryland 20910, USA
B1   Beckman Instruments, Inc.; Scientific Instruments Div., Fullerton, California 92634, USA
B2   Berkeley Controls Inc.; 2825 Laguna Canyoun Road, Laguna Beach, CA 95652, USA
C1   Cahn Instruments, Div. of Ventron Corp., 16207 South Carmenita Road, Cerritos, Calif. 90701, USA
C2   Chyo Balance Corp., 376-2 Tsukiyama-cho, Kuze, Minami-ku, Kyoto, Japan
C3   CI Electronics Ltd., Brunel Road, Churchfields, Salisbury, Wilts., England
C4   Columbia Scientific Industries, Inc., Analytical Instruments Div., 3625 Bluestein Boulevard, Austia, Texas 78762, USA
C5   Carlo Erba Strumentazione, Via Carlo Imbonati, 24, I-20159 Milano, Italy
C6   CEN, Division de Chimie, Saclay, France
D1   DuPont de Nemours & Co., Inc., Instruments Product Div., Wilmington, Delaware 19898, USA
F1   Fisher Scientific Co. Ltd., 711 Forbes Av., Pittsburgh, Pa. 15219, USA
H1   Harrop Laboratories, 3470 East Fifth Avenue, Columbus, Ohio 43219, USA
H2   W. C. Heraeus GmbH, Postfach 169, D-6450 Hanau, W. Germany
L1   Linseis KG, Vielitzer Str. 43, D-8672 Selb, W. Germany
M1   Mettler Instrumente, CH-8606 Greifensee, Switzerland
M2   MOM, Hungarian Optical Works, P.O. Box 52, H-1525 Budapest, Hungary
M3   Messtec KG, Friesenweg 4, D-2000 Hamburg 50, W. Germany
M4   Micromeritics Instrument Corporation, 5680 Goshen Springs Road, Norcross, Georgia 30093, USA
N1   Netzsch-Gerätebau GmbH, Wittelsbacherstr. 42, D-8672 Selb, W. Germany

464

P1   Perkin-Elmer Corp., Instrument Div., Norwalk, Connecticut 06852, USA
P2   Porous Materials, Inc., Cornell Industry Research Park, Ithaca, NY 14850, USA
Q1   Quantachrome Corporation, 6 Aerial Way, Syosset, New York 11791, USA
R1   Rigaku Corp., Segawa Bldg. 2–8 Kandasurugadai, Chiyoda-ku, Tokyo, Japan
S1   Sartorius Werke GmbH, Weender Landstr. 96–102, D-3400 Göttingen, W. Germany
S2   SETARAM, 101–103 Rue de Sèze, F-69451 Lyon, Cedex 3, France
S3   Shimadzu Seisakusho Ltd., 1 Nishinokyo-Kuwabaracho, Nakagyo-ku, Kyoto 604, Japan
S4   Stanton Redcroft (Div. of Oertling Ltd.), Copper Mill Lane, London SW17 0BN, England
S5   SADAMEL, Rue Jardinière 150, CH-2300 La Chaux de Fonds, Switzerland
S6   Ströhlein, Aderstr. 91, D-4000 Düsseldorf, W. Germany
T1   Theta Industries, Inc., 26 Valley Road, Port Washington, NY 11050, USA
U1   Ultramicrobalance Instruments, A.W. Czanderna, P.O. Box 27209, Denver, Colorado 80227, USA
V1   Voland Corp., 27 Centre Avenue, New Rochelle, NY 10802, USA
W1   Worden Quartz Products, Div. of Ruska Instruments, 6121 Hillcroft, Houston, Texas 77036, USA

References

1. E. Robens and R. Meyer, *Powder Metallurgy Int.*, **13**, 44 (1981)
2. R. Wilson, Some current work on particulate reference materials; paper presented at the Conference on Particle Size Analysis, Salford 1977
3. C. H. Giles, D. C. Havard, W. McMillan, T. Smith, and R. Wilson, in: S. J. Gregg, K. S. W. Sing, and H. F. Stoeckli (eds.), *Characterisation of Porous Solids*, Society of Chemical Industry, London, 1979, pp. 267–284
4. R. Meyer: Standardizing test methods for characterizing powders; paper presented at 'Powder Europa 78'
5. Short description and status of activities of B.C.R. Commission of the European Communities, BCR/100/76
6. E. Robens: Zertifizierte Referenzmaterialien und genormte Meßmethoden für feinteilige und poröse Substanzen; *Sprechsaal*, **110**, 12, 716–719 (1977)
7. R. Wilson, Some recently certified particle size reference materials. Paper presented at the 2nd European Symposium on Particle Characterisation, Nürnberg, Sept. 1979
8. Tätigkeitsbericht 1978/79 DIN Deutsches Institut für Normung, Berlin 1979
9. A. S. Joy: Work of the British Standards Institution Committee on Surface Area Determination, in: D. H. Everett, R. H. Ottewill (eds.), *Surface Area Determination*, Butterworths, London, 1970, p. 391–396
10. IUPAC, *Manuals of Symbols and Terminology*, Appendix 2, Part I: *Colloid and Surface Chemistry. Pure Appl. Chem.*, **31**, 578 (1976)
11. D. C. Havard and R. Wilson, Pore measurements on the SCI/IUPAC/NPL meso-porous silica surface area standard; *J. Colloid and Interface Science*, **57**, 2, 276–288 (1976)
12. B. Lippens, B. C. Linsen, and J. H. de Boer, *J. Catalysis*, **3** 32 (1964)
13. G. D. Halsey, *J. Chem. Phys.*, **16**, 931 (1948)
14. AFNOR Association française de normalisation, Tour d'Europe, F-92400 Courbevoie
15. *Annual Book of ASTM Standards and Special Publications*, Heyden, London
16. DIN Taschenbuch 133: *Normen über Siebböden und Kornmessung*; Beuth Bauverlag, Berlin, 1980

17. VDI-Handbuch, *Reinhaltung der Luft*, 4 vols, VDI & Beuth, Berlin 1958–76
18. RILEM Technical Committee 15-PM: Determination of pore properties of constructional and other materials. *Matériaux et Constructions*, **6**, No. 33 (1973)
19. H. Laurent (ed.), *Umfrage der Gemeinschaft über Standard-Referenz-Materialien*, EUR 4886 d,f,i,n,e; Europ. Community, Luxemburg, 1973
20. Service des Matériaux de Référence: *Catalogue des matériaux de référence français*, Paris: SMR-LNE, 1977
21. A. L. McClellan and H. F. Harnsberger, *J. Colloid Interf. Sci.*, **23**, 577 (1967)

Bibliography

Compilation of books in related subjects to the present work published between 1970 and 1982

A. W. Adamson, Physical Chemistry of Surfaces, 3rd edn, Wiley, New York 1976

J. R. Anderson (ed.), *Chemisorption and Reactions on Metallic Films*, Academic Press, London, 1971

J. R. Anderson (ed.), *Structure of Metallic Catalysts*, Academic Press, London, 1975

R. B. Anderson and P. T. Dawson (eds.), *Experimental Methods in Catalytic Research*, 3 vols, Academic Press, New York, 1976

M. V. Ardenne, *Tabellen zur angewandten Physik*, Vol. 1, 4th edn, Deutscher Verlag d. Wiss., Berlin, 1979

E. Bäder and H. von Kienle, *Aktivkohle und ihre industrielle Vertwertung*, Enke, Stuttgart, 1979

R. M. Barrer, *Zeolites and Clay Minerals as Sorbents and Moleculat Sieves*, Academic Press, New York, 1978

E. Bartholomé, E. Bickert, H. Hellmann, and H. Ley (eds.): *Ullmanns Encyclopädie der Technischen Chemie*, Vol. 2, 4th edn, Verlag Chemie, Weinheim, 1972

M. J. Katz, R. F. Walker, K. H. Behrndt, P. M. Waters, A. W. Czanderna, C. H. Massen, H. J. van Beckum, (eds.), *Vacuum Microbalance Techniques*, 8 vols, Plenum, New York, 1961–71

J. K. Beddow, *Particulate Science and Technology*, Chemical Publishing and Heyden, London, 1980

J. K. Beddow and T. P. Meloy, *Testing and Characterization of Powders and Fine Particles*, Heyden, London, 1979

B. E. P. Beeston, R. N. Horne, and R. Markham, *Electron Diffraction and Optical Diffraction Techniques*, North Holland, Amsterdam, 1973

T. Gast, E. Robens, S. C. Bevan, S. J. Gregg, N. D. Parkyns, C. Eyraud, M. Escoubes (eds.), *Progress in Vacuum Microbalance Techniques*, 3 vols, Heyden, London, 1972–75

B. Delmon, P. Jacobs, G. Poncelet, V. V. Boldyrev, M. Bulens, P. Grange (eds.), *Studies in Surface Science and Catalysis*, 3 vols. Elsevier, Amsterdam, 1975–78

C. H. Bramford and C. F. H. Tipper (eds.), *Reactions in the Solid State*, Elsevier, Amsterdam, 1980

D. H. Buckley, Surface Effects in Adhesion, Friction, Wear, and Lubrication, Elsevier, Amsterdam 1981

H. Chihara (ed.), Thermal Analysis: Proceedings of the Fifth ICTA Conference, Kyoto 1977. Heyden, London 1977

A. Clark, *The Theory of Adsorption and Catalysis*, Academic Press, New York, 1970

A. W. Czanderna and S. P. Wolsky (eds.), *Microweighing in Vacuum and Controlled Environments*, Elsevier, Amsterdam, 1980

H. Dagnall, *Exploring Surface Texture*. Rank Taylor Hobson, Leicester, 1980

E. Drauglis and R. I. Jaffee (eds.), *The Physical Basis for Heterogeneous Catalysis*, Plenum, New York, 1975

D. Dollimore, Proceedings of the Second European Symposium on Thermal Analysis, Heyden, London 1981

D. H. Everett and R. H. Ottewill (eds.), *Surface Area Determination*, Butterworth, London,. 1970

Forschung und Entwicklung zur Sicherung der Rohstoffversorgung. Part 3, Vol. 2: *Katalyse*. BMFT, Bonn, 1976

H. Freund and J. Grehn (eds.), *Handbuch der Mikroskopie in der Technik*, 7 vols, Umschau, Frankfurt am Main, 1975
S. Gál, *Die Methodik der Wasserdampf-Sorptionsmessungen*, Springer, Berlin, 1967
S. J. Gregg and K. S. W. Sing, *Adsorption, Surface Area and Porosity*, 2nd edn, Academic Press, London, 1982
S. J. Gregg, K. S. W. Sing, and H. F. Stoeckli (eds) *Characterisation of Porous Solids*, Society of Chemical Industry, London, 1979
H. B. Griffith, (ed) *Surfaces* 2nd ed., Cambridge University Press, Cambridge, 1981
M. J. Groves (ed.), *Particle Size Analysis*, Heyden, London, 1978
K. Hauffe and S. R. Morrison, *Adsorption*, De Gruyter, Berlin, 1974
P. C. Hiemenz, *Principles of Colloid and Surface Chemistry*, 2nd ed., Marcel Dekker, New York, 1977
J. W. Hightower (ed.), *Proceedings of the 5th International Congress on Catalysis*, North Holland, Amsterdam, 1973
L. Holland et al., *Vacuum Manual*, Methuen, London, 1974
L. Holland, W. Steckelmacher, and J. Yarwood (eds.), *Vacuum Manual*, Spon, London, 1974
P. Hopple (ed.), *Chemisorption and Catalysis*, Institute of Petroleum, London, 1970
IUPAC Manual of Symbols and Terminology on Colloid Science, Butterworths, London, 1982
H. Kambe, P. D. Garn (eds.), Thermal Analysis: Comparative Studies in Materials, Halsted Pr. 1975
M. Kerker, Surface Chemistry and Colloids, Butterworths, London, 1977
D. A. King, D. P. Woodruff (eds.), The Chemical Physics of Solid Surface and Heterogeneous Catalysis, 4 vols., Elsevier, Amsterdam 1981–82
C. J. Keattch and D. Dollimore, *An Introduction to Thermogravimetry*, 2nd edn, Heyden, London, 1975
F. Kneule, *Sorptions- und Desorptionsisothermen*, Berichtsheft Nr. 6. VDMA, Frankfurt am Main, 1964
F. Korte (ed.), *Methodicum Chimicum*, Vol. 1, Academic Press, New York, 1974
D. Langbein, Theory of van der Waals Attraction, Springer, Berlin 1974
R. R. LaPelle, *Practical Vacuum Systems*, McGraw-Hill, Maidenhead, 1972
M. Láznicka (ed.), *Physics of Solid Surfaces*, Elsevier, Amsterdam, 1982
L. L. Levenson, (ed.), Surface Properties of Materials, Elsevier, Amsterdam 1975
B. G. Linsen (ed.), *Physical and Chemical Aspects of Adsorbents and Catalysts*, Academic Press, London, 1970
G. Lombari, For Better Thermal Analysis, ICTA, Università di Roma, Rome, 1980
S. Lowell, *Introduction to Powder Surface Area*, Wiley Interscience, New York, 1979
W. C. McCrone and J. G. Delly, *The Particle Atlas*, 2nd edn, 4 vols, Ann Arbor Science Publ., Ann Arbor, 1975
R. G. J. Miller and B. C. Stace (eds.), *Laboratory Methods in Infrared Spectroscopy*, Heyden, London, 1972
K. L. Mittal, *Surface Contamination*, Plenum, New York 1979
Moderne Verfahren der Oberflächenanalyse. Dechema-Monographien 78. Dechema, Frankfurt am Main, 1975
S. Mordrý and M. Svatá, *Pore Structure and Properties of Materials*, 6 vol, Academia, Prague, 1973–74
Normen über Siebböden und Kornmessung, DIN Taschenbuch 133, Beuth Bauverlag, Berlin, 1980
Particle Size Analysis, Soc. for Analytical Chemistry, London, 1972
G. D. Parfitt and K. S. W. Sing, *Characterisation of Powder Surfaces*, Academic Press, London, 1976
J. B. Pendry, *Low Energy Electron Diffraction*, Academic Press, London, 1974
V. Ponec, Z. Knor, and S. Černý, *Adsorption on Solids*, Butterworths, London, 1974

468

W. Pupp, *Vakuumtechnik*, 2nd ed, Thiemig TB 43, Thiemig, München, 1972

I. D. Rattee and M. M. Breuer, *The Physical Chemistry of Dye Adsorption*, Academic Press, New York, 1974

L.V. C. Rees (ed.), *Zeolites*, Heyden, London, 1981

F. Ricca, (ed.), *Adsorption–Desorption Phenomena*, Academic Press, London, 1972

RILEM Technical Committee: *Determination of Pore Properties of Constructional and Other Materials. Matériaux et constructions*, **6**, no. 33 (1973)

M. W. Roberts, J. M. Thomas (eds.), Surface and Defect Properties of Solids, 7 vols., Am. Chemical 1970/78

J. J. Rooney and R. C. Pink, *Surface and Defect Properties of Solids*, The Chemical Society, London, 1973

A. Roth, *Vacuum Technology*, Elsevier, Amsterdam, 1976

J. Rouquerol and K. S. W. Sing (eds.), *Adsorption* at the Gas–Solid Interface, Elsevier, Amsterdam, 1982

J. S. Rowlinson and B. Widom, *Molecular theory of capillarity*, Oxford Science Publishers, Oxford, 1982

H. Rumpf and K. Leschonski (eds.), *Partikel-Meßtechnik*, DECHEMA-Monographien Vol. 79., Verlag Chemie, Weinheim, 1976

M. Schick (ed.), Surface Characteristics of Fibers and Textiles, 2 vols., Dekker, New York 1977

G. Schimmel and W. Vogell (eds), *Methodensammlung der Elekronenmikroskopie*. Wissenschaftliche Verlagsanstalt, Stuttgart, 1970

J. R. Smith (ed.), *Theory of Chemisorption*, Springer, Berlin, 1980

T. Sneck and H. Oinonen, *Measurements of Pore Size Distribution of Porous materials*, VTT, Helsinki, 1970

Standard and Test Methods for Metal Powders and Powder Metallurgy Products, Heyden, London, 1977

W. A. Steele, *The Interaction of Gases with Solid Surfaces*, Pergamon, Oxford, 1974

Surface Analysis Techniques for Metallurgical Applications, ASTM 1976

Surface and Colloid Science, 12 vols., Plenum, New York 1970/81

Surface Science: Proceedings Intern. Course Trieste, Unipub. 1974

F. C. Tompkins, Chemisorption of Gases on Metals, Academic Press, London 1978

Y. S. Touloukian and C. Y. Ho, Thermal Accomodation and Adsorption Coefficients of Gases, 2 vols., McGraw-Hill, New York 1981

K. K. Unger, *Porous Silica* (J. of Chromatography Library, Vol. 16), Elsevier, Amsterdam, 1979

P. L. Walker, Jr. (ed.), *Chemistry and Physics of Carbon*, 6 vols, Marcel Dekker, New York, 1970

Wasserdampf-Sorptionsisothermen. Berichtsheft 18 der Fachgemeinschaft Allgemeine Lufttechnik im VDMA, Frankfurt am Main, 1978

G. Wedler, *Adsorption*, Verlag Chemie, Weinheim, 1970

G. Wedler, *Chemisorption. An Experimental Approach*, Butterworths, London, 1976

W. W. Wendlandt, *Thermal Methods of Analysis*, Wiley, New York, 1974

W. W. Wendlandt and W. Collins (eds.), Thermal Analysis, Academic Press, New York 1976

H. G. Wiedemann (ed.), *Thermal Analysis*, 3 vol, Birkhäuser, Zürich, 1973

H. G. Wiedemann and W. Hemminger (eds.), *Thermal Analysis*, 2 vols, Birkhäuser, Basel, 1980

J. Yarwood, *High Vacuum Technique*, Chapman & Hall, London, 1975

Author Index

Pages on which the reference is shown in full are printed in italics.

476

Subject Index